Essentials of
Data Communications

Essentials of
Data Communications

David A. Stamper
and
The Saratoga Group

An imprint of Addison Wesley Longman, Inc.

Menlo Park, California • Reading, Massachusetts • New York • Harlow, England
Don Mills, Ontario • Sydney • Mexico City • Madrid • Amsterdam

Executive Editor: Michael Payne
Senior Acquisitions Editor: Maureen Allaire
Project Manager: Adam Ray
Assistant Editor: Susannah Davidson
Production Editor: Deneen Celecia
Art and Design Manager: Don Kesner
Composition and Film Manager: Lillian Hom
Composition and Film Coordinator: Vivian McDougal
Manufacturing Coordinator: Casi Kostecki
Marketing Manager: Melissa Baumwald
Copy Editor: Anna Huff
Proofreader: Joe Ruddick
Compositor: Bruce Saltzman of Digital Type & Image
Film House: Lazer Touch
Printer: Courier Westford
Cover Designer: Yvo Riezebos Design
Cover Photo: © Glenn Mitsui/Studio M.D.
Photo Credits: p. 50 Photo courtesy of Supra Corporation,
              p. 167, Photo courtesy of Wyse Technology

Library of Congress Cataloging-in-Publication Data
Stamper, David A.
        Essentials of data communications with software / David A. Stamper
        and the Saratoga Group.
               p.   cm.
        Includes index.
        ISBN 0-8053-7736-0
        1. Data transmission systems. 2. Computer networks. I. Saratoga
     Group.   II. Title
     TK5105.S735   1997
     004.6—dc20

                                                        96-12818
                                                          CIP

1 2 3 4 5 6 7 8 9 10—CRW— 2000 99 98 97 96

The Benjamin/Cummings Publishing Company, Inc.
2725 Sand Hill Road
Menlo Park, CA 94025

Table of Contents

Preface

....

Where are we heading as a society? Although we do not have a crystal ball that can accurately foretell the future, it is safe to assume that our future will be altered dramatically as a consequence of two technologies: computers and telecommunications. The evolution has already begun but the greatest changes lie ahead. For many years, computers and networks have influenced the way companies conducted their business, and that trend continues. The new aspect of computers and telecommunications is that they are now also having a significant influence on our personal lives and the ways in which we work, play, learn, and socialize.

The computer, once found only in commercial enterprises, is now a common household appliance. Furthermore, home computers are frequently used to connect to networks like the Internet and to information services like America Online, CompuServe, and Prodigy. These connections empower people to shop, bank, pay bills, make travel arrangements, and work remotely. In some instances, home computer users have also formed friendships over networks, and a few of these friendships have even led to marriage.

The events just cited are today's environment. The future holds additional promises. The ways in which we receive news, magazines, books, and entertainment in the home are presently affecting society as profoundly as the invention of the printing press. These changes will also further affect the way in which businesses function. Information will become a highly sought after commodity, and computers and computer networks will be the repository and delivery mechanism for information.

There is an important message here. The message is that you will use computers and data communications even if you do not work directly in the computer field. You will be a better user if you understand some of the underlying data communications technologies. Furthermore, if you work directly with computers, you may need to know the essentials of data communications.

As an example of these coming changes, this book—like a number before it—begins the transition from a print-based format to an electronic format. Some topics can be delivered much more effectively with computer-based modules that include text, graphics and animation, so we have incorporated supporting computer based modules into this text. If this book had been written five years later, it is likely that the book would be represented almost entirely by electronic media; the print based portion would consist of what the book covers and instructions on how to use it. Moreover, you would not go to a book store to buy it, you would download it from an electronic information market. Again, the new age of data communications in action.

The key to making this new technology work is how we pass data among computers. Fortunately, we have an excellent model for how this is done. The Open Systems Interconnection (OSI) Reference Model, has been developed by the International Standards Organization. The OSI Reference Model provides the general framework for implementations of transmission media, local area networks, wide area networks, network interconnections, network management, and related technologies. The chapters of this book are generally arranged to follow this seven layer model from the bottom up. As you read this text and step through the computer based modules, you are encouraged to continuously relate the material to the OSI reference model; this will help you place the topics their proper perspective relative to the overall objective, which is communicating.

HOW TO USE THIS BOOK

This book combines text and software to create an interactive learning package. The information on the computer based training (CBT) software disk accompanying this text is an integral part of the text material. In choosing the CBT topics, we attempted to select material that could be better explained via the integrated text, graphics, and animation inherent in that medium.

When you see a computer icon in the text, please stop reading and go to the computer module that is referenced. When you are finished with the computer module, return to the text. The CBTs appear in most chapters, and review questions for the CBT modules can be found at the end of the chapter. In order to answer all of the review questions, you will need to view the tutorials. Terms from the modules are also referenced in the index.

PEDAGOGY AND LEARNING AIDS

Chapter Introductions: Each chapter begins with an introduction to the material and sets several objectives for the reader.

End-of-chapter: At the end of each chapter is a summary of the key concepts, a list of key words, and a set of review questions. The end-of-chapter material gives the reader a guided reflection on the key points in the chapter.

Online glossary of terms: The accompanying CBT disk contains a comprehensive online glossary of data communications terms.

Online documentation: A complete online "help" feature is available for the CBT disk.

SUPPLEMENTS

The accompanying Instructor's Guide contains an instructor's manual, transparency masters, multiple choice, true-false, and fill-in test questions and answers.

For more information about *Essentials of Data Communications* and its supplements, please contact your Benjamin/Cummings Sales and Marketing Representative, or call the publisher directly at 800-950-BOOK.

ACKNOWLEDGMENTS

I am grateful to the numerous individuals who contributed to this textbook. I especially wish to thank the reviewers, who were instrumental in providing suggestions and constructive criticisms for development of this text. These people gave willingly of their time, and the text is much improved as a result of their contributions:

Gerald C. Canfield, University of Maryland, UMBC

Mary Ann Dase, Cal State Long Beach

Linda Ericksen, Umpqua Community College

David Haglin, Mankato State University

Charles W. Koop, DeVry Institute of Technology

M. Lisa Miller, University of Central Oklahoma

Sachi Sakthivel, Bowling Green State University

Roger Smith, Golden Gate University

Much appreciation goes to the editorial and production departments of Benjamin/Cummings Publishing. In particular, I wish to thank Vincent G. Vaccarello, Donald H. Czubek, and Nan Bowman from The Saratoga Group, and Larry Alexander at Benjamin/Cummings, who initially envisioned this project. I'd also like to thank Shawn Stamper for contributing his time in compiling the index.

Last, but not least, I wish to thank all of you—faculty, students and business professionals alike—who use this book. I will gladly receive any suggestions for improvements from you both formally and informally and your comments will be sincerely appreciated.

David A. Stamper

http://www.aw.com/bc/is/authors/stamper/edc/edc.html

1

·······················

INTRODUCTION TO DATA COMMUNICATIONS

··

CHAPTER OBJECTIVES

After studying this chapter you should be able to:

- Identify the essential elements of communication
- Describe different types of data communications applications
- Discuss the requirements of an online system
- List the seven layers of the OSI reference model
- Define some functions for each of the seven layers of the OSI reference model
- Describe the way in which a message is passed from one application to another using the OSI reference model

Computers are used to solve problems and process data. A data processing system may be viewed as an integration of subsystems that aid in solving business or scientific problems. Common subsystems include the operating system, database management, languages, applications, and data communications. Each subsystem is implemented as a combination of software, hardware, or both. This text discusses one part of the data processing system, the data communications subsystem, along with its interfaces with the other subsystems.

What is meant in this text by the term *data communications*? We define **data communications** as the transmission of data to and from computers and components of computer systems. More specifically, data communications is the transmission of data through a conducted medium such as wires, coaxial cables, or fiber optic cables, or by the use of wireless electromagnetic waves such as broadcast radio, infrared light, or microwaves. In reading this book, be aware that the field of data communications is so extensive that entire books are devoted to each chapter topic presented here. This text is intended to provide an overview of the entire field of data communications and to familiarize you with the terminology and capabilities of data communications systems. We begin the discussion by describing the essential elements of communication.

ESSENTIAL ELEMENTS OF COMMUNICATION

Communication of all types, be it everyday conversations or computer data exchange, requires a message, a sender, a receiver, and a medium. In addition, the message should be understandable and there should be some means of error detection. Figure 1-1 illustrates the sender, receiver, medium, and message in a telephone connection.

Figure 1-1

The Essential Elements of Communication

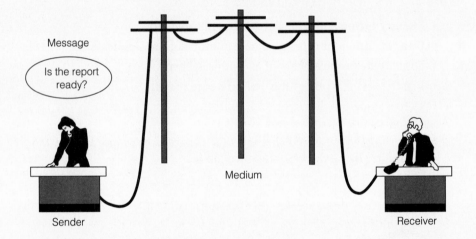

Message

For two entities to communicate, there must be a message, which can assume several forms and be of varying length. Types of data communications messages include a file, a request, a response, status, control, and correspondence. These are illustrated in Figure 1-2. Let us briefly look at each of them.

A File.   Today, many microcomputer owners subscribe to an information service such as the Internet, America Online, CompuServe, or Prodigy. One of the capabilities provided by these services is downloading or copying files. When an activity of this sort occurs, the message is the file being transferred.

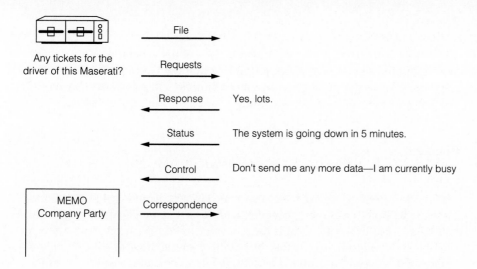

Figure 1-2

Types of Messages

A Request.   In online transaction processing, a user may request that the computer processor(s) take some type of action, such as displaying information, updating the database, or logging on or off the network.

A Response.   A request ordinarily receives a return message or response. For an information inquiry, the response is either the information requested or an error message saying why the data was not returned (such as "security violation," "information not on file," or "hardware failure"). For a database update transaction, the response could be either an explicit message that the action was performed, an error message, or an implicit acknowledgment that the transaction has been performed successfully, such as "progressing to the next transaction."

Status.   A status message, which can be sent either to all users or only to selected users, reveals the functional status of the system. If a system must be halted for scheduled maintenance, a status message might be broadcast to all users, enabling them to bring their work to an orderly halt.

Control.   Control messages are transmitted between system components. An automatic teller machine (ATM) might indicate to the controlling computer that it is out of cash; a printer might indicate that its buffer, or information storage area, is full and cannot receive additional data; or a network computer might notify other computers that a new computer has been added to the network and is available to accept and send messages.

Correspondence.   Correspondence involves messages sent from user to user. Such messages include those sent on electronic mail systems, where memos and correspondence may be routed among employees of a company. Some systems transmit document images, provide bulletin-board message posting, or enable telephone-like interactive communication.

Sender

The sender is the transmitter of the message—either a person or a machine. Frequently the sender is a computer or terminal with enough intelligence to originate a message or response without human intervention. The sender can also be a system user, sensor, badge reader, or other input device.

Receiver

Receivers include computers, terminals, remote printers, people, and devices such as drill presses, furnaces, and air conditioners. A message and a sender can exist without a receiver; however, without a receiver, no communication takes place. For example, signals have been beamed into space in an attempt to contact intelligent life forms, but until these signals are received and understood, no communication has occurred. In a computer system, a message could be sent to all terminals saying that a new system feature is available, but if all terminals happen to be turned off at that time, no communication will have occurred.

Medium

Messages are carried from sender to receiver through some **medium** of communication. In oral communication, sound waves are transmitted through air (the medium). Data communications uses several media to transmit data, including wires, radio waves, and light pulses. Media are discussed more thoroughly in Chapter 2.

Understandability

Even if all the components discussed above are present, if the message is not understood correctly, then accurate communication has not taken place. In human communication the most obvious obstacle is language differences, for which a translator or interpreter may be necessary. Computer systems have similar obstacles to communication. For instance, data can be represented by any of several different codes, the two most common being the American Standard Code for Information Interchange (ASCII) and the Extended Binary Coded Decimal Interchange Code (EBCDIC). Sometimes it is necessary to translate from one code to another to be sure that data is interpreted correctly.

Error Detection

In human communication, receivers can frequently detect errors because humans have the ability to reason and interpret. Grammatical errors, misspellings, and even some misstatements can usually be corrected by a human receiver. (If a teacher mistakenly gives the distance between the Earth and the sun as 93 million light years rather than 93 million miles, we would probably realize the error and, presumably, even correct it.) But computer networks do not reason. Even when a human computer operator realizes that a received message is erroneous, that operator may be unable to correct the error. When the receiver is a piece of hardware or software, incapable of reasoning and unable to detect or correct errors, it becomes necessary to employ special schemes for determining whether an original message has been distorted during transmission. All such error-detection schemes involve transmitting additional information along with the data, which increases the chances of detecting errors without eliminating the possibility that the received data actually may be erroneous. Error detection is discussed in Chapter 2.

DATA COMMUNICATIONS APPLICATIONS

There are several broad classes of data communications applications: batch, data entry, distributed, inquiry/response, interactive, and sensor-based. Note that the classes are not mutually exclusive; some transactions may fall into more than one class.

Batch Applications

Batch applications, including remote job entry (RJE), are characterized by large data transfers in two directions. In RJE applications, transactions are collected over time into what is called a **batch.** The batch of transactions is processed or transmitted as a whole. For example, a batch of inventory cards might be transferred from a warehouse to a remote computer center, and in return the warehouse would receive an updated inventory list. In some batch applications, large amounts of data flow in one direction only. When a sales representative records sales on a portable computer terminal but waits until the end of the workday to transmit the entire day's orders, a large amount of data flows in one direction and little or no data flows in the other direction.

Data Entry Applications

Data entry applications consist of lengthy inputs with short responses. In a credit authorization system, input for a group of charge receipts consists of credit card number, merchant number, and charge amount, plus the total of all charges in the group. The receiving system then calculates its own group total and compares it with the input total; if the figures agree, it is assumed the data entry was correct, and the only response is a prompt to continue entering the next group of receipts.

Distributed Applications

Distributed applications are characterized not so much by input and output size as by whether data or processing or both are distributed among several computers. Thus, requests as well as data flow between several system components, with possibly some parallelism in data access and processing. Order entry can be an example of this type of processing. When an order for an item is entered, the system tries to determine whether the item is in stock in any of its several regionally located warehouses. Because each warehouse has a computer system and maintains its local inventory, the system inquires into these remote databases to find a location with enough stock to fill the order. The system then updates the inventory at the location(s) from which the order is to be filled, updates the invoicing and accounts receivable at the accounting location, and supplies the ordering location with a shipment date and other relevant data.

Office automation systems on a **local area network (LAN)** are another example of distributed systems, with both data and processing distributed among several different computers. Applications such as word processing, communications among members of the corporation via electronic mail, spreadsheet analysis, and desktop publishing take place using the resources of several network computers, typically a workstation and a server.

Inquiry/Response Applications

In this type of application, inputs generally have only a few characters and output responses have many. **Inquiry/response applications** involve requests to display information. For example, a police inquiry might consist of a driver's license number and the response could be several thousand characters of information detailing the driver's name, address, driving record, and so on. In a hospital application, a nurse might enter the nurse's station number (relatively few characters) and the output would likely consist of several thousand characters giving each patient's name, status, and medical requirements.

Interactive Applications

An **interactive application** is characterized by relatively short inputs and outputs. The computer system prompts the user for an input, eliciting a short response. Because the sender and receiver are essentially conversing with each other, this application is sometimes referred to as conversational. Interactive applications are frequently used for online transaction processing with terminals that cannot accept an entire screenful of information. Applications in which the user's response dictates the next prompt, such as certain computerized games, are also interactive.

Sensor-Based Applications

Sensor-based applications involve special data collection devices for such uses as controlling temperature in buildings, monitoring and maintaining patient condition in hospitals, and controlling a manufacturing process. The processor receives data from the sensors and, if necessary, takes control action.

Combined Applications

The typical computer in a network of large systems supports more than one type of activity. It might have a batch processing requirement and one or more types of data communications applications. One task in designing a data communications system is to balance the workload to ensure effective and efficient use. Effective use means minimizing idle time for system components. It is not effective to have a data communications line idle for long periods and then have many users attempting to use it at once. Efficient use means using the components in an optimal manner. Efficient uses of a data communications line include compressing the data before transmitting it or eliminating sources of data errors.

REQUIREMENTS OF AN ONLINE SYSTEM

Although data communications applications are diverse, most have certain basic requirements: performance, consistency, flexibility, availability, reliability, recovery, and security.

Performance

System **performance** can be measured in several ways. Two very common measures are response time and throughput. **Response time** is the interval between entering a message and getting the response. Some define the measurement interval as being from the end of the entry to the appearance of the first response character; others define it as the interval from the end of the entry to receipt of the final response character. The difference between the two can be significant. For example, if the speed of the communications circuit is 30 characters per second and the response consists of 1200 characters, the response time by the first definition is 40 seconds less than that by the second definition. Response time has two major components: the time required for data transmission and the time required for processing. (Each component has subcomponents.) This text deals only with data transmission time.

Response times are quoted for transactions of a given type. A hospital application has response times for each of the following transactions:

- Patient admission
- Patient discharge
- Patient lookup
- Room occupants

In addition to each transaction having a response time, one transaction type may have different response times in different systems. This happens because of hardware differences or because the transactions are implemented in different ways. Table 1-1 illustrates the work Transaction A may do to admit a patient at one hospital, and Table 1-2 shows the work a patient admission transaction, Transaction B, does at another hospital. Even though these transactions have the same name, the work accomplished by each transaction is different; therefore, their response times differ. When comparing or evaluating transaction response times, you also need to evaluate the work done by those transactions.

TABLE 1-1   Activities for Transaction A

Obtain vacant room list header from memory location

Read vacant room record

Read patient record

Update vacant room list header in memory from room record

Rewrite room record linked to patient record

Rewrite patient record

TABLE 1-2   Activities for Transaction B

Obtain vacant room header from memory

Read vacant room record

Read patient record

Update vacant room header from room record

Rewrite room record linked to patient record

Read related charge record for room

Write charge record for patient

Read standard patient issue record

Write patient charge record for issue of supplies

Rewrite patient record

Throughput is the amount of work performed by the system per unit of time. It may appear that fast response time and high throughput are equivalent. Actually, the opposite is sometimes true. For example, transactions in which customers are involved usually need quick response time. Optimizing the speed of such transactions might slow down other processing activity, such as batch processing. Although response time in customer transactions might be better, the total amount of work accomplished may decline.

Consistency

Consistency describes a system that works predictably. For example, inconsistent response times for a transaction can be annoying to system users and is sometimes worse than a consistent response time that is slower than the fastest, inconsistent response time. It would be quite disconcerting if 50 percent of transactions took 3 seconds, 20 percent took 10 seconds, 15 percent took 30 seconds, 10 percent took 1 minute, and 5 percent took more than a minute. Such inconsistency not only is frustrating but also limits the effectiveness of the system. It might be better to have a more consistent response time of 10 seconds. Of course, complete consistency is difficult to achieve because of occasional periods of heavy processing. One common system design objective is for the response time of most transactions of a given type, such as 95 percent, to be lower than a certain threshold, such as 3 seconds.

Flexibility

One common aspect of online systems is that they change. Users might want to alter the types of transactions available, change the data format, expand an application, or add applications. **Flexibility** means that both growth and change can be accommodated with minimal impact on existing applications and users. The ability to increase processing power, terminals, communication circuits, and database capacity is critical to the long-term success of a system, and the network implementation ought to accommodate such changes. One of the best ways to ensure this ability is to use industry-standard network architectures and protocols. This method also helps when adding or upgrading equipment and gives users a wider variety of options from which to choose.

Availability

Availability requires that an online system be continuously available to the user community during the workday. In some cases this means 24 hours a day, every day of the year. In certain applications, if the online system is unavailable it can result in significant financial loss to a business. For example, an airline might be unable to sell seats on a flight if the reservation system is down, or it may overbook a flight, which will cause extra work for the employees and possible penalty payments to travelers for their inconvenience.

Reliability

Reliability, an important system attribute, is a measure of the frequency of system failure and in some ways combines consistency and availability. A system failure is any event that keeps users from processing transactions. This includes any hardware breakdown, such as a processor failure in a system that is not fault-tolerant, as well as an application or system software failure or the failure of the medium (such as a faulty data communications line). **Mean time between failure (MTBF)** is a measure of the average time until a given component may be expected to fail, and **mean time to repair (MTTR)** is the average time required to fix a failed component. Both figures are important in determining the frequency of failure and the time required to return the system to successful operation.

One way to improve the reliability of data communications systems is **fault tolerance,** which is the ability to continue processing despite component failure. In a fault-tolerant system, single points of failure do not cause system failure because every component in the system has a backup component that takes over if a failure occurs. Fault-tolerant **wide area networks (WANs)** are formed by combining fault-tolerant hardware with fault-tolerant software, and fault tolerance is also available for LANs. Fault tolerance is usually confined to a LAN's servers.

Recovery

Recovery addresses the fact that all systems, even those built for continuous operation, can fail. In some cases it may not be the system that fails but either the source of power or the people who operate the system. Regardless of the cause, the system must be able to recover to a consistent point—a point where the database has no partially updated transactions, no transactions have been processed twice, and no transactions have been lost. System users also should be advised of the state of all work they had in progress at the time of failure, to keep them from submitting a duplicate transaction or failing to reenter a transaction not received before the failure.

Security

Security has become increasingly important as the microcomputer has made computer networks accessible to almost everyone. As more businesses use data communications, the number of accessible computer systems continues to grow, thus making a vast amount of sensitive information available, including financial data and classified military information. Unfortunately, security has not always received a high priority in system and network design, so making up for these deficiencies is a necessity in the development of future systems and in the enhancement of existing ones. Systems security is discussed in more detail in Chapter 10.

INTRODUCTION TO NETWORKS

What exactly is a computer network? First, a computer network can be defined as a single computer, called a host, together with communications circuits, communications equipment, and terminals (see Figure 1-3). A network can also be defined as two or more computers connected via a communications medium, together with associated communications links, terminals, and communications equipment (see Figures 1-4 and 1-5). In these cases the computers are referred to as nodes. In Figures 1-4 and 1-5, the communications links are depicted by lines attached to the nodes. These are sample configurations only; actually, a wide variety of configurations is in use, and several viable configurations may exist for one application. In addition, a company may have several networks, such as several LANs and a WAN. In such instances, it is common to interconnect the various networks to provide communications among all network users, such as between LAN users on one LAN and LAN users on another LAN or between a LAN user and a WAN user. Such a network of networks is illustrated in Figure 1-6 and by the Internet, which connects several regional networks into one large, supernetwork. The Internet is discussed in Chapter 7.

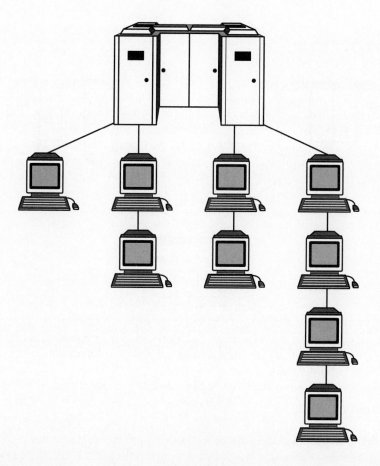

Figure 1-3

A Simple Data
Communications Network

Figure 1-4

Local Area Network

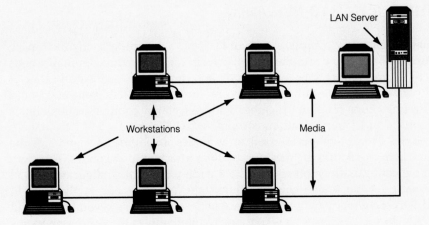

Figure 1-5

A Network of Computers

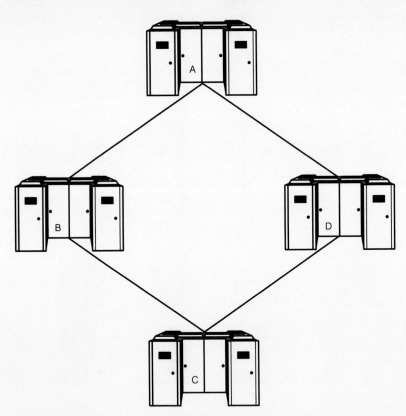

The following discusses several different applications and configurations of computer equipment. The chapters covering local and wide area networks provide details on network configurations and where they are used.

Company A

This company is an attorney's office with 12 partners and 22 support staff. The partnership maintains most of its documentation on a LAN. Each attorney

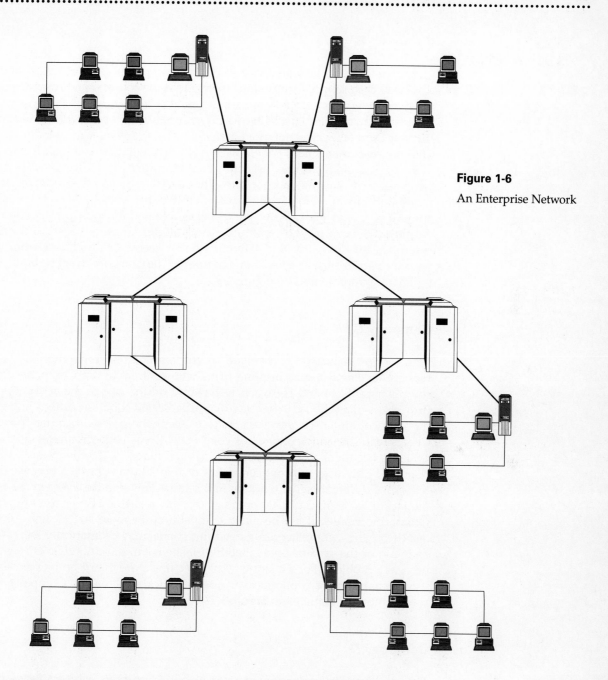

Figure 1-6

An Enterprise Network

and administrative support person has a microcomputer workstation that is attached to the network. Documents of a personal nature are stored on individuals' local disks whereas documents that are subject to sharing are stored on the network's file server. The **file server** is a repository for shared files such as completed contracts and wills, templates for legal documents and spreadsheets, and program files including word processors, spreadsheets, and desktop publishing. The file server also provides sharing of other resources such as printers, fax machines, and modems to be shared among the LAN users. Company A's network is generally represented by Figure 1-4.

Company B

This company provides a service to trucking companies that enables their drivers to cash script at truck stops throughout the country. The advantages are that drivers do not need to carry large amounts of cash for long trips, truck-stop owners are guaranteed against losses from bad checks, and the trucking companies need not provide significant cash advances to their drivers. The communications network consists of approximately 50 terminals located in the same building as the host computer in Company B's office. Truck-stop employees can telephone data entry personnel on a toll-free number to receive authorization to pay the driver (or advice to call the police). The total amount of money allocated to the driver is updated after each transaction. All links between the host computer and the terminals are local and are controlled by Company B, rather than being leased or purchased from a common carrier such as a telephone company. The Company B configuration is generally represented by Figure 1-3.

Company C

This service company is involved in the automated preparation of tax returns. Its clients are accounting firms who contract to use Company C's computer facilities and software. Depending on the size of the accounting firm, clients may choose to have a private, dedicated communications link to the host computer, or they can share a telephone link with other users. Clients who share a telephone link compete with each other for access to the available telephone lines. Suppose 50 lines are shared by 150 clients and each client typically uses the connection fewer than 2 hours per day. Because of time-zone differences, the workday is 12 hours long and the average use of the facility is 50 percent (300 hours of the 600 available connection hours). Ordinarily, there will not be much competition for these shared lines. But just before the income tax filing deadline, clients may dramatically increase their use of the system, so availability of the communications links might become a problem. For a client who needs a line more than 2 hours per day, it is probably more economical to use a dedicated line. The Company C configuration is depicted in Figure 1-7.

Company D

This multinational company manufactures and markets a broad range of computer systems. Every large sales office has a LAN and a demonstration computer, and all of these LANs and demonstration computers as well as the computers in the software development facility, home office, and manufacturing plants are linked in one large network, consisting of more than 200 WAN nodes, 3000 LAN nodes, and 1500 terminals. In addition to long-distance telephone lines and local, private lines, Company D uses coaxial cable and fiber optic cable for the LAN media and satellite communications for long-distance, high-volume transmissions between manufacturing plants and divisional offices. The Company D configuration is generally represented by Figure 1-6.

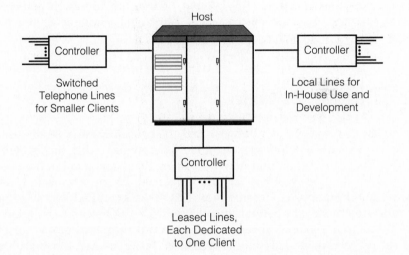

Host

Controller

Switched
Telephone Lines
for Smaller Clients

Controller

Local Lines for
In-House Use and
Development

Controller

Leased Lines,
Each Dedicated
to One Client

Figure 1-7

Company C's Network

These four companies have greatly different network configurations, yet each network is effective and cost-efficient for the business that uses it. Companies A, B, and C could have installed a network similar to that of Company D. Unfortunately, by doing so they would have to spend considerably more for their networks and thus might lose their competitive edge.

Many alternatives are available to a network designer, and several configurations will probably solve the communications requirements. A few such alternatives might be highly cost-effective, some may be only mediocre, and a few might drive the company into bankruptcy. It is important to realize that several "right" approaches usually exist.

System Complexity

Data communications systems may be simple or complex. A simple system might be composed of a single processor and some terminals, all located within a single building or a small LAN. Figure 1-3 illustrates the hardware components of a processor with terminals, and Figure 1-4 illustrates a micro-computer LAN with a dedicated file server and five workstations. A file server allows the microcomputers to share resources such as data, programs, and printers. A more elaborate system might consist of several LANs each of which is attached to a mainframe or minicomputer, which in turn is connected in a WAN. Also attached to the WAN processors are terminals that are distributed both locally and remotely. A network of this type is commonly called an **enterprise network,** which is two or more LANs connected to each other or one or more LANs connected to a WAN or to each other. Figure 1-6 depicts a system that meets this description. The computers and terminals in this figure are connected via an assortment of private wires, communications lines leased from a common carrier, and microwave and satellite transmission. Figures 1-3, 1-4, and 1-6 indicate the variety and complexity of communication systems. The illustrated components are discussed in detail in later chapters.

THE OSI REFERENCE MODEL

Regardless of the scope of a network and the equipment and media used, all networks share common functions. To contend with the growing number of different computer networks being developed, and in the belief that these diverse systems eventually need to be connected, the **International Standards Organization (ISO)** has identified and stratified the functions that every network must fulfill. The ISO recommendation is called the **Open Systems Interconnection (OSI) reference model,** or the OSI reference model. This model makes it easier to develop interfaces among different networks.

The OSI reference model does more than describe network interconnections; it also defines a network architecture. Many ISO standards relating to the reference model have been established, and more are being formulated. When the standards process is completed, network developers will have an alternative to proprietary corporate network architectures such as IBM's Systems Network Architecture (SNA). Details and examples of the OSI reference model are found in the following chapters. A brief description is provided here because the OSI reference model in general and standards arising from it are used for the development of networks. This discussion also provides an overview of communications systems.

The basic objective of a network of computers is for an application on one node to communicate with an application or device on another node. Although this may sound simple, some complexities are involved. You have just seen that many different WAN and LAN implementations are possible and, consequently, so are many different types of interfaces. This means you need one type of hardware and software to connect to one type of LAN and a different set of hardware and software to connect to a different type of LAN or to a particular WAN. Because of the variety of network types available and the frequent need to interconnect them, a thriving business has been created for establishing connections among networks. Building network interfaces is much simpler if the network is designed around an open architecture. An **open architecture** is one in which the network specifications are available to any company. This allows a variety of companies to design hardware and software components that can easily be integrated into new and existing networks based on the open architecture.

The Functions of Communications

To help motivate an understanding of the OSI reference model, consider how a worker might send a message from his or her office to a colleague in another location. This simple act can closely resemble sending a message in an OSI network. A possible scenario for this transmission might be as follows:

1. The worker dictates a memo on a tape recorder and delivers it to her or his administrative assistant.

2. The administrative assistant makes the memo presentable by typing it, correcting grammatical mistakes, and so on. The administrative assistant places the memo in an interoffice envelope and places the envelope in the outgoing mailbox.

3. The mail-room clerk picks up the mail, takes it to the mail room, sorts it, and determines a route for the message. Possible routings are internal mail, postal mail, and private express mail carriers. Because this message must go to a distant office and no priority is assigned, the clerk places the interoffice envelope in an external mailing envelope, possibly with other correspondence for that office, addresses it, and deposits the envelope in the external mailbox.

4. The mail carrier picks up the mail, including the worker's message, and takes it to the post office, where it is sorted and placed on an outgoing mail truck.

5. The post office physically delivers the mail to the mail room of the destination office. That mail-room clerk opens the outer envelope and sorts its contents.

6. The mail-room clerk delivers the memo in its interoffice envelope to the recipient's administrative assistant.

7. The recipient's administrative assistant takes the memo out of the envelope and prepares the memo for the recipient. The administrative assistant may time-stamp the memo, summarize it, make comments, set a priority for the recipient's reading it, and so on.

8. The recipient receives the memo, reads it, and reacts to the worker's message.

The preceding scenario describes a variety of different functions necessary to move a message from the sender's desk to the recipient's desk. The functions consist of message composition, presentation services, address determination, enveloping, selecting transmission routes, physical transmission, and so on. In general, these same functions must be performed when transmitting a message between computers in a network. The OSI reference model explicitly identifies seven layers of functions that must be performed in network interconnections: application, presentation, session, transport, network, data link, and physical. Figure 1-8 represents the OSI layers in two network nodes, a sending and a receiving node.

In the letter-routing example, each functional layer on the sending side performed a specific set of functions, and each function was performed for a peer layer on the receiving side. Placing the correspondence in the interoffice envelope was done by the sending administrative assistant and undone by the receiving administrative assistant. In the OSI reference model, each layer in the sending network node is designed to perform a particular set of functions for its corresponding (peer) layer in the receiving network node. The application layer in the sending node prepares the data for the application layer in the receiving node. The application layer then passes the message to the presentation layer. The presentation layer formats the message properly for the presentation layer on the receiving node, passes the data to the session layer, and so on. In Figure 1-8 the solid line shows the physical route of the message, and the dotted lines show the logical route, from peer layer to peer layer. Also notice that each layer has a well-defined interface through which it communicates with adjacent layers.

Figure 1-8

OSI Peer Layer
Communication

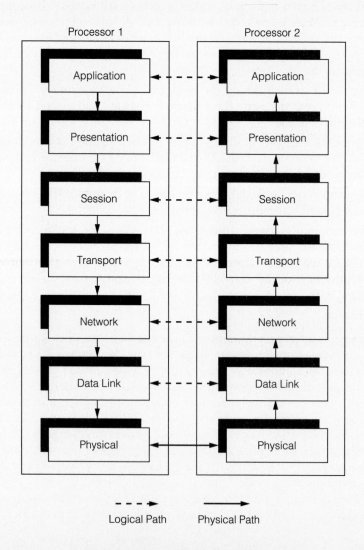

Functions of OSI Layers

The functions of each OSI layer are briefly described below. More extensive explanations of several of these layers are given later as needed.

Application

The **application layer** is functionally defined by the user. Sometimes application programs must communicate with each other. The content and format of the data being exchanged are dictated by the needs of the organization. The application determines which data is to be transmitted, the message or record format for the data, and the transaction codes that identify the data to the receiver. Suppose an order-entry transaction started on a sales node needs to pass product shipping information to a warehouse node. In this application, the message contains the ship-to address, part identifiers, quantities to be shipped, and a message code showing the action to be taken by the receiving application.

Presentation

The **presentation layer** formats the data it receives from the application layer. If certain data preparation functions are common to several applications, they can be resolved by the presentation services rather than being embedded in each application. The types of functions performed at the presentation level are encryption, compression, and conversion from one transmission code to another (such as EBCDIC to ASCII).

Session

The **session layer** establishes the connection between applications, enforces the rules for carrying on the dialogue, and tries to reestablish the connection if a failure occurs. The dialogue rules specify both the order in which the applications are allowed to communicate and the pacing of information so as not to overload the recipient. If an application is sending data to a printer with a limited buffer size, the agreed-upon dialogue may be to send a buffer-size block to the printer, wait for the printer to signal that its buffer has been emptied, and then send the next block of data. The session layer must control this flow to avoid buffer overflow at the printer.

Transport

The **transport layer** is the first layer concerned with the world external to its processor. It generates the address of the end user and ensures that all blocks or packets of data have been received, that there are no duplicate blocks, and that blocks have not been lost in transmission.

Network

The **network layer** does end-to-end routing of packets or blocks of information, collects billing and accounting information, and routes messages.

Data Link

The **data link layer** must establish and control the physical path of communication to the next node. This includes error detection and correction, defining the beginning and end of the data field, resolving competing requests for a shared communications link (deciding who can use the circuit and when), and ensuring that all forms of data can be sent across the circuit. The conventions used to accomplish these data link functions are known as **data link protocols**.

Physical

The **physical layer** specifies the electrical connections between the transmission medium and the computer system. It describes how many wires are used to carry the signals; which wires carry specific signals; the size and shape of the connectors or adapters between the transmission medium and the communications circuit; the speed at which data is transmitted; and whether data (represented by voltages on a line, modification of radio waves, or light pulses) is allowed to flow in both directions and, if so, whether the flow can be in both directions simultaneously.

OSI Reference Model

You now have an opportunity to look at an example of the activities that occur at each level of the reference model as an application on one network node transmits a message to an application on another network node. At this time, you should shift to the computer-based training (CBT) module entitled "OSI Reference Model". While you study this module, note how each layer prepares the message for both its peer layer and its lower layer.

THE SOFTWARE ENVIRONMENT

Before we begin the technical discussion of the data communications system, an explanation of how it supports applications is worthwhile. Let us take a brief look at the application environment of a data communications system. Within the central processing system resides an operating system, together with data communications, database, and application software. This is illustrated in Figure 1-9. These software subsystems perform the following functions.

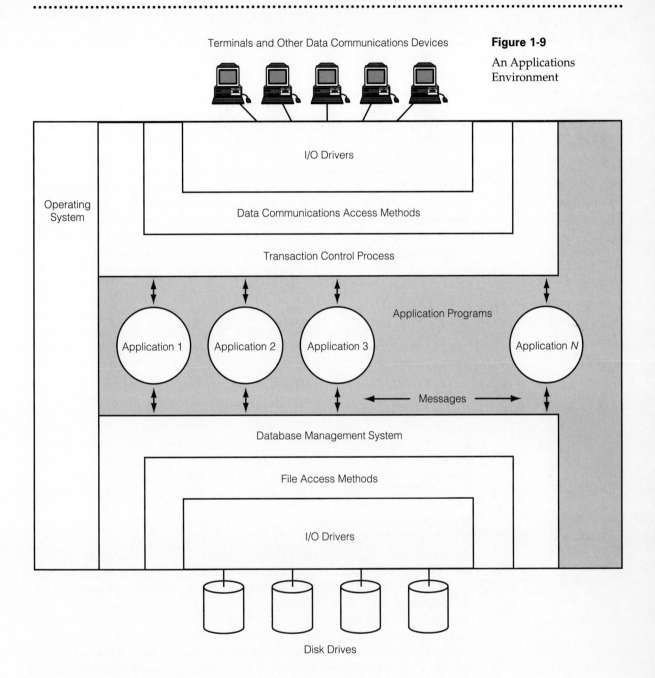

Terminals and Other Data Communications Devices

Figure 1-9

An Applications
Environment

Application Programs

Application programs are the heart of the system. They are the sole reason
for having a computer and associated software and hardware. Application
software may be purchased from the computer vendor or a third party or
developed locally. There are many varieties of application programs. For
example, an inventory system has many programs, each of which performs

one or more inventory functions, such as inventory update, inventory listings, printing packing lists, and so on. A banking system consists of many programs that provide functions such as creating new accounts, deleting accounts, updating accounts, reporting account statuses, and so on.

To make the development process efficient, programmers should not have to concern themselves with the intricacies of data communication and data storage. This is why application support software, such as the operating system, data communications system, and database system, is used. The purpose of these systems is to allow application developers to concentrate on solving business problems rather than on the specifics of devices such as terminals and disk drives. By isolating applications at this level of detail, a company can also introduce devices into a system with minimal or no impact on existing application programs.

For example, it is typical to have a variety of workstations within a computer network. The way data is displayed on these devices often differs from one workstation to the next. The capabilities supported by the devices also may differ. One workstation may have a color display, and another, a monochrome display. Requiring each application to keep track of these differences would place a heavy, unnecessary burden upon the application programmer. The data communications system accommodates device differences and provides a standard interface that allows an application to deal with any type of device.

Operating System

The **operating system** manages the resources of the computer. It manages memory; controls access to the central processing unit (CPU); and provides interfaces to users, the input/output (I/O) subsystems, and the file system.

Data Communications

The data communications subsystem is responsible for interfacing to devices that are attached via communications lines. These devices are distinguished from locally attached peripherals such as disk drives, printers, and tape drives. In addition to the function defined above, the data communications system provides a bridge between applications and the devices with which they must communicate. In this capacity, it switches messages between workstations and applications and becomes involved in recovery in the event of a system failure. The data communications component that provides this service in a large computer system is called a **transaction control process (TCP).**

Database Management System

The **database management system (DBMS)** serves as an interface between the application programs and the data they need to resolve business problems. The functions provided by the DBMS are data definition, data manipulation, and data management and control. **Data definition** provides the ability to define fields; to combine fields into records; and to define files, data access methods, and associations. **Data manipulation** allows users to retrieve, insert, delete, and modify data in the database. **Data management and control** allows the database administrator and operations personnel to start, stop, monitor, and reorganize the database.

We can see how these software components work together by tracing a transaction through a system. For simplicity, consider a mainframe computer with attached terminals as illustrated in Figure 1-3. A **transaction** is a user-defined piece of work that, from the perspective of the database, performs a series of operations that leaves the database in a consistent state. Either the entire transaction must be completed or the database must be left in the state it was in before the transaction started. For a transaction that transfers money between two accounts, there are three database states: (1) at the start of the transaction, (2) after taking money from one account, and (3) after placing the money in the second account, or the end of the transaction. The database is inconsistent in the second state.

Transaction Processing

A particular example of a transaction would be adding an employee to the database. This process consists of inserting two records into the database; an employee record and a payroll record. The transaction starts at a terminal in the personnel department; the activity is shown in Table 1-3.

TABLE 1-3   User Interaction

Transaction control process (TCP) displays menu on terminal

User selects "add employee" activity and sends TCP

TCP responds to terminal with data entry screen

User fills out screen and sends to TCP

TCP checks data for consistency and writes data to transaction log

TCP begins transaction

TCP sends message to application to process transaction

Application formats data and calls DBMS routine to add employee record to database

DBMS processes application request and returns completion status to application

Application formats data and calls DBMS routine to add payroll record to database

DBMS processes application request and returns completion status to application

Application sends completion status to TCP

TCP ends transaction

TCP sends completion status to user at terminal

From an opening menu displayed on the terminal, the operator selects an option for adding a new employee. This selection is transmitted to the data communications system, which determines that an employee input form is required. This screen template or input form is transmitted to the terminal, where the operator enters the required information. The terminal access method is responsible for ensuring that the proper control characters are inserted to format the data for the type of terminal being used. The lower levels of the data communications system provide the logic to properly place the data on the communications line, to detect transmission errors, and to provide the proper electrical signals for transmission.

The operator enters the data pertaining to the new employee and transmits it back to the computer, where it is received by the data communications system. The TCP checks the message for transmission errors, logs the message to a transaction log file, and determines the transaction type. Because this transaction updates the database, the TCP formally begins a transaction for recovery purposes. The TCP recognizes that it is a message for an application, determines which application should process the transaction, and sends the message to the proper application.

The application program receives the message—to insert two new records into the database—from the data communications system and begins to process it. It formats the records and makes the DBMS requests to insert them. The DBMS accepts the records and inserts them into the database. Before inserting the records, however, the DBMS logs the record images, both before and after making the changes. These before and after images can be used for recovery if a failure occurs. Upon successful completion of the record insertions, the DBMS returns a successful completion status to the application program. The application program then responds to the data communications system that the transaction has been successfully processed. The TCP ends the transaction and sends the completion status back to the terminal operator.

Throughout the transaction the operating system is actively involved, transferring control from one software subsystem to another, interfacing with the peripheral devices, and managing memory. Through the interaction of all the software systems, the transaction is completed. The operating system, the data communications system, and the DBMS support the application process in performing its work.

The preceding example was presented in the context of a network using a single host processor. With only minor modifications the discussion may also be applied to a LAN configuration or a WAN. Let us briefly look at the way in which these activities would occur on a LAN.

A user at a LAN workstation may begin by running a database program located on the file server. The database program will be transferred over the LAN medium into the workstation's memory. From the user's perspective the file server appears to be a disk drive because the application's request to run a program results in that program being loaded into the workstation's memory just as though the program was on the workstation's local disk drive. The database processing logic will thus be carried out entirely by the workstation's processor. The database application will periodically need access to records stored in a shared database on the file server. A request is sent from the workstation to the file server asking the file server to access the desired record. The file server accepts the request, accesses the records from its disks, and transmits the records to the requesting workstation. In this example, the file server responds to requests by simply providing the workstation with the requested records. The file server does not participate in processing database records.

In a different LAN scenario we may find a database server that cooperates with the workstation in carrying out database requests. With this alternative the workstation sends the database server a request for database processing rather than a request for individual records. The request might be something like, "Give me the total sales for the Northwest Region." The database server will act on the request and return the single-figure answer rather than the set of records essential to deriving the answer.

There is a common thread in each of the above examples: A user or program made a request that was acted on by one or more other processes. In one example, all of the cooperating processes were running in one processor. In the LAN examples the software was resident in two different processors. The networking trend, particularly for LANs, is to distribute the processing for a single application over two or more network nodes. An application at one node makes requests that software programs on other nodes process. The requester is called a **client process** and the processes that act on those requests are called **server processes.** This general concept is called **client/server computing.** With client/server computing, the network is called upon to solve application problems rather than having a single node responsible for all application requirements. In essence, then, the network becomes the computer! We discuss client/server computing more extensively in Chapter 10.

SUMMARY

Data communications is the electronic transmission of computer-readable data. For two entities to communicate, four essential elements—message, sender, receiver, and medium—must be present. The message also must be understood by the receiver and there ought to be a means for detecting transmission errors.

The data communications industry experienced tremendous expansion during the 1970s and 1980s, largely as the result of lower prices for both equipment and transmission media. During these two decades network hardware and software became faster and more sophisticated to meet the requirements of an online system: performance, consistency, reliability, flexibility, recovery, availability, and security.

As networks proliferated, so did the ways in which they were built. In many cases this resulted in the inability of computers on one network to communicate with computers on another network. The International Standards Organization developed the OSI reference model to remedy this.

The OSI reference model describes seven functional layers—application, presentation, session, transport, network, data link, and physical—for moving data from an application in one network node to an application in another node. Many standards have been developed based on the OSI reference model. The key to the model is that the interfaces and protocols are open to all, and networks designed around the model and standards can be more easily interconnected.

KEY TERMS

application layer   19

application program   21

availability   9

batch   5

batch application   5

client process   25

client/server computing   25

consistency   9

data communications   1

data definition   23

data entry application   5

data link layer   20

data link protocol   20

data management and control   23

database management system (DBMS)   22

data manipulation   23

distributed application   6

enterprise network   16

fault tolerance   10

file server   13

flexibility   9

inquiry/response application   6

interactive application   6

International Standards Organization (ISO)   16

local area network (LAN)   6

mean time between failure (MTBF)   10

mean time to repair (MTTR)   10

medium   4

network layer   20

open architecture   16

Open Systems Interconnection (OSI) reference model   16

operating system   22

performance   7

physical layer   20

presentation layer   19

recovery   10

reliability   10

response time   7

security   10

sensor-based application   7

server process   25

session layer   19

throughput   9

transaction   23

transaction control process (TCP)   22

transport layer   19

wide area network (WAN)   10

REVIEW QUESTIONS

1. Characterize each of the following types of application:
   a. Inquiry/response
   b. Interactive
   c. Batch
   d. Data entry
   e. Distributed
   f. Sensor-based

2. What are the requirements of an online system?

3. What is a fault-tolerant data communications network? How does fault tolerance improve the reliability of a network?

4. List the seven layers of the OSI reference model.

5. List two functions of each layer in the OSI reference model.

6. Distinguish between the OSI service data unit (SDU), protocol control information (PCI), and protocol data unit (PDU) (see CBT module).

7. Describe the encapsulation process at a layer in the OSI reference model. That is, what is received from a higher layer, what is added, and what is produced as a result of the addition (see CBT module)?

2

MEDIA AND DATA TRANSMISSION

CHAPTER OBJECTIVES

After studying this chapter you should be able to:

- Describe the major data communications media
- Compare and contrast selected data communications media
- Describe how signals are represented
- Explain the functions of a modem
- Describe the three basic flow control protocols used in data communications
- Explain the types and sources of errors that can affect data transmissions
- Describe the ways errors are detected and corrected
- Compare and contrast digital and analog data transmission
- Characterize the transmission services provided by common carriers

*I*n Chapter 1 we examined the essential features of communication, one of which was a medium. We also gave an overview of the OSI reference model. In this chapter we examine some aspects of the OSI physical layer by looking at the various media available for transporting information, the strengths and weaknesses of each medium, and the ways to represent data during its transmission.

TRANSMISSION MEDIA

The transmission media commonly used in today's data communications networks can be divided into two major classes: conducted and wireless. **Conducted media** use a conductor such as a wire or a fiber optic cable to move the signal from sender to receiver. Conducted media include telephone wires, coaxial cables, and fiber optic cables. **Wireless media** use radio waves of different frequencies or infrared light broadcast through the air or space and hence do not need a wire conductor to convey signals. Wireless media include broadcast radio, microwave radio, satellite radio, spread spectrum radio, and infrared light. These options are listed in Table 2-1.

Table 2-1　Transmission Media

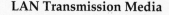

Conducted Media	Wireless Media
Electrical Conductors	Radio Frequency
Wires	Broadcast
Coaxial cable	Microwave
Light Conductors	Spread spectrum radio
Fiber optics	Light Frequency
	Infrared

Modems & Media

The conducted media most commonly used are twisted-pair wires, coaxial cable, and fiber optic cable, and microwave and satellites are the most commonly used wireless technologies. To learn more about microwave and satellite transmission, consult the CBT module entitled "Modems & Media".

LAN Transmission Media

Twisted-pair wires, coaxial cable, and fiber optic cable are commonly used in local area networks (LANs). To learn about the use of these media in LANs, you should shift to the "LAN Transmission Media" CBT module. During your exploration of this module, pay particular attention to those characteristics (speed, security, distance, and susceptibility to error) that make each medium desirable or undesirable in different situations. These attributes together with cost form the basis of the media selection criteria discussed later in the chapter.

In addition to microwave and satellite transmissions, several other wireless media are beginning to have expanded use in data communications. Among these are broadcast radio, spread spectrum radio, and infrared transmission.

Broadcast Radio

Broadcast radio employs not only the radio frequencies typical of AM and FM radio stations, but shortwave and short-distance radio frequencies as well. Broadcast radio's primary applications are in paging terminals, the devices carried by people (such as doctors) who are on call; for cellular radio telephones; for mobile computing; and in wireless LANs. When broadcast radio is used with LANs, cables connecting each computer are eliminated. The elimination of cables makes installing workstations and changing their location easier and reduces the problems of loose connections that can occur as a result of people walking or pulling on cables.

Mobile computing has significantly expanded the role of broadcast radio in data communications. The importance of mobile computing and mobile communications is such that major reallocation of the available radio frequencies may result. Mobile computing, of course, requires a wireless medium, and broadcast radio is being increasingly used in this manner. This new application of radio transmission is placing ever higher demands on a limited range of broadcast frequencies. The demand is reaching the point where some experts suggest that countries need to reevaluate the entire use of the frequency spectrum and use radio frequency transmission only for mobile communications. Nonmobile communications such as television would be delivered exclusively by conducted media, thus freeing those frequencies for mobile communication devices such as portable computers and personal communicators.

The most common media for mobile computing communications are cellular radio, radio nets, and low-orbit satellites. Cellular radio as currently implemented tends to be costly and operates at low speeds, typically 19,200 **bits per second (bps)** or lower, but higher speeds are likely as this technology expands. This makes cellular radio primarily suitable for transfers of small amounts of data such as electronic mail messages. Cellular radio transmission for data is also subject to high error rates. Low-orbiting satellites offer another communication alternative. Unlike the geosynchronous satellites, low-orbit satellites do not remain in a fixed position relative to the Earth. However, by using several low-orbit satellites, it can be assured that at least one is always in position to accept and relay signals. Use of this technology for commercial mobile computing is still in its infancy. Each of these three technologies has the disadvantages of low speed, possibility of signal interference, and lack of security.

Spread Spectrum Radio

The primary application of **spread spectrum radio (SSR)** for data communications is wireless LANs. SSR has long been used by the military to provide reliable radio communications in battlefield environments, where signal jamming can be expected. Two methods, frequency hopping and direct sequencing, are used to provide SSR signals. With **frequency hopping,** data is transmitted at one frequency, then the frequency is changed and data is transmitted at the new frequency, and so on. Each piece of data is transmitted over several frequencies to increase the probability that it will be successfully received. **Direct sequencing** sends data over several different frequencies simultaneously. When used in wireless LANs, SSR distances are limited to approximately 1000 feet, making it useful for small LANs or as the medium for small segments of larger LANs. Examples of SSR being used in a large LAN include the use of portable computers and providing LAN connections in an area in which it is difficult or expensive to install conducted media. SSR signals can penetrate normal office walls but signal strength is reduced considerably by concrete and metal walls. Like most wireless media, SSR has the disadvantage of being susceptible to signal interference and signal interception. The speed of data transmission (2 Mbps) also is slower than that of many of today's LANs using conducted media, but the speed of this technology will likely increase.

Infrared Transmission

Infrared transmission uses electromagnetic radiation of wavelengths between visible light and radio waves. Infrared transmission, like satellite and microwaves, is another line-of-sight technology. It is used to provide local area connections between buildings and also is the medium used in some wireless LANs. Data transmission rates are typically on the order of 4 Mbps or less, but, as with most transmission technologies, speed improvements can be expected. The frequencies of various wireless media are given in Table 2-2.

When deploying media for a network, a company has various choices. One alternative is to purchase and maintain the media. This is the common method used when connecting devices within a building complex. Whenever long distances must be covered, a common carrier such as a telephone company is typically used to provide communications media. Let us now look at some of the common carrier services.

COMMON CARRIER SERVICES

In the past, high-speed data links were quite expensive and were dedicated to carrying only data. Today's high-speed transmission facilities are available at low cost and, furthermore, we are able to combine data, voice, and graphic images on some of these high-speed communications links. Thus, the modern data communications manager may be responsible for the entire spectrum of corporate electronic communications; knowledge of the basic services and operations of the common carriers is important. Major offerings are briefly summarized below.

TABLE 2-2   Frequency Spectrum Classification

Frequency (Hz)	
10^{16}	X rays, gamma rays
10^{15}	Ultraviolet light
	Visible light
10^{14}	Infrared light
10^{13}	
	Millimeter waves
10^{12}	
10^{11}	Microwaves
10^{10}	UHF television
10^9	VHF television
	VHF TV (high band)
10^8	FM radio
10^7	VHF TV (low band)
	Shortwave radio
10^6	AM radio
10^5	
10^4	
10^3	Very low frequency
10^2	
10^1	

Switched Lines.   When a microcomputer user connects the microcomputer to a modem and telephone line and then dials the number for a bulletin board service or for an information utility, a **switched line** is being used. Switched lines simply make use of the existing telephone circuits and switching equipment to establish a connection between sender and receiver. This facility is available wherever telephone wires exist.

Leased Lines.   **Leased lines** are dedicated lines that are obtained from a common carrier, typically a telephone company. When a company leases a line, the circuit is allocated between the sending and receiving ends and is dedicated to the company. The circuit is always available for transmission, and the company pays only the monthly leasing fee. The fee is based on the speed of the line and the distance covered. For better reliability, leased lines may be conditioned to reduce error rates, which allows higher transmission speeds. The speed of leased lines is usually at least 9600 bps and can exceed a million bps.

Wide Band Transmission.   **Wide band transmission** allows very high data transmission rates. Transmission rates in this category are in the range of 56 Kbps and higher. Most wide band services available today are digital rather than analog.

T-1 Service.   **T-1 service,** also referred to as **DS-1 signaling,** provides digital transmission rates of 1.544 Mbps. A T-1 communications link can be created by multiplexing (combining) a number of lower speed lines. Although the implementation may vary, generally a T-1 circuit can be created by multiplexing 24 64-Kbps lines. Even higher speeds are available with **T-3** and **T-4 services,** also referred to as **DS-3** and **DS-4 signaling,** respectively. T-3 service provides a data rate of 45 Mbps and is derived from multiplexing 672 64-Kbps lines. T-4 service provides transmission at 274 Mbps and is derived from multiplexing 4032 64-Kbps lines. T-1 is the most common option; however, as the need for speed increases and the rates for T-3 and T-4 services decline, higher speed services such as T-3 are likely to become more common. One of the needs for high-speed data circuits is illustrated by the Internet, a network of networks having thousands of nodes and millions of users. During peak usage periods, billions of bits per second may be transmitted. On those Internet circuits with high utilization, T-3 and T-4 speeds are necessary to provide the expected performance.

Fractional T-n Service.   A T-1 service that began to appear in the late 1980s is known as **fractional T-1 service.** Before fractional T-1, high-speed transmission options were 56 or 64 Kbps or 1.544 Mbps with few options in between. Fractional T-1 is intended to fill this void by providing a portion of a T-1 line to customers. Organizations needing data rates higher than 64 Kbps but less than the 1.5 Mbps of a T-1 line can subscribe to fractional T-1 service. For speeds between T-1 and T-3, fractional T-3 services are available. Fractional T-n service allows a user to share a T-n line with another subscriber by using only a portion of the 64 Kbps lines that are multiplexed together to form the T-n circuit. A fractional T-1 subscriber could subscribe to 64, 128, 192, 256, and so on Kbps. Some common carriers limit the available increments by allowing multiples of 1, 2, 4, 6, 8, and 12 channels for speeds of 64, 128, 256, 384, 512, and 768 Kbps. Fractional T-n services allow the subscriber to optimize the line speed and the cost of the service.

Switched Multimegabit Data Service.   **Switched multimegabit data service (SMDS)** is a high-speed connectionless digital transmission service. **Connectionless** means the sender and receiver do not need to be connected via a dedicated line. In SMDS, the common carrier provides the user with access points for both sender and receiver. With SMDS, data is broken down into 53-byte cells for transmission. The common carrier provides high-speed switching equipment that routes these cells to their destination address. SMDS speeds are 44 Mbps but 155 Mbps services are soon likely. SMDS can be used for high-speed data transmissions such as the long-distance interconnection of LANs.

Asynchronous Transfer Mode and Frame Relay.   **Asynchronous transfer mode (ATM)** and **frame relay** are similar services that provide high-speed switching of data packets. Both provide data transfers ranging into the hundreds of megabits per second. Although differences exist between the two, we use ATM as an example of both. In ATM a user starts the transmission process by sending a block of data addressed to the recipient. The data is broken into 48-byte data packets for transmission. Five bytes of control data are appended to the 48-byte data packets, forming a 53-byte transmission frame. These frames are then transmitted to the recipient, where the 5-byte control data is stripped and the message is reassembled.

WATS.   **Wide area telecommunications** (or telephone) **service,** or **WATS,** offers both inbound and outbound services. The inbound WATS service is the familiar toll-free 800-prefix telephone numbers. A customer may subscribe to an inbound service, an outbound service, or both. The common carrier charges a flat monthly fee for the service, which provides for a specific number of hours of connect time to designated regions. The total cost of the service is based on both the number of hours of connect time and the distance to be covered by the service. When WATS service is used for data transmission, the effect is the same as using switched lines, but the cost of the call differs.

Packet-Switching Network Service.   This service allows users to establish connections between many locations for a fixed monthly fee plus a cost per packet of data sent. This facility is discussed in more detail in Chapter 8.

Satellite Service.   Users may rent satellite transponder time from a number of common carriers.

Integrated Services Digital Networks.   Increased use of common carrier facilities for data communications has prompted providers of such services to evaluate their networks. One conclusion that has been drawn is the need for the **integrated services digital network (ISDN),** which is one network capable of transmitting data in various forms. These forms could include digital data, voice, facsimile (fax), graphics, and video. The benefits to the user community of this type of network are higher transmission speed and potential cost reductions for communications services resulting from the ability to combine multiple data forms onto one network. Two objectives of ISDNs are to allow this integration of data types over one medium and to provide international data exchange. The first mission of the ISDN program has been to define the functions and characteristics of the network and to establish implementation standards. In 1984, the **Consultative Committee on International Telegraph and Telephony (CCITT)** produced the first of what is likely to become several standards for ISDN implementations. This standard provides for several different types of service so it can meet the needs of diverse users.

The ISDN system specifies three basic types of channels designated as B, D, and H types. Table 2-3 shows the various channel types and options that are available. ISDNs will initially provide two interface structures designated as basic service and primary service. The basic service is designated as $2B^{64}$ + D^{16}, which indicates that it consists of two type B channels and one 16-Kbps type D channel, for an aggregate speed of 144 Kbps. The primary service has a different configuration for North America and Japan than for Europe. The North American and Japanese specification is designated as $23B^{64}$ + D^{64}, for an aggregate speed of 1.544 Mbps. This is the same speed as the T-1 service. In Europe, the primary service is designated as $30B^{64}$ + D^{64}, for an aggregate speed of 2.048 Mbps, equivalent to the European version of T-1 transmission.

Table 2-3   ISDN Channel Types and Options

ISDN Channel Types

   B—64 Kbps

   H0—384 Kbps(=6B)

   H11—1.544 Mbps (=23B + ID^{64})—North America and Japan

   H12—2.048 Mbps (=30B + $ID^{64)}$—Europe

Control Data

   D—Both 16 and 64 Kbps

Basic Service Options

   $2B^{64}$ + D^{16} = 144 Kbps

Primary Service

   $23B^{64}$ + D^{64} = 1.544Mbps—North America and Japan

   $30B^{64}$ + D^{64} = 2.048 Mbps—Europe

As an emerging technology, ISDNs have great potential for data transfer and the integration of different forms of data. All the uses for ISDNs have not yet been identified, but possible applications include:

- Digital voice transmission
- LANs (see Chapter 5 for additional information)
- Office automation (routing and access to documents)
- Security via transmission of graphic images, such as signatures for check cashing verification or freeze-frame images to security guards
- High-speed switched data lines, for example to provide faster Internet access
- Video telephone service
- Concurrent transfer of voice and data (for example, two users can be engaged in a telephone conversation while simultaneously transmitting data between their workstations)

Cellular Radio Telephone. **Cellular radio telephone** provides mobile telephone connections. The telephones often are installed in vehicles, but that is not required. A mobile telephone can be carried by a pedestrian or cyclist. Currently cellular telephones are available only in major metropolitan areas because it is not economical to establish the facilities in areas of low population density. It is likely that satellite transmission will be added to existing systems and thereby overcome this limitation.

Figure 2-1 shows a diagram of a cellular system. Transmission is via FM radio broadcast. Before cellular technology, signals for a major metropolitan area were broadcast from a central site like ordinary radio station signals. Because of the limited available channels (dictated by the assigned frequencies), only a limited number of calls could be in progress at one time. With cellular technology, the calling area is divided into cells, each of which is serviced by a transmitting station. The transmissions are low power and thus serve only that cell, allowing the same frequency to be used concurrently by nonadjacent cells. As a mobile user moves from one cell to another, the responsibility for transmission is passed from the cell being exited to the cell being entered. Because cellular technology provides connection to line-based telephone networks, the full range of data transmission capabilities that exists for regular telephone service is available. Some cars are now equipped with facsimile machines for mobile fax transfers, and it is possible to connect portable computers in mobile stations to computer networks.

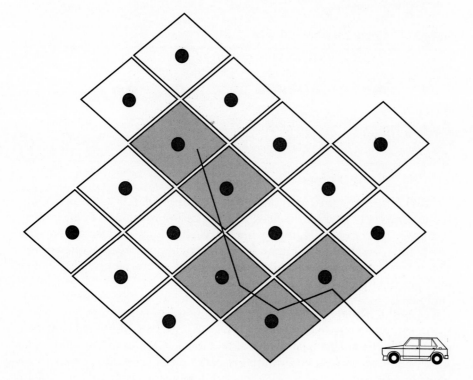

Figure 2-1

A Cellular Radio
Telephone System

PBX and Centrex Services.   Private branch exchange, or **PBX,** can be used as a delivery mechanism for a LAN. **Centrex service** is essentially a PBX service provided by a common carrier. Instead of the switching equipment being located on the customer's premises, the common carrier provides the switching equipment on the common carrier's site. Several locations in a city can share the same switch and use the same calling prefix, thereby allowing extension dialing as though the telephones were located in one building and served by an onsite PBX. As with a PBX, Centrex service can be used to transmit data as well as voice.

MEDIA SELECTION CRITERIA

Several factors (Table 2-4) influence the choice of a medium for a data communications network. Because every configuration has its own set of constraints, not all factors apply in every situation; in some situations, there may even be only a single viable alternative. However, system designers must consider each criterion, either implicitly or explicitly. The factors also may influence one another. For example, a strong correlation often exists between a medium's application and its required speed, so much so that the application usually dictates a minimum acceptable transmission speed (although other factors such as cost and expandability can also pertain).

Table 2-4   Media Selection Criteria

Cost	Security
Speed or capacity	Distance
Availability	Environment
Expandability	Application
Error rates	Maintenance

Cost.   A dramatic expansion in the application of data communications began during the 1970s, influenced strongly by improvements in technology and lower costs. Cost reductions were the result of improved technology and competition among the common carriers providing transmission services. The technological advances included communications equipment capable of supporting higher data transmission rates at lower costs, as well as the commercial availability of fiber optics and satellite transmission. The costs associated with a given transmission medium include not only the costs of the medium but also ancillary fees, such as the costs for additional hardware and software that might be required. A deferred ancillary cost that is important to consider when making an initial selection is the cost of expansion. An emerging marketing organization located in Houston, Texas, might initially select the specific market areas of New York City, Chicago, Houston, and

Los Angeles. The logical choice for connecting the remote offices to the host computer in Houston is to lease a line from a common carrier. As the corporation expands into other cities, however, a satellite link could be more economical because the expense of adding new satellite locations might be less than that of leasing more land lines.

Speed.   A tremendous range of transmission speeds is available. Low-speed circuits transmit at rates less than 100 bps; high-speed circuits, at more than 100 Mbps. Within a given medium, higher speeds mean higher costs, though this is not necessarily attributable to the medium itself. Higher data transmission rates require more sophisticated (expensive) communications equipment. Two factors dictate the required speed of a medium: response time and aggregate data rate. Design goals for an online application should include the expected response time for each type of transaction. **Aggregate data rate** refers to the amount of information that can be transmitted per unit of time. Commonly used media speeds are summarized in Table 2-5.

Table 2-5   Media and Their Common Transmission Speeds

Switched line	300, 1200, 2400, 4800, 9600, 14,400, 19,200, 28,800, 38,400
Leased line	2400, 4800, 9600, 19,200, 56,000, 64,000
T1, T2, T3, T4	1.5M, 6.3M, 45M, 274M
Unshielded twisted pair	1M, 10M, 16M, 100M
Shielded twisted pair	1M, 10M, 16M, 100M
Coaxial cable	1M, 2M, 10M, 50M, 100M (over 400M potential)
Fiber optics	over 2 Gbps
Microwave	to 45M
Broadcast radio	9600, 19,200
Spread spectrum radio	2M
Infrared light	1M, 4M
Satellite	to 50M

Response Time.   Response time has two components, transmission time and processing time, and each of these can be broken down into subcomponents. Suppose the design objective is a response time of 3 seconds for 95 percent of one type of transaction. If processing takes 1 second, transmission must take 2 seconds or less. If the transaction involves the exchange of 500 characters of information, then the speed of the medium must be at least 250 characters per second (500 characters divided by 2 seconds), which represents approximately 2400 bps. This assumes there is no sharing of the communications link. If the line is shared, allowances must be made for the amount of time that the line might be unavailable to a specific user. Chapter 6 discusses several ways that one communications line can be shared among several users.

Aggregate Data Rate.   In applications such as bulk data transfers, aggregate data rate may be the factor dictating line speed. Suppose the application just discussed required that the line be available to office personnel during the day for inquiries and updates and that within an hour of closing time a file of 2 million characters had to be transmitted to a host computer. The business-day requirements for response time could be satisfied with a 2400-bps channel, but the file transfer would require an aggregate data rate of about 555 characters per second (2 million characters per hour divided by 3600 seconds per hour), which is a 7200-bps channel. (Note: These examples do not allow for any overhead or re-transmissions due to errors.)

Availability.   Availability has two aspects: (1) Is the medium available when it is needed, and (2) is there sufficient carrying capacity to handle the volume of data? An operation that uses a switched telephone line would be at a disadvantage when phone lines are busy, as on certain holidays. Imagine a fast-food chain with stores throughout the United States that maintains a central file of sales and inventory data. Each store's terminals record the daily receipts and foods dispensed. At the end of the business day the central location dials the phone number of each store's computer, transfers and processes the data collected during the day, and then orders supplies for each restaurant. On Mother's Day the phone circuits are extremely busy, which interferes with the chain's ability to contact all of its locations. This lack of availability would not be catastrophic for this application, but for a process control or factory control application, lack of availability could produce disastrous results.

Shared Lines.   Shared lines also can create problems of availability. One user may monopolize the line, thus making it unavailable to others. Suppose two terminals share a line, and one user is attempting interactive queries into a database while the other attempts to copy a lengthy file to an attached printer. The line's capacity may be taken up with the file transfer, making the line unavailable to the other user.

Distance.   Distance includes not only transmission distance but also the number of locations served. If the distances are short (within one building or complex of buildings), private media such as wires, coaxial cable, or fiber optics may be feasible. With greater distance or number of locations, it usually becomes necessary to obtain media from a common carrier. As the number of locations to be reached becomes very great, or when it is necessary to communicate with remote locations, a broadcast medium such as a satellite may be the only viable solution.

Environment.   The constraints of environment can eliminate certain types of media. Even when the distance between two buildings to be connected in a data communications network is small enough to make private lines feasible, local ordinances may prohibit the user from installing such lines. If a locale prohibits the stringing of wire over or under a public street, the user might have to pick a medium other than private wires. Direct satellite links in leased office facilities might be impossible because the lease prohibits installing Earth stations on the premises. Private lines that must be strung through areas with considerable electrical or magnetic interference might be impractical because of the potential for inducing errors in transmission.

Application.   Certain applications (such as environmental monitoring) employ devices designed to connect to a system in a very specific way and at specific speeds. In such applications, the characteristics of the required equipment may dictate the type of medium and interfaces to be used. As noted above, the particulars of an application also help determine other required characteristics of the medium, such as speed, security, and availability. For instance, the most obvious media for a high-speed LAN are twisted-pair wires, coaxial cable, and fiber optics, whereas the private branch exchange telephone system would be a lower speed alternative.

Maintenance.   Just as all media are subject to error, all are subject to failure. In some cases repair or replacement is simple: A telephone cable severed in an excavation accident can be repaired within several days, and while repairs are being made an alternate path might be made available. Repair or replacement of a defective satellite, however, is a lengthy process, which is why communications companies frequently have a backup transponder available. Maintenance concerns may not have a high priority because such failures are infrequent. Nonetheless, system designers must consider the impact of medium failures and their probable duration and must prepare a backup or contingency plan so communications can continue while repairs are being made. In a recent study of financial institutions, over 60 percent estimated they would be out of business if their computer systems were down for over two days. To provide high reliability, a major bank in Australia that depended heavily on its computer center established multiple computer centers, each serviced by different telecommunications trunk lines. It also made provisions for switching lines from one center to another should the communications links to one of the centers be severed. As a result, no failure at a single point was able to disrupt the bank's ability to process data.

A comparison of the principal data communications media is provided in Table 2-6. In some instances it is difficult to separate one criterion from another. Consider the expandability of a network that uses wires. One expansion option may be to add new hardware instead of new lines. Suppose a company needs to add two more terminals in a location that currently has only one. Instead of adding two new communication lines, a hardware device called a multiplexer can be installed at each end of the connection. A multiplexer will allow all three terminals to share the same line. (Multiplexers are covered in Chapter 6.)

Table 2-6   Media Comparison Table

	Wires	Coaxial Cable	Fiber Optics	Microwave	Broadcast Radio	Satellite
Availability	Good	Good	Good	Good	Possible contention	Fair to good
Expandability	Fair	Good in local areas	Good	Good	Good	Good
Errors	Fair	Good	Good	Fair	Fair	Fair
Security	Fair	Fair	Good	Poor	Poor	Poor
Distance	Good	Poor	Good	Good	Good	Good
Environment	Fair	Good	Good	Fair	Fair	Fair

Another expansion option is to allow the three terminals to share the same line using a technique called polling. Polling is also discussed in Chapter 6. Another alternative is to add two new communication lines. If this last alternative is chosen, there is usually no problem in obtaining the circuit. Unfortunately, the cost may be high, which is why this cell in table 2-6 is assigned a rating of fair. Table 2-6 should be used in conjunction with Table 2-5, on transmission speeds, because it is important that each device communicating on a medium have sufficient access and speed to perform its task. Configurations such as the line-sharing ones just mentioned will reduce the availability of the medium to individual attached devices. This means that with one type of multiplexer on a 9600-bps line with four devices, the available speed to an individual device will be only 2400 bps.

DATA FLOW

Every data communications network must have some mechanism of control over the flow of data. This is accomplished at two levels. The first level provides for contention control, which determines which stations may transmit, the conditions under which transmission of data is allowed, and the pacing of data transmission. Contention control is discussed in subsequent chapters. The other, more basic level of data flow relates to the transmission equipment used: lines, modems, and devices. The three elementary types of data flow are simplex, half duplex, and full duplex.

Simplex Transmission.   In **simplex transmissions** data may flow in only one direction, like traffic on a one-way street. Radio and television transmissions, illustrated in Figure 2-2(a), are examples. One station assumes the role of transmitter and the other station is the receiver; these roles may not be reversed. Although this may appear rather limiting, simplex transmission has numerous applications. Receive-only devices such as keyboards, microcomputer monitors, and optical character recognition (OCR) scanners involve simplex communication. A building environmental monitoring system also operates in this mode, sending temperature and humidity readings to a computer that controls the heating and cooling of the building. Simplex lines are less common in business applications than half duplex or full duplex.

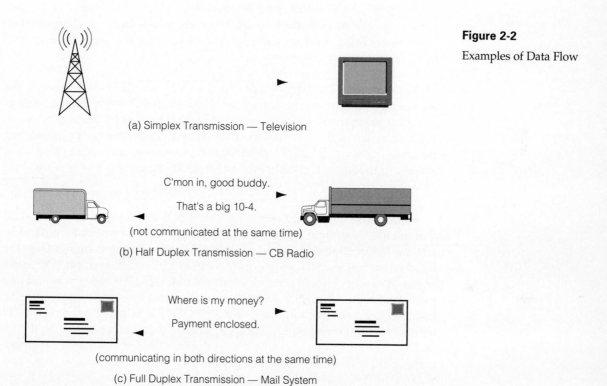

(a) Simplex Transmission — Television

C'mon in, good buddy.

That's a big 10-4.

(not communicated at the same time)

(b) Half Duplex Transmission — CB Radio

Where is my money?

Payment enclosed.

(communicating in both directions at the same time)

(c) Full Duplex Transmission — Mail System

Figure 2-2

Examples of Data Flow

Half-Duplex Transmission. In **half-duplex transmission,** data may travel in both directions, although only in one direction at a time, like traffic on a one-lane bridge. Figure 2-2(b) shows the example of citizens band (CB) radio, where radio operators on the same frequency may be either sender or receiver but not both at the same time.

Full-Duplex Transmission. In **full-duplex transmission,** data can be traveling in both directions simultaneously, like traffic on a two-way street. An example of data transmission using full-duplex capabilities is the postal service: Letters can be transmitted in both directions simultaneously, as illustrated in Figure 2-2(c).

SIGNAL REPRESENTATION AND MODULATION

As noted above, each medium has individual characteristics that determine how and where it might be used. The medium serves as a conduit for data. It is also important to understand how data can be represented on the medium. The two basic classes of representing data are analog and digital. Let us now look at how data are transmitted.

Bit Rates, Baud Rates, and Bandwidth.   Up to this point, data transmission speed has been discussed exclusively in bits per second, or **bit rate.** This bit rate is the most appropriate unit for systems analysis; however, two other terms also are commonly used: bandwidth and baud rate.

Bandwidth.   The **bandwidth** of a channel is the difference between the minimum and maximum frequencies allowed. A voice-grade channel that can transmit frequencies between 300 and 3400 hertz (Hz) has a bandwidth of 3100 Hz. Bandwidth is a measure of the amount of data that can be transmitted per unit of time and is directly proportional to the maximum data transmission speed of a medium. The higher the bandwidth, the greater the data-carrying capacity.

Baud Rate.   The **baud rate** is a measure of the number of discrete signals that can be transmitted per second. Unfortunately, the terms *baud rate* and *bit rate* are frequently used interchangeably. But the bit rate is higher than the baud rate when a signal represents more than 1 bit of information. Suppose a signal represents 1 bit of data. If the signal changes 1200 times a second, the baud rate would be 1200 and the bit rate would be 1200 bps. Suppose, instead, that a signal could represent 2 bits. This is possible if the signal can assume four different states, one each for the bit combinations of 00, 01, 10, and 11. This technique is referred to as **dibits.** Given this situation, suppose a signaling rate of 1200 changes per second is maintained. The baud rate remains at 1200, but the bit rate doubles to 2400 bps because each signal represents 2 bits. Figure 2-3 shows the transmission of the bit pattern 1001001 using dibits (with 1 bit added to make the number of bits even). Similarly, 8 signal levels could represent 3 bits with each signal, a technique referred to as **tribits.** If 16 different signaling levels were used, 4 bits per signal could be represented, a technique referred to as **quadbits.** Hence, with current technology the bit rate equals the baud rate or a multiple thereof (two, three, or four times the baud rate). **Phase-shift keying (PSK)** or a derivative is the most common method of achieving dibit and tribit transfer; **quadrature amplitude modulation (QAM)** is the most common method for quadbit transfer. Later in this chapter we explain how PSK and QAM are implemented.

Digital versus Analog Representation.   All the computers we are considering store data in digital form and transmit this data in analog or digital form. In **digital transmission,** data is represented by a series of distinct entities. In data communications equipment this series is almost always a binary digit, or bit—either 0 or 1. **Analog transmission** refers to measurable physical quantities, which in data communications take the form of voltages and variations in the properties of waves. Data is represented in analog form by varying characteristics of a wave. Translation from digital format to analog format and back to digital format is accomplished by a device known as a **data set** or **modem** (an abbreviation for *modulator-demodulator*). A modem functions to accept digital data (a string of bits), transform the data into an analog signal, and pass the signal along a medium to another modem. The receiving modem translates the analog signal back into digital data. Because the telephone companies' original communications systems transmit information in analog form, data communication systems must change digital data to analog form to meet the requirements of data communications transmission facilities. In a subsequent section we discuss modem capabilities. First, we look at a method for representing data in analog format.

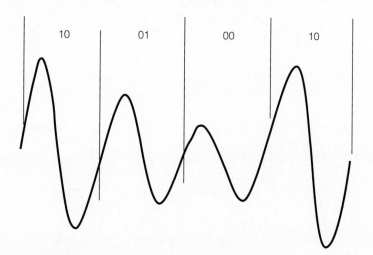

Figure 2-3

Example of Dibits Using Amplitude Modulation

Carrier Signals. One of the trigonometric relationships between angles in a right triangle is called the sine of the angle. The values for the sine of an angle vary from 1 to −1, and a continuous curve of this function can be plotted. Figure 2-4 depicts a simple sine wave. A wave of this form has the potential for carrying information. If the wave continues without change, as depicted, no information can be discerned. Such an unmodulated signal is called a **carrier signal.** The purpose of a modem is to change, or modulate, the characteristics of the carrier wave so a receiver can interpret information. The simple sine wave has several properties that can be altered to represent data: amplitude (height), frequency (period), and phase (relative starting point). Modems alter one or more of these characteristics to represent data.

$y = \sin x$

Figure 2-4

A Simple Sine Wave

Amplitude Modulation. The simplest characteristic to visualize is **amplitude modulation (AM).** Figure 2-5 represents two sine waves superimposed on one another. One curve represents sin x and the other represents $2 \sin x$. Note that the $2 \sin x$ curve has twice the amplitude of the sin x curve. (Varying the amplitude of a curve is similar to changing the voltage on a line.) How is this variation used to convey information? Suppose the bit pattern 1001001 is to be transmitted. If a 1 bit is represented by the curve of $2 \sin x$ and a 0 bit by the curve traced by sin x, the bit pattern would be represented by the modulated sine curve depicted in Figure 2-6.

Figure 2-5

Superimposed Sine Waves, Example 1

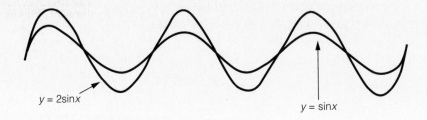

Figure 2-6

Amplitude Modulation

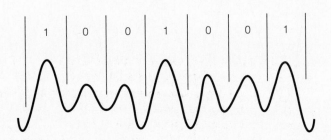

Frequency Modulation.   The period, or frequency, of a sine curve is the interval required for the curve to complete one entire cycle. In the simple sine curve the period is 2 pi, where pi is approximately 3.14159. In data transmission such intervals are measured in fractions of a second, so the period is the number of seconds required for the wave to complete one cycle. The mathematical function that alters the period is sin nx. Figure 2-7 shows the curve of sin $2x$. When the horizontal axis represents time, the period is frequency (oscillations) per unit of time. Hertz (Hz) is the term used to denote frequency; one hertz is one cycle per second. The human ear can detect sound waves with frequencies between 20 and 20,000 Hz. Telephone systems use the much smaller frequency range between 300 and 3400 Hz, which is satisfactory for carrying voice transmission.

To convey information by **frequency modulation (FM)** is to vary the frequency of the transmission. To transmit the binary pattern 1001001 by frequency modulation on a voice-grade line, a frequency of 1300 Hz can represent the 1 bit and a frequency of 2100 Hz can represent the 0 bit (the actual values used by some modems). The signal received must be within 10 Hz of these values to be acceptable, which means the range for a 1 bit is 1290–1310 Hz. These frequency values must be different enough to minimize the possibility of signal distortion altering the values transmitted. Thus, if the 1 bit were represented by 1500 Hz and the 0 bit by 1510 Hz, a decrease of only 10 Hz would change a 0 bit into a 1 bit. Figure 2-8 shows an example of frequency modulation for our selected bit pattern 1001001.

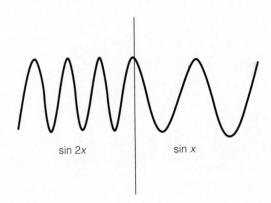

Figure 2-7

The Curve of Sin $2x$

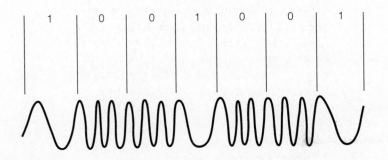

Figure 2-8

Frequency Modulation

Phase Modulation. A third modulation technique is **phase modulation** (phase shifting). If the simple sine curve is represented by sin x, then a change of phase is represented by sin $(x + n)$. Figure 2-9 shows the curve of sin x, Figure 2-10 shows the curve of sin $(x +$ pi$)$, and Figure 2-11 shows the two curves superimposed on one another. Transmitting the bit pattern of 1001001 using phase modulation — where a 1 bit is represented by no phase change and a 0 bit by a change in phase of pi radians — yields the curve in Figure 2-12.

Phase modulation is often used for high-speed modems because it lends itself well to the implementation of dibits, tribits, and quadbits. Figure 2-13(a) shows eight different angles in a full circle. Suppose each angle is used as a phase shift in phase modulation. Thus, with eight different signals we can represent 3 bits of information per signal, or tribits. In Figure 2-13(b) the eight angles are combined with two levels (amplitudes) of signal, providing 16 different signals, each of which can represent 4 bits. This combination provides a quadbit capability known as quadrature amplitude modulation (QAM). QAM on a 2400-baud line can provide transmission of 9600 bps. The most common modulation techniques in data communications are frequency modulation, also known as **frequency-shift keying (FSK),** and phase modulation, also known as phase shift keying (PSK). Also available are variations known as **differential phase-shift keying (DPSK)** and QAM.

Figure 2-9

The Curve of Sin x

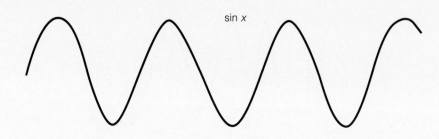

$\sin x$

Figure 2-10

The Curve of Sin $x + \pi$

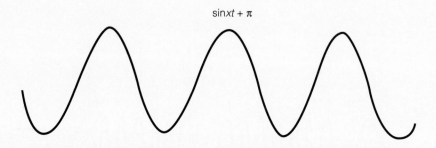

$\sin xt + \pi$

Figure 2-11

Superimposed Sine Waves, Example 2

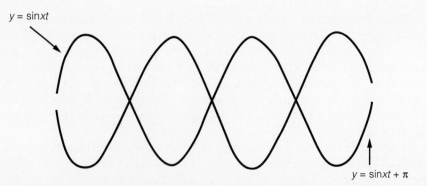

$y = \sin xt$

$y = \sin xt + \pi$

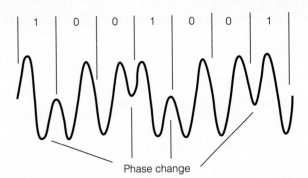

Figure 2-12

Phase Modulation

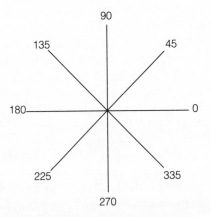

(a) Eight different phase changes,
    suitable for tribits

Figure 2-13 (a)

Phase Modulation Angles

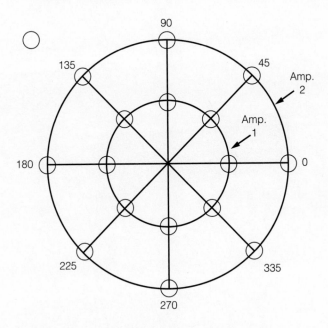

(b) Eight phase changes plus two amplitudes yields 16
    different signals, for quadbits
    The 16 different signals are represented by circles

Figure 2-13 (b)

Phase Modulation Angles
and Amplitudes

The analog representation just described is used in many common carrier communications networks. Be aware, however, that there are other ways of representing data in analog format. For example, changing the voltage on a wire can also be used to represent data. No voltage may represent a 0 bit and three volts may be used to represent a 1 bit.

MODEMS AND THEIR CAPABILITIES

Modems fall into two categories; copper-based and fiber optic. Copper-based modems are used to interface to twisted-pair wires, and fiber optic modems are used with fiber optic cable. The principle of both types of modems is essentially the same: changing signals from one format to another and then back again. Copper-based modems change a device's digital signals to analog electrical signals, whereas fiber optic modems change a device's digital signals to optical digital signals. When the supplier of fiber optic cable is a common carrier, the common carrier is responsible for signal generation. A company that installs its own fiber optic cables may need to purchase its own fiber optic modems.

Modems that are used to transmit data over communications links are always used in pairs. The modems in a pair must be configured alike. Most modems have a variety of available options. Figure 2-14 shows a modem. Some modem capabilities are presented in Table 2-7, and a terminal-computer connection using modems is illustrated in Figure 2-15. Most modems on the market do not offer all of these capabilities. Some options are explained here; the remainder are discussed in Chapter 6.

Figure 2-14

A High-Speed Modem

Table 2-7 Some Modem Capabilities

Speed and variable speed

Auto-answer

Manual answer

Auto-dial

Manual dial

Auto-disconnect

Manual disconnect

Programmable control (e.g., computer-controlled dialing and setting of data rate)

Automatic redial

Keyboard dial

Speaker (to monitor dialing and connection)

Synchronous or asynchronous

Full or half duplex

Compression

Reverse channel

Secondary channel

Multiport

Line conditioning capabilities (equalization)

Self-testing mode

Voice-over data

Fax

Compatibility with:

    Bell modems

    Hayes modems

    Microcomputer Network Protocol (MNP)

        MNP4—error correction

        MNP5—data compression

Consultative Committee on International Telegraph and Telephony (CCITT) standards

Elecronic Industries Association (EIA) standards

U.S. government standards

Figure 2-15

Terminal Computer
Connection Using Modems

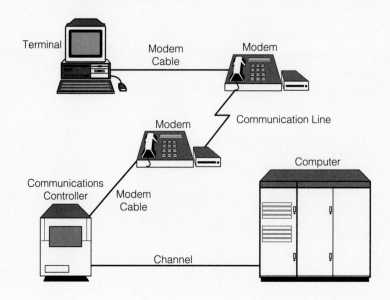

Speed.   All modems are designed to operate at a specific speed or range of discrete speeds. A variable-speed modem can be set via switches on the modem, via program control, or by automatic adjustment to the transmission speed.

Telephone Options.   Auto-answer, manual-answer, auto-dial, auto-disconnect, auto-redialing, and keyboard dialing all refer to use of switched telephone lines. Most modems can react to the ring indicator on the line and automatically answer a call. For a manual-answer modem, someone must help in making the connection. This "inconvenience" actually promotes security. Auto-dialing means the modem can dial a number itself. Many modems can remember frequently called numbers. Each memory location can usually be associated with a code name, making dialing even easier. For example, the code name "school" can be used to represent the telephone number for the school's computer center. The user can then direct the modem to dial school rather than selecting the specific number. With autodisconnect a modem terminates a call automatically when the other party hangs up or a disconnect message is received. Auto-redialing modems automatically redial a call that resulted in a busy signal or no connection. Finally, keyboard or programmable dialing means the number can be dialed using the keyboard of a terminal or via program control. For mobile computing, cellular radio, broadcast radio, and pocket modems are available. Pocket modems are pocket-sized modems used primarily for portable computers. Modems conforming to the Personal Computer Memory Card International Association (PCMCIA) standards are available for notebook-class computers. Pocket, PCMCIA, and radio frequency modems are relatively recent technologies and show that mobile computing is becoming an important segment of the data communications market.

Self-Testing.   Most new modems, and many older models, have some type of self-testing mode. These include a loop-back test, in which the modem's outgoing signal is looped back to itself; memory diagnostic checks; and modem-to-modem test transmissions. These self-tests are quite valuable in isolating problems in the communications equipment.

Compatibility.   A variety of modem standards exist, and adherence to widely accepted standards helps establish modem compatibility. In the past, governing standards were supplied by AT&T and the Hayes Corporation. Today, the controlling modem standards are provided by the CCITT

Modems & Media

You can learn some of the details of several CCITT standards through the CBT module entitled "Modems & Media".

TRANSMISSION ERRORS

All data transmissions are subject to error, although some media are more susceptible than others. Contextual recognition of errors is usually impossible in data communications systems. If the data transmitter and receiver are computers, it is virtually impossible for editing routines to determine whether one or more bits have been changed; even if data is displayed on a terminal, the operator may be unable to discern all the errors. If a bank teller interrogates a customer's account balance as illustrated in Figure 2-16, it is unlikely that the teller would recognize that a 1-bit error had altered the balance from $100 to $228. Errors can be induced during data transmission in a number of ways.

Figure 2-16

A Transmission Error

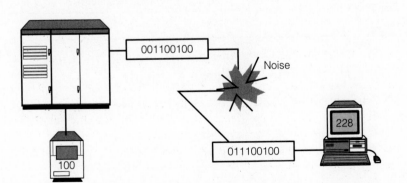

Perhaps you have experienced signal distortion on your television, radio, stereo system, or telephone resulting from a loose connection or a connection disrupted because someone stepped on or otherwise disrupted the wires. This static or distortion called **impulse noise,** is disconcerting for music or speech but may be disastrous for data communications because it might change a 0 bit to a 1 bit or vice versa. Errors of this nature are called **impulse errors** and are one of the most common causes of errors in data communications. Other sources of impulse errors are lightning strikes and interference from the environment. For example, when data communications wires are strung through an elevator shaft, through a machine shop, or over fluorescent lights, the electromagnetic fields emitted in these environments can cause signal disruption in unshielded wires.

When talking to a person, you have undoubtedly noticed that the voice signals fade over distance, a phenonenom known as **attenuation.** Data transmitted over any medium suffers from weakening over distance. Telephone companies overcome this problem with amplifiers or repeaters that regenerate the signal to maintain its original strength. Other problems we experience in transmitting data include echoing of signals and **crosstalk,** or the spilling of signals from one communications channel onto another channel.

Impact of Data Errors

Table 2-8 shows the possible effects of impulse noise of various durations, for different line speeds. It is significant that fewer bits are subject to error when transmission is at lower rather than higher speeds. Although the figure applies to any type of noise for the same durations, impulse noise was chosen because it is one of the most common types of noise affecting telephone wires. The most significant thing shown by Table 2-8 is that the potential number of bit errors increases with both duration of the noise and line speed. Although the ideal is to eliminate all errors in data, a goal of fewer than 1 error per 100,000 bits is considered adequate. (Most line media and radio-wave transmission systems are designed for fewer than 1 error per 1 million bits transmitted.)

Table 2-8   Potential Number of Corrupted Data Bits

Line Speed (bps)	Impulse Noise Duration (milliseconds)				
	0.2	0.4	0.6	0.8	1.0
300	0.06	0.12	0.18	0.24	0.30
1200	0.24	0.48	0.72	0.96	1.20
2400	0.48	0.96	1.44	1.92	2.40
4800	0.96	1.92	2.88	3.84	4.80
9600	1.92	3.84	5.76	7.68	9.60
19,200	3.84	7.68	11.52	15.36	19.20

ERROR PREVENTION

The best method to guard against data errors is to correct their source. Eliminating all noise is impossible, but error prevention techniques can reduce the probability of error corruption in the data. Such techniques include telephone line conditioning, reducing transmission speed, shielding, line drivers, and using better quality equipment.

Telephone Line Conditioning.   When a line is leased from a telephone company, **conditioning,** sometimes referred to as equalization, can be included for an additional charge. The two classes of conditioning are Class C and Class D, with four commercial levels of Class C conditioning: C1, C2, C4, and C5. Each level of Class C conditioning provides increasingly stringent constraints on the amplitude and phase distortion permitted on the line. A line with C5 conditioning should be more error-free than a line with C1 conditioning. One useful aspect of the relatively new Class D conditioning is that the telephone company will inspect the circuits available between the desired communication points to select the circuit with the least amount of noise. Users can also obtain equipment, such as certain modems, that aids in the conditioning of lines.

Lower Transmission Speed.   A bit error is much less likely to occur at lower transmission speeds. Some modems adjust their speed automatically or via program control to accommodate noisy lines. With a high-quality line, such a modem may operate at 28,800 bps; if the quality of the line deteriorates, the modem has the capability of switching to a lower speed, for example 14,400 bps.

Shielding.   Although additional shielding of leased telephone cables is not a user option, shielding can be provided for private lines to reduce the amount of crosstalk and impulse noise from the environment. Media shielding in the form of coaxial cable or shielded twisted-pair wires is frequently used for LAN media.

Line Drivers (Repeaters).   **Line drivers,** or **repeaters,** can be placed at intervals along a communications line to amplify and forward the signal. Digital signal noise can usually be eliminated, because the signal is being regenerated. For analog signals, however, it is difficult to separate most noise from the signal; noise that is picked up also will be amplified by the repeaters. The function of repeaters is to restore signals to their full strength and overcome signal loss due to attenuation.

Better Equipment.   Because some older mechanical equipment and some older transformers and power supplies are more likely to produce noise than newer equipment (such as electronic switches), replacing older components with better equipment can reduce the amount of noise.

ERROR DETECTION

Unfortunately, the remedies just cited to minimize the number of errors may be impractical from either a cost or a feasibility standpoint. Because error elimination is impossible, it is also necessary to determine whether a transmission error has occurred and, if errors have occurred, to return the data to proper form. Error detection algorithms in data communications networks are based on the transmission of redundant information. In telegraphy, one way to ensure correctness of data is to transmit each character twice. This is not entirely error-proof, so it could be taken one or more steps further by sending each character three or more times. Although this might increase the reliability of the transmission, line utilization drops dramatically. As the error rate approaches zero, so does the effective utilization of the medium. Some middle-ground approach clearly is required that can detect almost all errors without significantly reducing the data-carrying capacity of the medium.

Parity Check

One of the simplest and most widely used forms of error detection is known as a **parity check** or **vertical redundancy check (VRC).** A parity check involves adding a bit—known as the parity bit—to each character during transmission. The parity bit is selected so the total number of 1 bits in the code representation of each character adds up to either an even number (even parity) or an odd number (odd parity). Each character is checked upon receipt to see whether the number of 1 bits is even or odd. Consider the string of characters DATA COMM as coded in 7-bit ASCII with odd parity. The representations of these characters plus the parity bit for odd parity are given in Table 2-9. It can be seen that the number of 1 bits in each eight-bit sequence (octet) is always odd (either one, three, five, or seven); it is the parity bit that ensures this. If even parity were chosen, the parity bit would be selected so the number of 1 bits would always be an even number.

Table 2-9   Parity Bit Generation

Letter	ASCII	Parity Bit	Transmitted Bits
D	1000100	1	10001001
A	1000001	1	10000011
T	1010100	0	10101000
A	1000001	1	10000011
space	0100000	0	01000000
C	1000011	0	10000110
O	1001111	0	10011110
M	1001101	1	10011011
M	1001101	1	10011011

In the odd parity example in Table 2-9 each character transmitted consists of eight bits—seven for data and one for parity. Parity enables the user to detect whether one, three, five, or seven bits have been altered in transmission, but it will not catch whether an even number (two, four, six, or eight bits) has been altered. One common error situation involves burst errors, or a grouping of errors (recall the possible effect of impulse noise during high transmission rates). The likelihood of detecting errors of this nature with a parity check is approximately 50 percent. At higher transmission speeds this limitation becomes significant. (A burst error for the duration of two bits does not necessarily result in two bit errors. None, one, or two bits could be affected.)

Longitudinal Redundancy Check

We can increase the probability of error detection beyond that provided by parity by making, in addition, a **longitudinal redundancy check (LRC).** With LRC, which is similar to VRC, an additional, redundant character called the **block check character (BCC)** is appended to a block of transmitted characters, typically at the end of the block. The first bit of the BCC serves as a parity check for all of the first bits of the characters in the block, the second bit of the BCC serves as parity for all of the second bits in the block, and so on. Table 2-10 is an example of LRC. An odd parity scheme has been chosen to perform the redundancy check, so each column has an odd number of 1 bits.

Table 2-10   Longitudinal Redundancy Check (LRC) Generation

Letter	ASCII	Parity Bit	Transmitted Bits
D	1000100	1	10001001
A	1000001	1	10000011
T	1010100	0	10101000
A	1000001	1	10000011
space	0100000	0	01000000
C	1000011	0	10000110
O	1001111	0	10011110
M	1001101	1	10011011
M	1001101	1	10011011
BCC	1000011	0	10000110

LRC combined with VRC is still not sufficient to detect all errors (no scheme is completely dependable). Table 2-11 presents the same DATA COMM message transmission, with errors introduced in rows and columns marked by an asterisk. Although both LRC and VRC appear correct, the data received is not the same as that transmitted. Adding LRC to VRC brings a greater probability of detecting errors in transmission.

Table 2-11   LRC Transmission Errors

Letter	ASCII	Parity Bit	Transmitted Bits
D	$\overset{**}{1000100}$	1	10001001
A	1000001	1	10000011
T	*1100100	0	10101000
A	*1110001	1	10000011
space	0100000	0	01000000
C	1000011	0	10000110
O	1001111	0	10011110
M	1001101	1	10011011
M	1001101	1	10011011
BCC	1000011	0	10000110

Cyclic Redundancy Check

A **cyclic redundancy check (CRC)** can detect bit errors better than either VRC or LRC or both. A CRC is computed for a block of transmitted data. The transmitting station generates the CRC and transmits it with the data. The receiving station computes the CRC for the data received and compares it to the CRC transmitted by the sender. If the two are equal, then the block is assumed to be error-free. CRC can detect:

- All single-bit and double-bit errors
- All errors in cases in which an odd number of bits are erroneous
- Two pairs of adjacent errors
- All burst errors of 16 bits or fewer
- More than 99.998 percent of all burst errors greater than 16 bits

Because of its reliability, CRC is becoming the standard method of error detection for block data transmission (as opposed to transmission of one character at a time).

Message Sequence Numbers

Suppose you send someone one letter per day for five days through the postal system. There is no guarantee that the letters will be received in the order sent. Several might arrive on the same day (and out of order), one might be lost, or all five might arrive at the same time. If the letters are intended to be read in order, you can number them sequentially, such as 1/5, 2/5, 3/5, and so on. This alerts the recipient to the order and allows him or her to detect missing messages. A similar scheme can be used for data communications messages.

One sequencing technique appends a message sequence number to each data block transmitted between two stations. If a processor is communicating with two different stations, each link would have its own sequence number. Every time a message is transmitted, the sequence number is sent along with the message. The receiving station compares the received sequence number with a number maintained in its memory. If the message numbers agree, no messages have been lost; if the received message number disagrees with the expected message number, an error condition is created and the receiver requests that the sender retransmit the missing messages.

Error-Correction Codes

Some error detecting schemes allow the receiving station not only to detect errors but also to correct some of them. Such codes are called forward error-correcting codes, the most common being Hamming codes. As with straight error detection codes, additional, redundant information is transmitted with the data. Error-correcting codes are convenient for situations in which single-bit errors occur, but for multiple-bit errors the amount of redundant information that must be sent is cumbersome. The effectiveness of forward error-correcting codes is reduced by transmission noise that frequently creates bursts of errors, so these codes are not used as commonly as are error detection schemes. Error-correcting codes have good applications in other areas, such as memory error detection and correction, where the probability of single-bit errors is higher. Some semiconductor memories use a 6-bit Hamming code for each 16 bits of data to allow for single-bit error correction and double-bit error detection.

Message Acknowledgment

The mechanism used to effect retransmission is the positive or negative acknowledgment, often referred to as ACK and NAK, respectively. When a station receives a message, it computes the number of error detection bit(s) or characters and compares the result with the check number received. If the two are equal, the message is assumed to be error-free and the receiver returns a positive acknowledgment to the sender. If the two are unequal, a negative acknowledgment is returned and the sending station retransmits the message. Of course, the sending station must retain all messages until they have been positively acknowledged.

Retry Limit

In some instances a second message attempt also will be received in error, perhaps due to an error-prone communications link or to faulty hardware or software. To cut down on continual retransmission of messages, a retry limit—typically between 3 and 100—can be set. A retry limit of 5 means a message received in error will be retransmitted five times; if the message is not successfully received by the fifth try, the receiving station either disables the link or disables the sending station itself. The objective of a retry limit is to avoid the unproductive work of continually processing corrupted messages. Once the cause of the problem has been corrected, the communications path is reinstated.

DIGITAL DATA TRANSMISSION

All communications media are capable of transmitting information in either digital or analog form. Despite the fact that computer data is represented in digital form, originally computer data was transmitted mostly in analog form. The primary reason for this is that the providers of communications transmission facilities had established analog facilities for voice transmission. However, advances in digital technology and lower prices for digital transmission electronics are bringing about a change to digital transmission. Within several decades most major metropolitan areas will have made the transition; were it not for the considerable existing investment in analog transmission facilities, the changeover might come even sooner. If telephone companies were to begin today, it is likely that their transmission facilities would be digital rather than analog. There are four primary reasons for this.

Advantages of Digital Transmission

The advantages of digital transmission for data communications are lower error rates, higher transmission rates, elimination of the need to convert from digital format to analog and back to digital, and better security.

Lower Error Rates.   Current telephone networks transmit signals over wires or via radio broadcast, continually amplifying the signals to overcome weakening from attenuation. Long-distance transmission demands that the signals be amplified multiple times to overcome attenuation. Because any frequency within the bandwidth is acceptable, it is difficult to filter out introduced noise or distortion, so both are amplified and propagated along with the original signals. Like analog signals, digital signals also lose strength due to attenuation. Figure 2-17(a) shows a digital signal as it is originated. Figure 2-17(b) illustrates a possible effect of attenuation on that signal. A digital signal represents only two discrete values, so it is possible to completely regenerate the signal. Restored to its original state and strength, the data can be forwarded to the next regeneration point or to the final destination without any associated noise. This is accomplished by a digital regenerator. Figure 2-17(c) shows a regenerated signal.

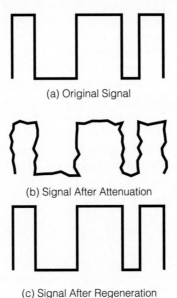

(a) Original Signal

(b) Signal After Attenuation

(c) Signal After Regeneration

Figure 2-17

Digital Signal
Regeneration

Higher Transmission Rates.   Another benefit of digital transmission is increased transmission speed. With digital transmission, switched connections can operate at speeds up to 56 Kbps. The current limit is 38,400 bps for switched circuits.

No Digital to Analog Conversion.   Digital transmission theoretically avoids the need for conversion between formats. Unfortunately, not all locations are serviced by digital networks, whose implementation has been restricted thus far to highly populated urban centers. In addition, the connection from a given location to the digital transmission and switching equipment is still an analog link in many cases. This makes it necessary to convert a signal from digital to analog and back to digital for transmission to the message's destination. The device that converts the analog signal to digital is known as a **codec,** an abbreviation for coder-decoder.

Security.   Companies are becoming increasingly concerned about security of data and voice transmissions. One method for protecting these transmissions is encryption. You may be familiar with this concept as voice scramblers used on secure telephone lines. Although encryption algorithms exist for both analog and digital formats, digital encryption algorithms are more advanced and hence more secure and difficult to crack. Therefore, digital transmissions have the potential of greater security.

Digital Voice Using Pulse Code Modulation

In converting from analog to digital transmission lines, telephone companies are faced with the opposite problem faced by the data communications industry: On a digital line it becomes necessary to transform analog voice patterns into digital representation and then convert the digital patterns back to analog format. The device that does this is called a **codec** and is illustrated in Figure 2-18. A variety of conversion techniques exist, but the most commonly used is known as **pulse code modulation (PCM).** On a communications wire, PCM is represented as pulses of current. A pulse of three volts could represent a 1 bit, and zero voltage could represent a 0 bit. In some schemes a 1 bit would be represented by a voltage of +1.5 and the 0 bit by a voltage of −1.5. The first technique is referred to as unipolar signaling; the latter is polar signaling. These techniques are illustrated in Figures 2-19(a) and 2-19(b), respectively.

Figure 2-18

Codec Converting Analog and Digital Signals

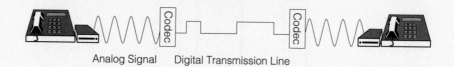

Analog Signal   Digital Transmission Line

Figure 2-19

Pulse Code Modulation

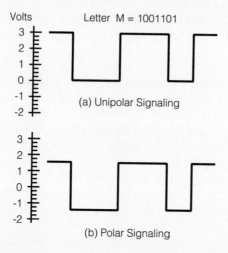

INTERFACES

Once a medium has been selected, it is necessary to connect it to the computer equipment. The two classes of equipment in data communications are **data communications equipment (DCE)** (modems, media, and media-support facilities such as telephone switching equipment, microwave relay stations, and transponders) and **data terminal** (or terminating) **equipment (DTE)** (including terminals, computers, concentrators, and multiplexers, all of which are covered in Chapter 6). The physical interface is the manner in which these two classes of equipment are joined together. Figure 2-20 depicts a data communications linkage with the DCE and DTE components identified.

The interface between DCE and DTE can be divided into four aspects: mechanical, electrical, functional, and procedural. The mechanical portion includes the type of connectors to be used, the number of pin connections in the connectors, and the maximum allowable cable lengths. The electrical characteristics include the allowable line voltages and the representations for the various voltage levels. The functional interface specifies which signals—timing, control, data, or ground leads—are to be carried by each pin in the connector. Table 2-12 lists the signals assigned to each of the 25 pins in an RS-232-C interface.

Table 2-12   RS-232-C Interface Connector Pin Assignments

Pin Number	Circuit	Description
1	AA	Protective ground
2	BA	Transmitted data
3	BB	Received data
4	CA	Request to send
5	CB	Clear to send
6	CC	Data set ready
7	AB	Signal ground (common return)
8	CF	Received line signal detector
9	—	(Reserved for modem testing)
10	—	(Reserved for modem testing)
11		Unassigned
12	SCF	Secondary for pin 8
13	SCB	Secondary clear to send
14	SBA	Secondary transmitted data
15	DB	Transmission signal timing
16	SBB	Secondary received data
17	DD	Receiver signal timing
18		Unassigned
19	SCA	Secondary request to send
20	CD	Data terminal ready
21	CG	Signal quality detector
22	CE	Ring indicator
23	CH/CI	Data signal rate selector
24	DA	Transmit signal element timing
25		Unassigned

Figure 2-20

DTE and DCE
Components

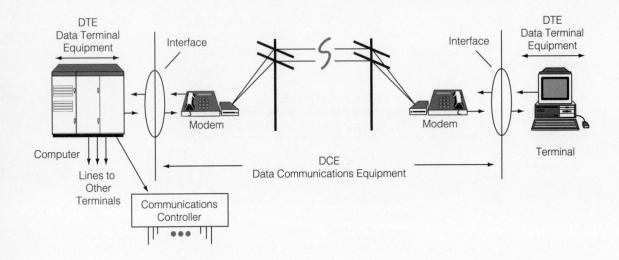

Procedural characteristics define how signals are exchanged and delineate the environment necessary to transmit and receive data. One pin or conducting wire in the connector might represent the ability of a terminal to accept a transmission; when the terminal is ready to receive data, a signal will be raised on that lead. When no signal is raised on that circuit, transmission to the terminal is not valid. Table 2-13 shows a procedural interface to transmit from a processor to a terminal.

Table 2-13   Procedural Interface between Processor and Terminal

1. Processor and terminal raise DTR (data terminal ready) signal to modem

2. Modems raise DSR (data set ready) signal.

3. Processor raises RTS (request to send) signal.

4. Processor's modem sends a carrier signal.

5. Terminal's modem detects carrier and raises CD (carrier detect) signal to processor's modem.

6. Processor sends data on TD (transmit data).

7. Processor's modem modulates data onto the carrier wave.

8. Terminal's modem demodulates data onto RD (received data).

9. Processor lowers RTS signal.

10. Processor's modem drops CTS and carrier wave.

11. Terminal's modem drops CD.

12. Transmission is complete.

Interface Standards

Numerous standards are adhered to in establishing an interface between DCE and DTE. There are too many such interfaces to describe here. However, one of the most common interface standards is the RS-232-C standard for serial data transmission. This is the standard used to transmit data over a microcomputer's serial port. A brief overview of this standard is given below, and its capabilities are generally characteristic of other interface standards.

The RS-232-C Interface Standard

Currently in the United States the predominant interface standard is the Electronic Industries Association (EIA) **RS-232-C standard,** established in October 1969 and reaffirmed in June 1981. RS-232-C encompasses serial binary data interchange at rates up to 20,000 bps and a recommended distance of up to 50 feet; longer distances are possible for shielded wires. (Shielded wire is certified by the manufacturer as capable of spanning 500 feet at 9600 bps.) Because of the speed limitations, RS-232-C has its greatest application in interfacing to wire media, where this bit transmission rate is most common. It covers private, switched, and leased connections, with provisions for auto-answer switched connections. In serial binary transmission (or bit serial transmission), bits are transmitted in single file. This is contrasted with bit parallel transmission, wherein bits are transmitted in parallel. Figure 2-21 illustrates the difference between these two techniques.

Message to Be Transmitted: LINE
Representation: ASCII

```
L    1001100
I    1001001
N    1001110
E    1000101
```

```
1001100  1001001  1001110  1000101
   L        I        N        E
```

(a) Bit Serial Transmission

```
1 1 1 1
0 0 0 0
0 0 0 0
1 1 1 0
1 0 1 1
0 0 1 0
0 1 0 1
L I N E
```

(b) Bit Parallel Transmission

Figure 2-21

Serial versus Parallel Transmission

The RS-232-C standard does not specify size or type of connectors to be used in the interface. It does define 25 signal leads, 3 of them unassigned, 2 reserved for testing, and the remaining 20 used for grounding, data, control, and timing. In the absence of a standard, one connector—a 25-pin connector—has become common in implementing RS-232-C connections. Figure 2-22(a) depicts this type of connector. Actual transmissions typically use fewer than 25 signal leads. A simple modem interface can require that only 7 pins be active, yet on occasion, connectors supporting 15, 9, and 7 pins are used to interface with these devices. A 15-pin connector and a 9-pin connector are illustrated in Figures 2-22 (b) and 2-22 (c). The RS-232-C standard covers all four aspects of the interface: mechanical, electrical, functional, and procedural. This is significant because other interface specifications treat them separately, which means two or three standards may be cited that together form the equivalent of what is specified by RS-232-C.

Figure 2-22

Cable Connectors

(a) 25-pin connector for RS-232-C or CCITT V.24 interface

(b) 15-pin connector for RS-232-C or CCITT V.24 interface

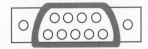

(c) 9-pin connector for RS-232-C, RS-449, or CCITT V.24 interface

SUMMARY

A wide variety of transmission media are available to the network designer, and many networks employ several of them. If the telephone companies' use of fiber optics, microwave, and satellite channels is considered, most long-distance networks are a combination of media. Numerous factors influence the selection of transmission media. Each medium has information-carrying capacity, which varies from a few characters per second to millions of characters per second. The terms *bit rate, baud rate,* and *bandwidth* are used to describe a medium's carrying capacity, and these measures are interrelated.

In transmitting information between devices in a computer network, it is frequently necessary to convert a device's digital signals to analog format. There are several ways to do this; frequency modulation, phase modulation, and phase modulation plus amplitude modulation are the most common.

The device that translates digital signals to analog signals and then back again is known as a modem or data set. Modems differ greatly in the bit rate provided as well as in the options available. The three basic types of data flow are simplex, half duplex, and full duplex. Most business data communications systems use either full or half duplex.

All media are subject to error. Detecting errors requires that redundant information be transmitted with the data. The three most common error detection schemes in data communications are vertical redundancy check (VRC), longitudinal redundancy check (LRC), and cyclic redundancy check (CRC). The most effective is CRC. In some protocols, sequence checking is also used to improve the reliability of transmission.

Digital data transmission provides both higher transmission speeds and fewer errors. The common carriers are gradually making the conversion from analog transmission equipment to digital equipment. Digital transmission has led to new transmission capabilities, specifically the integration of different services over one medium. It is now common for both data and voice to be transmitted over the same circuits. One of the technologies rapidly being implemented to provide this capability is the integrated services digital network, or ISDN.

Interface standards exist regarding connections between data terminal equipment (DTE) and data communications equipment (DCE). Both domestic and international standards address mechanical, functional, procedural, and electrical interfaces; unfortunately, these standards do not always agree.

KEY TERMS

aggregate data rate   39
amplitude modulation (AM)   46
analog transmission   44
asynchronous transfer mode (ATM)   35
attenuation   54
bandwidth   44
baud rate   44
bit rate   44
bits per second (bps)   31
block check character (BCC)   57
broadcast radio   31
carrier signal   45
cellular radio telephone   37
Centrex service   38
codec   62
conditioning   55
conducted media   30
connectionless   34

Consultative Committee on
   International Telegraph and
   Telephony (CCITT)   35
crosstalk   54
cyclic redundancy check (CRC)   58
data communications equipment
   (DCE)   62
data set   45
data terminal equipment (DTE)   62
dibits   44
differential phase-shift keying
   (DPSK)   48
digital transmission   60
direct sequencing   32
DS-1 signaling   34
DS-3 signaling   34
DS-4 signaling   34
fractional T-1 service   34

REVIEW QUESTIONS

1. Distinguish between switched lines and leased lines.

2. Compare shielded and unshielded twisted-pair wires. Give an example of where each can be used effectively.

3. Explain the need for repeaters when using twisted-pair wires.

4. Describe the composition of coaxial cable. (see CBT module LAN Transmissin Media)

5. Rank wires, coaxial cable, and fiber optics with respect to speed, cost, and resistance to noise. Which is fastest? Which is least expensive? Which is least error prone?

6. Describe:
   a. Amplitude modulation
   b. Frequency modulation
   c. Phase modulation

7. Compare broadcast, microwave, and satellite radio.

8. How does spread spectrum radio work? What is its primary data communications application?

9. Why do some experts believe that television signals should be transmitted by conducted media rather than by wireless media? Do you agree or disagree with this premise? Explain your conclusion.

10. Explain how the terms *baud rate, bit rate,* and *bandwidth* are used to describe the speed of a communications link.

11. Describe what a modem does.

12. Compare the CCITT V.22, V.29, V.32, and V.33 standards. (see CBT module "Modems & Media")

13. Define:
    a. Simplex transmission
    b. Half-duplex transmission
    c. Full-duplex transmission

14. Describe four ways to prevent transmission errors.

15. Describe how parity checking works.

16. Explain why CRC is a better error detection scheme than parity or longitudinal redundancy checks.

17. What are the advantages of digital data transmission?

18. Why are interface standards important?

19. What are ISDNs? Give two examples where ISDNs might be used for data transmission.

20. How does a cellular radio telephone system work?

21. Briefly describe:
    a. Switched multimegabit data service (SMDS)
    b. Asynchronous transfer mode (ATM)
    c. Fractional T-n service

3

INTRODUCTION TO
NETWORKS

CHAPTER OBJECTIVES

After studying this chapter you should be able to:

- Define the characteristics of a local area network (LAN) and a wide area network (WAN)
- Compare and contrast a LAN and a WAN
- Discuss the rationale behind LANs and WANs
- Describe major LAN and WAN applications
- Define several common network terms

The 1970s brought significant growth in wide area network (WAN) technology, and one of the biggest growth segments of the communications industry during the 1980s was local area network (LAN) technology. The LAN boom has resulted from lower hardware costs, availability of network and application software, and the integration of microcomputers into the workplace. This is not to say that all LANs use microcomputers as workstations. LANs were in operation before microcomputers became commonplace, and high-speed LANs are still used to connect large computing systems. The 1990s are likely to be characterized by the continued growth of LANs; the widespread interconnection of networks of all types; mobile networking; expansion of the use of multimedia over networks; integration of telecommunications networks such as telephone, computer, radio, and television networks; and a significant increase in network speeds. In a few years the differences between WANs and LANs may be slight and we will be able to once again just talk about networks. Until that time, we need to recognize the existence of the two basic network types and where each fits in the world of data communications.

In this chapter we first define LANs and WANs, including the reasons for having them and applications that lend themselves to these types of network. We also introduce common network terms. Some of these terms are generic to all network types and some are specific to either a LAN or a WAN. This chapter also introduces the concept of network management. An understanding of this material will aid in your understanding of the details of network hardware, topologies, media access control, system software, and network implementations, which are covered in Chapters 4 and 5 for LANs and Chapters 6 and 7 for WANs. We start by comparing WANs and LANs.

THE RATIONALE BEHIND NETWORKS

The first type of network to be developed was the WAN. The major motivations for WANs were to overcome distance, to overcome the computational limitations of a single computer, and to provide for departmental computing. Companies that are national or international frequently have multiple computing sites. Networks are used to connect these geographically dispersed sites, and to provide for the exchange of data and software. In some instances, the computing needs at one location exceeded the capacity of a single computer. In these instances multiple computers were installed at one location and then networked to provide resource sharing as well as greater computing capacity. Resources that were shared included hardware and data. As computers became smaller and less expensive with the introduction of minicomputers, some departments purchased computers to better control their computing environment. The department-level computers usually were networked with corporate computers and other department-level computers.

The last two motivations for WAN networking resulted in several computers being located in a small geographical area. The mode of interconnection, however, was basically the same as that being used to connect computers over long distances. LAN technology developed to overcome the speed limitations of this type of network. Originally LANs were installed to connect mainframes and minicomputers, and most LANs were implemented for two reasons: high-speed data transfer and resource sharing in a local area. Today there are several additional reasons including group-oriented software, communication among workers, management control, cost-effectiveness, and downsizing in which large computer systems are replaced by LANs. We now consider each motivation.

Large Data Transfers

In a large data-processing installation with a variety of processors, moving data from one system to another once was accomplished by magnetic tape or low-speed communications links (less than 100 Kbps). Magnetic tapes provide high data transfer rates but have two disadvantages. First, manual intervention is required to effect data transfers. Operators are required to mount and dismount tapes. This not only tends to slow down the transfer but also often means the transfer must be scheduled, reducing the potential for as-needed transfers. Second, incompatibilities between tape formats on different systems must be accommodated when tapes are used as a transfer medium. When using communications links slower than 100 Kbps, large file transfers are very time-consuming. If we consider a speed of 56 Kbps in transferring 1 million records of 100 bytes each, the transfer requires

(1,000,000 records) (100 bytes per record) (8 bits per byte)/56,000 bits per second
= 14,286 seconds = 238 minutes = 3.97 hours

The above figures assume that the line is operating at 100-percent capacity and that there is no protocol overhead, both ridiculous assumptions. The actual transfer time would likely be more than 6 hours. The corresponding time for a 100-Mbps LAN is 8 seconds.

A LAN can provide the best attributes of each of the above solutions: high speed coupled with operator-free implementation. LANs operating at speeds of 10–100 Mbps are approximately 200 to 2000 times faster than the 56-Kbps link. A caveat is required at this point: Although the medium can transmit data at a rate of 100 Mbps, actual transfer between two systems is often considerably slower because of the CPU time necessary to send and receive the message. Still, the transfers both are time efficient and can be initiated under program or user control without operator intervention.

Resource Sharing

Resource sharing is best exemplified by microcomputer LANs. Early microcomputer LAN systems were primarily oriented toward printer and file sharing—print server and file server technology. Printer sharing allows several users to direct their printed output to the same printer. In Chapter 5 we explain how this is done. With file sharing, two or more users can share a single file. The file can be an application program, a database file, or a work file such as a spreadsheet or word processing document. In the next two chapters we consider server technology and ways in which files can be shared. LANs now are used to share more than printers, disks, and data. Other hardware shared on a LAN includes facsimile (fax) machines, modems, and terminals.

Groupware

LANs have expanded the potential of the microcomputer from individual productivity to work-group productivity; however, work-group software is not exclusively a microcomputer technology. Work-group productivity tools, collectively referred to as **groupware,** have their roots in WANs. Groupware allows a group of users to communicate and coordinate activities. Several work-group applications are described below.

Electronic Mail.   One of the earliest workgroup applications was **electronic mail** or **e-mail.** An e-mail system has many of the capabilities of a conventional postal system, such as collecting and distributing correspondence of various sizes and types and routing the correspondence to recipients in a timely manner. We have, however, come to expect many more capabilities from an e-mail system than from a conventional postal system. Today's e-mail systems allow correspondents to exchange communications containing text, graphics, and voice images in batch or real-time mode. For many companies, e-mail has become a primary mode of communications.

Electronic Appointment Calendars.   Electronic appointment calendars are stored on the network. One user can consult other users' appointment calendars to find a time at which each user is available for a meeting. The electronic calendar system can then schedule the meeting for each participant.

Electronic Filing Cabinets.   E-mail and other machine-readable documents can be stored in disk folders in **electronic "filing cabinets"** that are equivalent to file folders in conventional filing cabinets. Messages and documents in the folder can later be retrieved, modified, or deleted. Most filing systems maintain an index of the folders and their contents.

File Exchange Utilities.   **File exchange utilities** allow files to be easily copied from one network node to another.

Project Management Systems.   **Project management systems** assist in planning projects and allocating resources. The introduction of LAN implementations has allowed these systems to be integrated more completely into the work group. A manager and team member can agree on the parameters of a task, the team member can update his or her progress, and the manager can monitor the progress. Projects can therefore be managed more effectively.

Group Decision-Support Systems.   **Group decision-support systems (GDSSs)** assist individuals and groups in the decision-making process and help them set objectives. There are two levels of GDSSs. A lower-level GDSS does not have an underlying decision-support system, but simply serves as a bulletin board for the exchange and development of ideas. A higher-level GDSS includes a decision-support system that provides more tools for group users than a lower-level GDSS.

Electronic Meeting Systems.   **Electronic meeting systems** go beyond simple teleconferencing. The inclusion of networks allows participants to exchange machine-readable information in the form of graphics, text, audio, and full-motion video. If electronic meeting systems are combined with decision-support system software, meeting participants can work in parallel to reach solutions.

Document Management Systems.   **Document management systems** help an organization manage and control its documents. Capabilities include indexing documents, finding documents based on keywords contained in the document, controlling document changes, and allowing several users to collaborate on document editing.

The motivation for using microcomputer LANs has evolved from that of simple hardware resource sharing, to data and application sharing, to idea sharing and personnel coordination. Although LANs are still used to share hardware, software, and data, the biggest benefit of LANs may lie in groupware applications.

Communication

Most of us view telephone networks as a way to allow people to communicate. We use data communications networks for the same reason. However, in a data communications network, the entities that communicate with each other are not necessarily people. The network depicted in Figure 3-1 represents a variety of users and applications communicating: a person-to-person communication, a person-to-application communication, and an application-to-application communication.

Figure 3-1

Objects Communicating in a Network

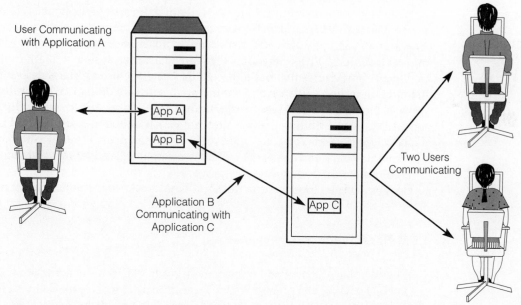

The "messages" being exchanged can also differ. The person-to-person communication may be an electronic conversation with the two parties exchanging messages in real time as illustrated in Figure 3-1. User A types a message on the terminal and presses the Enter key, and the message is immediately displayed on User B's workstation. The person-to-application communication may be a user making an inquiry into the corporate database. In Figure 3-1, the user communicating with the application might be checking on a shipment for a customer. The application-to-application communication may be the transfer of a file from one node to another.

Management Control

Another reason for using a LAN is **management control.** A LAN can help a company standardize its microcomputer environment. Application standards can be set up more easily in a network because most application programs can be installed on one or more network nodes called **servers.** In general, a server provides a service commonly needed by applications. Some common server classes are file, database, print, terminal, and modem. Servers in these classes allow applications to share the hardware and capabilities that the servers provide. Users access these services over the network. In a small network, all users may run the same word processing program that is located on a specific network node. All users will use the same version of the same word processor, making document interchange a simple matter. Contrast this with two or more users having different versions of the same word processor or, worse yet, completely different word processing software. In this case, documents created under one system would likely need to be converted and possibly reformatted before being used by the other word processing system.

LANs can also help control one of the most unsettling problems facing computer users today: computer viruses. A **computer virus** is a segment of code that attaches itself to a file (usually a program), to memory, or to system portions of a disk. A computer virus is intended, first, to replicate itself and, second, to disrupt the normal functioning of the computer. With diskless workstations and virus-detection software, management can reduce the risk of viral infections. **Virus-detection software** analyzes a system and attempts to discover any viruses that have infected the system. Once a virus is detected, the virus-detection software or a complement software utility can be used to remove the virus. A **diskless workstation** has no local disk drives, which reduces the ways a virus can be introduced. An added security benefit of diskless workstations is that a company's workers are unable to copy software or corporate data for personal gain. The disadvantage of diskless workstations is the complete dependence on the network. They cannot be used in a stand-alone mode or in a location that does not have access to the network.

Cost-Effectiveness

Communicating, sharing, and management control are three benefits of using networks. However, the primary reason for using a network is cost-effectiveness. The ability to share resources has a direct impact on an organization's expenses. If users can share hardware, less hardware is needed. If a network were used only for resource sharing, it would be cost-effective when installing; and operating the network is less expensive than or equal to the hardware, software, data preparation, and other costs in a non-networked environment. Less obviously, cost-effectiveness may derive from the ability of users to communicate and thus improve their productivity. One direct benefit is the reduction of paperwork. Electronic data exchange is converting paper offices to electronic offices.

Downsizing

In some companies, LANs have been used to downsize the data processing hardware, software, and personnel requirements. **Downsizing,** also sometimes referred to as rightsizing, refers to using smaller computer platforms in place of large computers or to choosing the correct size of computer for the job. Some companies have replaced their mainframe computers with one or more microcomputer LANs. These companies found they could provide better data processing services for their users. The better services were obtained at lower hardware, software, and personnel costs; however, reduced costs are not always the result of downsizing. Other companies that have downsized have not realized reduced costs as a result. Diagrams of one company's computer configuration before and after downsizing are shown in Figure 3-2(a) and Figure 3-2(b), respectively.

NETWORK APPLICATIONS

In Chapter 1 we generally characterized network applications. In this section we concentrate on applications common to both WANs and LANs. Many applications fall into this category. The more common include office automation, multimedia applications, computer-aided design (CAD), computer-aided manufacturing (CAM), and computer-aided instruction (CAI). Some of the functions performed in these application areas are described below.

Office Automation

Over time, a few technologies have significantly affected office procedures. Among these are telephones, calculators, copy machines, and computers. Two of the most recent influences are microcomputers and LANs. Microcomputers have provided office workers with some autonomy regarding their processing needs. The vast array of microcomputer software with user-friendly interfaces has given end users significant local processing capability. This ability, coupled with shared access to centralized databases and documentation, has added a new dimension to data access and manipulation. Together with electronic mail and document exchange systems, these capabilities have led to **office automation** and significantly changed the way many offices conduct business. Some office activities an office worker can perform include:

- Distributing memos to a list of recipients using the electronic mail system.
- Scheduling a meeting by accessing electronic appointment calendars. The scheduler software chooses a time at which all participants are available. The calendars of the attendees can be accessed over the network, a common convenient time determined, and appointments made in affected calendars without contacting each participant personally.

- Running an application stored on a file server's disk. The speed at which the application is transferred to the workstation is relatively equal to that of executing the software from a locally attached disk drive.

- Accessing a shared plotter or color printer to output a graph.

- Accessing a document for editing and returning the changes to a central repository, the shared disk drive.

- Extracting data from a centralized database and manipulating the data locally with spreadsheet, database management system, word processor, or other software.

- Composing a portion of a document and submitting it to a centralized system for integration with work accomplished elsewhere.

- Inputting transactions for processing on another node in the network.

- Transmitting data from the LAN to other corporate users on a WAN or another LAN.

- Accessing public or quasi-public networks such as America Online, CompuServe, Prodigy, or the Internet. Networks such as these provide a wide range of services including electronic mail; information databases; and services such as banking, stock trading, and catalog shopping.

Multimedia on LANs

Multimedia technology extends a computer's capabilities by adding audio and video to data. Multimedia is much more than just being able to produce sound, pictures, and animation on a computer. The promise of this technology is the full integration of audio and video into existing software. Additional hardware is needed to bring these capabilities to a computer. Typically, the components of a **multimedia personal computer (MPC)** are a **compact disk–read-only memory (CD-ROM)** drive, an audio board, a computer with a fast processor, a high-resolution color monitor, and ample memory and disk capacity. Multimedia technology is rapidly expanding on both stand-alone microcomputers and LANs. In this section we do not address the technology of multimedia; instead, we examine its impact on LANs.

Multimedia on LANs is already being used. A multimedia server on a LAN delivers digitized audio and video signals to client workstations capable of supporting the technology. The issue is not whether multimedia can be done on LANs but how to do it successfully. The current problem with this technology is the speed of the common LAN. Today's LANs operate at approximately 4–16 Mbps. These speeds are inadequate for extensive use of multimedia. Full-motion video to a monitor with a resolution of 640 by 480 picture elements (pixels) with 24-bit true color at a frame rate of 30 frames per second requires a data rate of 240 Mbps. This is far in excess of common LAN speeds. Still-frame video and audio signals do not require such high bit rates, but sustained transfers of between 16 and 384 Kbps are needed for the duration of many multimedia video and audio sessions. At the higher rate,

30 users would require more than the entire capacity of a 10-Mbps LAN. It also is not possible to sustain a 10-Mbps data rate over a 10-Mbps network because of overheads in the data link protocol, transmission errors, and delays in media access. LANs operating at 10 Mbps are not designed to sustain such constant high data rates.

Figure 3-2

Computer Configuration Before and After Downsizing

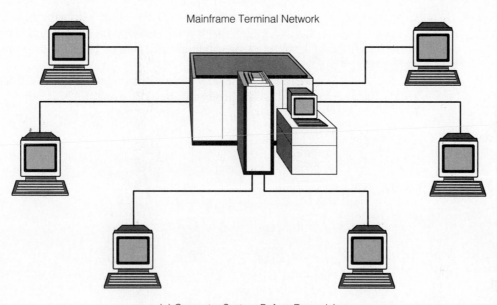

Mainframe Terminal Network

(a) Computer System Before Downsizing

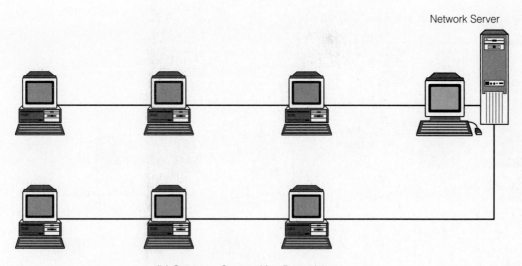

Network Server

(b) Computer System After Downsizing

A combination of several techniques will likely be necessary to realize the full potential of multimedia for large numbers of users. Among these are data compression, higher-speed networks, LAN segmentation, and the asynchronous transfer mode switches described earlier.

Data compression reduces the number of bits that need to be transferred. You may be familiar with this technology through disk compression programs that approximately double the storage capacity of disk drives. Thus, an 80-MB disk might be able to store 160 MB of data via compression. If data is compressed prior to transmission and then decompressed at the receiving end, the demand on the transmission media can be significantly lowered. Compression/decompression chips are available that perform these two operations faster than software. Equipping multimedia clients and servers with compression/decompression capability will help by reducing the number of bits being transferred.

Even with compression, the capacity of LANs running slower than 20 Mbps will be strained by several concurrent multimedia users. LANs with a large

Figure 3-3

Segmenting a LAN for
Multimedia Applications

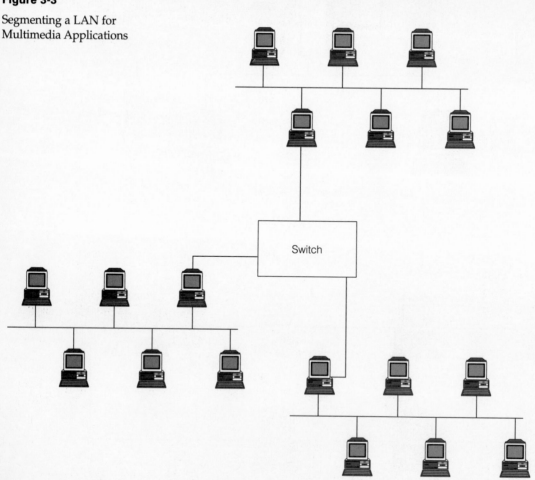

number of users and without multimedia are already candidates for higher speed transmissions. Several options are available to accommodate these users as well as those moving to heavy multimedia use. **High-speed network technologies** are described in Chapter 4.

Even 100-Mbps LANs will be unable to meet the needs of large numbers of concurrent multimedia users. **LAN segmentation** may be required to allow for greater numbers of concurrent multimedia users. LANs would be broken down into small segments as illustrated in Figure 3-3. Each multi-media segment can be serviced by a dedicated multimedia server or by a multimedia server on a high-speed backbone network, as shown in Figure 3-4. With few users on each segment, the data-carrying capacity of each segment will not be exceeded. It is even conceivable that an individual intensive multi-media user will need to be placed on a LAN segment by him- or herself.

Figure 3-4

A High-Speed Backbone Network for Multimedia Applications

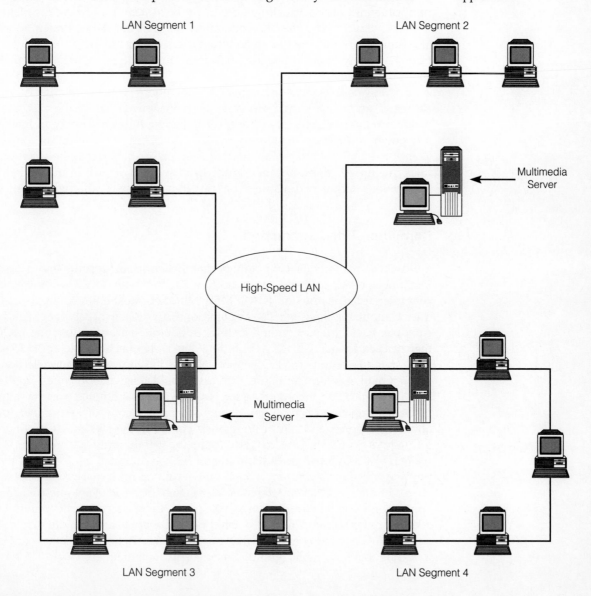

CAD/CAM

In addition to the office automation functions above, networks can serve as the communications medium for **computer-aided design/computer-aided manufacturing (CAD/CAM)** applications. In a CAD/CAM application a user can check out a drawing and continue work on it, compose a new drawing, and exchange information with other users of the system. The draftsperson can access a designer's notes, change or create a drawing from those notes, and print the drawing on a shared device such as a plotter. Engineering drawings are usually represented by very large data files; LAN transmission speeds are essential to effectively transfer these drawings from one node to another. CAD is used extensively by automobile, aerospace, computer, and engineering corporations. With a CAD system, an engineer can go directly from drawings, to constructing a model of the system, to sending the plans, to manufacturing, in a seamless operation. *Seamless* means the flow of work and control is highly integrated and the system user is not aware of the interfaces in going from one operation, such as an engineering drawing, to another, such as model construction.

CAM systems control assembly line operations, robots, manufacturing processes, and machinery. CAM systems are designed to make the manufacturing process more efficient through automation. In the aerospace industry, computer control of machinery effects precision fabrication of parts. Computer-controlled robots are used to weld bodies on automobile assembly lines. As in CAD applications, transmission speed is critical in many CAM applications because events must be triggered at precisely the right time.

Computer-Aided Instruction

Educational institutions have found that networks in general and LANs in particular can facilitate the education process with what is known as **computer-aided instruction (CAI).** Most education capabilities of stand-alone microcomputer systems are also available on LANs. These capabilities include computer-based instruction and testing. In educational institutions the LAN may be used for many reasons, including device sharing, access to application software, and electronic mail. Other possible uses include assignment, collection, and return of exercises. An English professor could assign a term paper, require that it be "typed" on a word processor, have the papers submitted electronically, grade the papers, insert grading comments, print a copy of each paper for archival purposes, and return the graded papers to the students. Clubs and committees can use the LAN to post information for other students on electronic bulletin boards. **Electronic bulletin boards** are the computer equivalent of the physical bulletin board. Users of the LAN typically access the electronic bulletin board through a switched telephone connection. Once attached, the user can "post" notices on the board, such as asking how to connect a specific printer to a LAN printer server. A user also could post answers to existing questions or make software or hardware available. In general, the electronic bulletin board is a clearinghouse for public (group) dialogue and equipment exchange.

NETWORK CHARACTERISTICS

The applications described above share one or more of the following attributes:

- Communication between a variety of devices
- Utilization of several different applications
- High-speed data transfer
- High reliability
- Device and data sharing
- Transparent interface to shared resources
- Adaptability to meet changing hardware and software requirements
- Potential access to other networks such as a WAN or a LAN
- Security from interference from other users, either accidental or intentional
- Need for management

This, then, is the basis for a network: multiple devices of different types and capabilities providing transparent access to diverse resources, all requiring reliability and rapid response for common services needed by the devices. The network must be manageable, able to accommodate changing requirements and devices, and able to interface to other communication networks. Most important, the network must contribute to the solving of business problems.

High speeds over limited distance make LANs very suitable for joining computers in a building or building complex. Typically, LAN speeds are 1 million (M) bits per second (bps) or faster, and speeds of more than 2 billion (G) bps have been attained. The distance spanned depends on the specific implementation. Usually workstations are not dispersed over a distance of more than a few miles, although a few LAN implementations support distances of 100 miles or more. The LAN itself consists of communications software, a communications medium, nodes, connectors that attach the nodes to the medium, and network software.

In contrast, a WAN usually consists of data terminal equipment owned or controlled by the user and data communications equipment provided by a common carrier; however, some WANs are implemented as totally private networks without using the services of a common carrier. It also is common for LANs and WANs to be connected into a larger enterprise network, and the distinction between the two regarding speed and distance is decreasing.

NETWORK TERMINOLOGY

Network and Node.   The term **network** as used in Chapters 4 through 8 means a group or set of computer systems and their attached communications devices, such as terminals and multiplexers. Each computer system is called a **network node.** *Computer system* is the term used rather than *processor* or *computer* because of the existence of multiple processor systems. Thus, a node is one or more processors that collectively serve as a termination point for a communications link with another node.

Link, Path, and Circuit.   In Chapter 1 you read about the data link layer and how it helps move data from one node to another. We can also talk about the path a message takes to get from the sender to the receiver. There is often a difference between a link and a path: A **path** represents end-to-end message routing, whereas a **link** connects one node to an adjacent node or one node to a terminal. A link is also known as a **circuit,** because a circuit is a conduit for data and in some instances multiple, lower-speed, individual connections are combined to form a single, higher-speed connection through a technique called **multiplexing.** In Figure 3-5, the lines represent communications links connecting nodes. Figure 3-5 shows two paths available for communication between Node A and Node C (the path A —> B, B —> C and the path A —> D, D —> C), with two links on each path. We sometimes also refer to a **virtual circuit,** which is a connection established between a sender and a receiver upon setting up a communications session. In a virtual circuit, all messages are sent over the same path.

Figure 3-5

Links and Paths in a Network

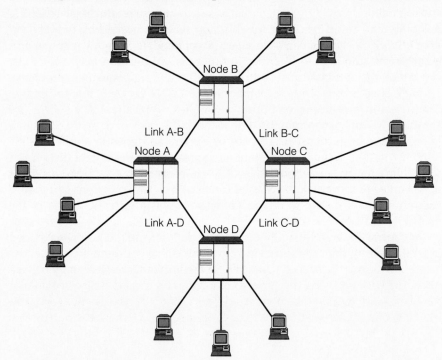

Routing.   **Routing** is a function of the OSI network layer and refers to how the path from sending node to receiving node is determined. In general, routing in a LAN is simple: The message is broadcast to all nodes. This can be done efficiently because of the speed of data transmission. In WANs routing is usually more selective in that a single optimum path is selected for sending data, or several paths may be used concurrently. It is seldom the case, however, that a message is sent to all nodes as in a LAN.

Session and User. Session refers to a communications dialogue between two users of a network and is a function of the OSI session layer. A **user** can be a terminal operator, an application, or any other originator of messages. In some systems, sessions are quite formal, with well-defined conventions for establishing, continuing, and terminating the dialogue.

Packet Switching and Packet Distribution Networks. Packet switching refers to the technology of transmitting a message in one or more fixed-length data packets. A packet-switching network is also sometimes referred to as a **packet distribution network (PDN), public data network** (also **PDN), X.25 network** (X.25 is a standard designation), or **value-added network (VAN).** Henceforth, the abbreviation **PDN** is used. A PDN generally connects a user and the nearest node in the PDN. The PDN routes the data packets to their final destination by finding the best route for each packet (packet switching).

Store-and-Forward. In **a store-and-forward system,** messages may be stored at nodes along the transmission path before these nodes deliver the messages to the next node. There are several reasons for using store-and-forward. First, there is the responsibility for being able to resend the message. If Node A is transmitting a message to Node Z, the path between the two may pass through several intermediate nodes. To ensure delivery, either Node A must keep the message until it is delivered or an intermediate node that has received the message must assume this responsibility. In a store-and-forward system, a node that receives the message will write it to disk or store it in memory and then acknowledge to the sender that the message has been received. This relieves the sender of accountability for the message. Store-and-forward is attractive for financial transactions because it provides a trace of the progress of the transaction.

Second, store-and-forward algorithms are used for time-staged delivery systems. These systems allow users not only to send messages but also to specify a required delivery time, providing several benefits. Corporations with offices in various time zones can assign a delivery time for their mail messages. If the delivery time is not immediate, the system can process the message during a period of low activity. Suppose a mail message is posted at 2:00 p.m. for delivery to a time zone that is four hours later, where it is 6:00 p.m. If the delivery time is set as 9:00 a.m. the next day, the message can be stored locally and sent at midnight when both the sending and receiving systems are less busy. Time-staged delivery of large files can also allow their transmission to be paced over time, making the communications links more available for other transmissions.

Third, store-and-forward systems may be used if no path to the destination is available. If a link fails during the process of sending the message and the message cannot be delivered, the node at the point of failure can store the message. When the link is restored, the message is forwarded to the next node in the path. This practice relieves the message originator from the responsibility of saving the message until it reaches its destination.

Finally, store-and-forward techniques can be used in systems where messages have different priorities. Low-priority messages may be stored for later delivery to give higher-priority messages better access to a link during periods of congestion.

Network Architecture and Topology.   The physical layout of a network, which is the way that nodes are attached to the medium, is referred to as the **network topology.** The **network architecture** is the way that the media, hardware, and software are integrated to form the network.

SUMMARY

A LAN is a high-speed network serving a limited geographic area. Originally, LANs were used primarily for sharing hardware and software and high-speed data transfers. Recent reasons for using a LAN include the ability to use work-group software or groupware, serving as a communications vehicle among workers, downsizing applications, and management control of computing resources. Four classes of LAN applications are office automation, computer-aided manufacturing, computer-aided drafting and design, and computer-aided instruction. LANs extend the capabilities of stand-alone computers. LANs also mean additional responsibilities. Stand-alone microcomputers are managed by those who use them. A LAN requires more centralized management and control. This is a part-time responsibility for small LANs but a full-time responsibility for one or more employees for medium to large-scale LANs. Poor management can ruin the effectiveness of even the best configured LANs.

A WAN is a network that may be confined to a limited geographical area but more typically is geographically distributed. The speeds of the circuits are usually much slower than those of a LAN. Although most of today's LANs are composed of microcomputers, WANs ordinarily have larger computers as nodes. In the complex world of data communications it is common to have enterprise networks that are formed from the interconnection of WANs and LANs.

KEY TERMS

circuit 84

compact disk–read-only memory
  (CD-ROM) 78

computer virus 76

computer-aided design (CAD) 82

computer-aided instruction (CAI) 82

computer-aided manufacturing
  (CAM) 82

data compression 80

diskless workstation 76

document management system 74

downsizing 77

electronic appointment calendar 74

electronic bulletin board 82

electronic filing cabinet 74

electronic mail (e-mail) 74

electronic meeting system 74

file exchange utilities 74

REVIEW QUESTIONS

1. What is the difference between a link and a path?

2. What is a store-and-forward system?

3. What were the motivating factors for the development of LANs?

4. What are the distinguishing features of a LAN? What are those of a WAN?

5. What is a computer virus?

6. Describe three LAN applications.

7. Describe four LAN hardware components.

8. Describe three LAN software functions.

4

....

LAN HARDWARE, TOPOLOGIES, AND MEDIA ACCESS CONTROL

....

CHAPTER OBJECTIVES

After studying this chapter you should be able to:

- Identify the major classes of LAN servers
- Compare and contrast file and database servers
- Identify the principal hardware components of a LAN
- Discuss LAN hardware needs
- Recognize the tradeoffs made in designing LAN hardware
- Describe several important LAN standards
- Compare and contrast the three major LAN topologies
- Describe the LAN media access control protocols
- Recognize the advantages and disadvantages of each media access control protocol
- Compare and contrast the major LAN architectures

When selecting and installing a LAN you have several important decisions to make. You must choose the medium, media access control protocol, topology, hardware, and software. We discussed media in Chapter 2. In this chapter we look at the principal hardware components of a LAN, three LAN topologies, and two media access control protocols. A wide variety of hardware components are available—servers, workstations, adapters, and so on—but the key to success is choosing components that can be integrated to form an effective system. We begin the discussion by looking at LAN servers.

SERVER PLATFORMS

To make an informed decision regarding server hardware, you must understand what the server does. A variety of services can be provided by a server including file, database, printer, terminal, modem, facsimile (fax), and remote access. A terminal server allows terminals to be attached to a LAN; the terminal server provides the necessary computation capabilities. Modem and facsimile servers allow users to share modems and fax machines. A remote access server provides LAN services to users who access the LAN remotely via telephone lines. File, database, and printer servers are the most common server types and are the focus of our attention in this chapter. We begin by comparing file and database servers.

File Services

File services is one of the primary jobs of a server. The objective of file services is to provide users access to data, programs, and other files stored on the server's disk drives. It should be transparent to the user that the data or files he or she is using are located on the server's disk drives rather than on a local disk drive. Over time several technologies have been developed to provide file services. File and database servers are the most commonly used today.

File Servers

A **fileserver** allows users to share files. If several LAN users need access to an application such as word processing, only one copy of the application software needs to reside on a file server. Individual users can share this application provided the users' company has observed the product's license agreement. In this case, one copy of the program files can satisfy the needs of all application users. When a user enters a command to start an application, that application is downloaded into the user's workstation. Consider the savings in disk space in a company having 100 users for a product that requires 5 MB of disk storage. Storage on a file server requires only 5 MB of disk space for all users. Storing the same application on 100 users' local disk drives will require 500 MB of disk space. File server technology is illustrated in Figure 4-1.

When a user needs data from the file server, that data is transferred to the user's workstation. This is suitable for small files, but consider the impact of such technology when accessing a large database. If a user enters a request that requires looking at thousands of records, each record must be transferred over the LAN to the user's workstation.

Suppose you want to determine the average grade point average (GPA) for all students in your school and that there are 40,000 records in the student file. With file server technology the database application runs on your workstation; it is downloaded to your workstation when you start the application. When you make your request to find the average GPA, each student record is transferred over the network to your workstation, where the grade-point-average data is extracted and computations are made. Transferring all 40,000 database records over the network can place a heavy load on the medium and reduce its performance. In a case like this it is more efficient to have the server do the calculations and pass only the response over the network. A database server performs this function.

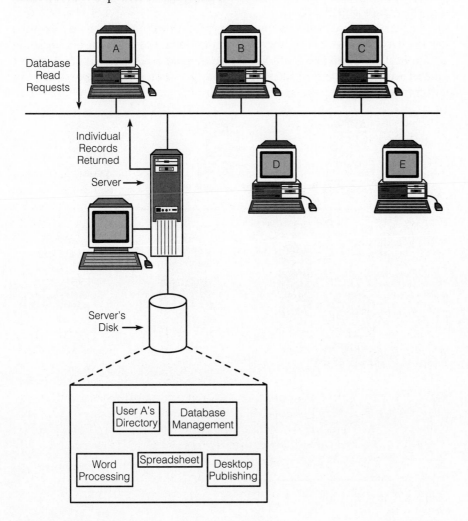

Figure 4-1

File Server Technology

Database Servers

The **database server** was developed to solve the problem of passing an entire file over the medium. The most common example of a database server is the SQL server. **Structured Query Language (SQL)** is a standard database definition, access, and update language for relational databases. An SQL server accepts a database request, accesses all necessary records locally, and then sends only the results back to the requester. In the GPA example, all 40,000 student records still must be read, but the computation is done by the SQL server.

Only one record containing the average GPA is sent back over the network to the requester. This reduces the load on the network medium, but it does place an extra load on the server. The server not only must access the records, but also must perform some database processing. This can affect other users who are also requesting SQL services. The SQL server must be powerful enough to provide effective services for all users and avoid becoming a performance bottleneck.

An interface also must exist between the application software making the database request and the SQL server. The interface must be capable of translating an application's data needs into an SQL statement. This means an SQL server cannot work unless the application or an application interface exists that can generate the SQL syntax. SQL server technology is illustrated in Figure 4-2.

Figure 4-2

SQL Server Technology

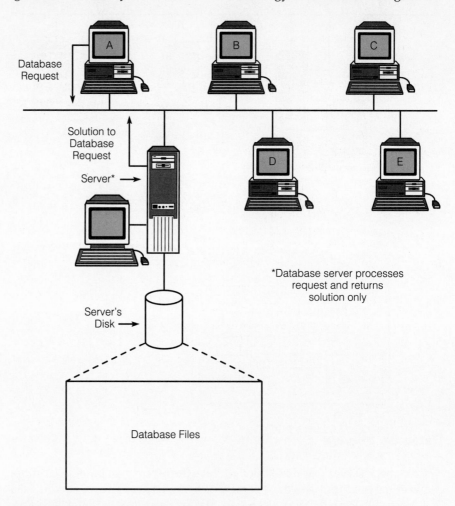

The Server's Disk Subsystem

File and database servers share a common need to efficiently access data. When choosing a file or database server, you should carefully select the server's disk subsystem, which consists of the disk drives and the disk controllers. Two factors are critical when choosing a disk drive: storage capacity and average access time.

Server disk drives are typically high-capacity units, which means they can store large amounts of data and have fast access times. The capacity to store large amounts of data is important because the server must store many data and program files. A file server is essentially each user's hard disk. Individual data storage, together with shared storage needed for application software, databases, several versions of operating system software, utility programs, and electronic mail messages, can easily require several hundred or several thousand megabytes of storage. Some operating systems alone require more than 10 MB of disk storage. An SQL server holds database files as well as the SQL server software. Organizations adopting SQL server technology will likely have large databases and high-volume storage needs.

The need for large amounts of data storage might be satisfied with one high-capacity drive or with several lower-capacity ones; both alternatives offer benefits. Having fewer disk drives provides a configuration that is easier to manage. Having several smaller-capacity drives is beneficial because several disks can be working simultaneously to satisfy user requests, and the impact of a disk failure can be lessened. Suppose you need 1000 MB of storage. You could select one 1000-MB drive or three 350-MB drives. With one drive it is simple to determine file allocation: All files are placed on that drive. With three drives your objective should to be to spread the files over the three drives to provide equal access and to ensure equal activity.

If an application requires 45 disk accesses per second, a single fast disk drive may have difficulty keeping up with this load. With three drives and a good distribution of files, you would have only 15 requests per drive per second. This configuration may be more expensive but it provides better performance. Remember, for file or SQL server disk drives, you should select those with sufficient storage capacity and speed to meet your performance objectives. A powerful processor with a slow disk subsystem can cripple your network. This point cannot be emphasized enough.

A second factor to consider when choosing a disk drive is the access time of the disk itself. The three components of disk access are seek time, latency, and transfer time. The **seek time** is the time required to move the read/write heads to the proper cylinder. Once the heads are positioned, you must wait until the data revolves under the read/write heads; this is called **latency.** The average latency is one-half the time required for the disk to make a complete revolution. **Transfer time** is the time required to move the data from the disk to the computer's memory. Fast disks will have average access times of approximately 15 milliseconds or less. In contrast, many floppy disk drives have access times of approximately 200 milliseconds. Your file server should have disks with fast average access times.

Finally, you also need to consider the **disk drive interface,** or the controller. The disk drive interface sets the standards for connecting the disk drive to the microprocessor and the software commands used to access the drive. There are a variety of disk drive interfaces. Some are well suited for server operations and some are too slow for most LANs. You must choose an interface supported by your LAN operating system. The two interfaces most commonly used for microcomputer-based servers are the small computer system interface (SCSI, pronounced "scuzzy") and the integrated drive electronics (IDE) interface. Both interfaces provide high-speed data transfers and large-capacity disk drives. SCSI generally provides more efficiency and is currently the interface of choice.

Server Memory

A server is a combination of hardware and software. The software should be designed to take full advantage of the hardware, and in the next chapter you will learn techniques for ensuring this compatibility. Memory is often a good hardware investment, because many software systems can take advantage of available memory to provide better performance. High-speed cache memory can significantly improve a computer's performance. Today, microcomputer memories operate at speeds of 70–80 nanoseconds. High-speed **cache memory** operates at speeds of approximately 15 nanoseconds, and is thus 4 to 5 times faster than RAM. Obviously, it is faster to fetch instructions from cache memory than from RAM. The processor first looks for the instruction in cache memory. If it is found in cache, the fetch is very efficient. If the instruction is not in cache, it and a block of the following instructions are transferred from RAM into cache. This increases the chances that the next instruction will be efficiently found in cache memory.

Another form of caching is called disk caching. **Disk caching** is similar in function to cache memory except that main memory serves as a high-speed buffer for slower disk drives. In both types of cache, memory is used as a buffer for lower-speed hardware. When choosing a LAN operating system that provides disk caching, you need to configure the server with sufficient memory to make caching effective. The fundamental premise of disk caching is that a memory access is faster than a disk access. A disk cache therefore attempts to keep highly accessed data in memory. Essentially caching works as follows: If a user's request for data is received, cache memory is searched prior to the data being physically read from the disk. If the data is found in cache memory—a process known as a **logical read**—then the data is made available almost instantly. If the data is not found in cache memory, then it is read from disk, which is called a **physical access.** As data is read from disk, it is also placed into cache memory so any subsequent read for that data might be a logical read.

Disk caching taken to the fullest extent results in all data residing in memory and all reads being logical reads. This is rarely the case. However, it should be clear that effective use of cache memory can significantly improve performance. Because disk caching requires memory, sufficient memory must be available to provide a large percentage of cache hits. A **cache hit** means that the data being read is found in cache memory.

Suppose that LAN data requests cycle through four records—A, B, C, and D—and that you only have enough cache memory for three records. When additional space is needed, the cache-management scheme typically replaces the record that has been dormant the longest with a new record. Records A, B, and C have been read in that order and are in cache memory as illustrated in Figure 4-3(a). A request is issued for Record D, but it is not in cache memory, so a physical read is required. Record D is read and must be inserted into cache memory. Because Record A is the least recently used, Record D replaces Record A, as illustrated in Figure 4-3(b). Next a request is received for Record A. Because it is not in cache memory, a physical read is issued and Record A replaces the least recently used record, Record B. Cache memory now looks like Figure 4-3(c). Next a request is made for Record B, which is also not in cache memory. Record B is read and replaces Record C as illustrated in Figure 4-3(d). Unfortunately, Record C is the next record to be read and again requires a physical read. It is read into cache memory, replacing Record D. Then the cycle repeats again. In this simple example, the cache is one record too small and is totally ineffective. In fact, it is counterproductive, as it only incurs extra overhead by searching cache memory for records that are not cache resident.

Figure 4-3

Example of Disk Cache Memory

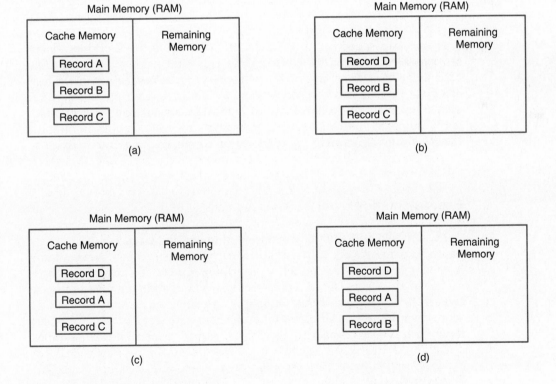

The problem of insufficient cache memory can be corrected by expanding the cache memory. In the example, just one more record slot results in 100 percent cache hits after the four initial reads. Of course, this example is contrived, and 100 percent cache-hit rates are rarely attainable. The example demonstrates that there is a critical threshold for cache memory. If the available memory is under this threshold, cache can be ineffective. When the available cache memory is over this threshold, cache can be very effective. Some users have experienced cache hits as high as 80 to 90 percent. The hit rate depends on the access patterns, so do not expect this figure to hold true for all systems.

An ample amount of memory is important for reasons other than disk caching. You also should have sufficient memory to avoid disk swapping. Most of today's memory-management schemes are based on **virtual memory management,** which uses the disk as an extension of memory so each program has virtually all the memory it needs. Virtual memory management allows the real memory of a system to be less than the aggregate memory required by all the running applications. To do this, application code and data are swapped back and forth between the disk and memory. The swap rate goes up if the available memory is too small. When the swap rate increases, the operating system is spending extra time managing memory and less time is available for doing application work. The amount of application work done per unit of time decreases as the swap rate increases.

Processor Speed

The **processor speed** of the server is also a critical factor. It seldom makes sense to select a server that has fast disks and sufficient memory but a slow CPU. In general, the server ought to be one of the fastest (if not the fastest) computers on the network. One exception to this generalization is a server providing small amounts of data to graphics workstations. Most graphics applications require high-speed processors to create and print graphic images. In these networks the workstation computing power may equal or exceed that of the server.

Expansion and Power

A server should have sufficient expansion capability and the power to effectively use the expansion slots. Network server capacity can be expanded by adding hardware to the existing server or by adding servers. Expanding the capabilities of an existing server is less expensive than adding a new server, so the server you choose should support expansion. This allows you to add more memory, disks, printers, or other hardware devices that users can share, such as modems, facsimile machines, tape drives, and optical disk drives.

System Bus

A computer's **system bus** provides the connection among system components such as the CPU, memory, and device controllers. The size, speed, and type of bus affect the computer's performance. The bus size determines how many data bits can be transferred among system components at one time. A server with a 16-bit bus will take twice as many transfers for 1000 bytes of data as a system with a 32-bit bus, and the operation will take approximately twice as long to perform. A 64-bit bus will provide better performance than a 32-bit bus. The speed of the bus determines how fast data is transferred along the bus. A faster bus will provide better performance than a slower one. The type of the bus refers to the interface standard the bus supports. Microcomputers use three main bus architectures: **industry standard architecture (ISA), extended industry standard architecture (EISA),** and **microchannel architecture (MCA).** The ISA bus is the one on which the original IBM PC was based and is still widely used. The EISA and MCA buses represent improvements over the original ISA bus and are better suited for high-capacity servers. Some systems have more than one bus, such as a separate bus for the monitor and for disk drives. Having two or more buses allows multiple data paths between devices and can further improve performance.

WORKSTATIONS

Some LANs are homogeneous, which means all the workstations are of the same basic type, all are running the same level of the same operating system, and all use essentially the same applications. It is easier to configure this type of network than one that is heterogeneous, but homogeneous networks are less common. Often a network is assembled from workstations acquired over time. These workstations usually represent different levels of technology and perhaps use different versions of operating systems. Consider a network with the following workstations:

- IBM or compatible with an industry standard architecture (ISA) bus
- IBM or compatible with an extended industry standard architecture (EISA) bus
- IBM or compatible with a microchannel architecture (MCA) bus
- Apple Macintosh or compatible
- Sun workstation

If you are selecting components for a heterogeneous network, your hardware and software options are more limited than for a homogeneous network. You may be limited in your choice of network operating systems (see Chapter 5) or LAN adapters. The limitations arise from the inability of some LAN software to support different workstations or from the limited availability of required hardware, such as a LAN adapter. You will find many options for a LAN with only IBM-compatible workstations and several for LANs with only Apple workstations, but some of these options will not support both types of microcomputers. Fortunately, interoperability of different hardware platforms on a single LAN is becoming more common.

Diskless Workstations

You may want to consider diskless workstations when configuring your LAN. A diskless workstation does not have any local disk drives. Instead a diskless workstation has its operating system boot logic in a read-only memory (ROM) chip. This chip contains the logic to connect to the network and download the operating system from the server. A diskless workstation cannot be used in a stand-alone mode; it is fully dependent on the server for all of its software, and it cannot function if the network or server is not operating. This is the disadvantage of a diskless system. Its advantages are lower cost, better security, and tighter control.

Because diskless workstations have no disk drives, they are inherently less expensive than those with disk drives. The maintenance costs for diskless systems also are less than for systems with disk drives. Diskless systems provide extra security because users are unable to copy the organization's data onto local hard or floppy disk drives. This is important because an organization's primary security risk is its employees. Diskless systems also provide a greater measure of control because employees cannot introduce their own software into the system. This not only ensures that standard software and data are used but also reduces the chances of computer viruses being introduced into the network.

Workstation Memory and Speed

Like servers, workstation memory configurations are important. If you have stand-alone microcomputer systems, each with the minimum application memory configuration, you may need to add more memory to those systems to run the same applications on a network because LAN software must also run in the workstations. In addition, LAN software stays memory resident. Suppose you have a microcomputer with 512 KB of memory and that this is just enough to load the operating system and your database management system. Placing that same microcomputer on a network requires that some of the memory be allocated to the LAN interface software; you may be unable to run your database management system because of insufficient memory. The solution is to expand the computer's memory. The amount of memory required for LAN software varies from one LAN to another. Some require fewer than 20 KB, and some require more than 70 KB of resident memory.

The speed of the workstation's processor needs to be compatible with the type of work for which the workstation is being used. If you use the workstation for word processing, a low-speed processor probably is satisfactory. A workstation used for graphics work requires a high-speed processor. Basically it is the application and not the LAN that determines the required power of the workstations.

BACKUP DEVICES

No LAN is complete without a backup device. One of the LAN administrator's most important duties is to make periodic file backups. A **backup** is a copy of files at a specific time and is used to restore the system to a workable state following a system failure or an event that damages the data, or to restore data that needs to be available only on a periodic basis. Research data needed only once or twice a month and year-end payroll data needed temporarily to file workers' tax notices can be backed up and then replaced on disk on an as-needed basis.

The principal backup device is a magnetic tape drive. Removable disk drives and optical disk drives are alternatives. The primary backup technologies are described below and are listed in Table 4-1.

TABLE 4-1   Primary Harware Backup Technologies

Diskette Backup
> 360 KB
> 720 KB
> 1.2 MB
> 1.44 MB
> 2.88 MB
> 20 MB

Hard Drive, Fixed
> Multiple capacities

Hard Drive, Removable Cartridge
> 40 MB to more than 250 MB

Tape Backup
> 4mm or 1/4-inch
>> to 5 GB
>> 60MB, 150 MB, 160 MB, 500 MB, 1.2 GB, 2.2 GB are common

> 8mm or VCR
>> to 2.2 GB

> 9-track
>> to 100 MB

(Some backup systems provide autoloading multitape systems with capacities to 100 GB.)

Optical Drives
> WORM (write once, ready many)
>> to 4 GB

> Rewritable
>> to 4 GB

Magnetic Tape Drives

Magnetic tape drives are inexpensive relative to the other backup options. Magnetic tapes can hold large volumes of data, are easy to use and store, and generally provide good performance. A variety of tape backup devices are available. The drives themselves are less expensive than disk or optical drives with comparable storage characteristics, and a wide range of data capacities are available. Tape drives vary in the size of the tape and the recording method. If more than one tape drive is to be used in one organization, it is best to establish a standard tape configuration so the tapes can be exchanged among the different drives.

Like other hardware, the tape drive must be compatible with the server or workstation on which it is installed. A drive usually has a controller that must be installed in the computer, so you must select a drive that has a controller compatible with your equipment. You also need backup software and procedures to make your backups. Backup software is covered in the next chapter.

Other Backup Options

You may use floppy disks as the backup medium. The major disadvantage of this backup method is the low capacity and speed of the backup medium. Floppy disk backup for LANs with small disk requirements or for backing up a few small files can be practical, but for large-disk systems, the number of disks needed to store all the data is too high to be time effective. Backing up to floppy disks is slow, subject to errors, and requires handling many disks.

A hard disk drive on either a server or a workstation may also be used for backup. The arguments for and against this alternative are much the same as those for floppy disks. The major difference is that the capacity of hard disks is greater than that of floppy disks. If the hard disk is not removable, however, it is difficult to keep multiple generations of backups, a procedure that is important for a comprehensive backup plan.

Optical disk drives are gaining popularity as backup devices. The reasons for this are their decreasing costs and large storage capacity, and the recently introduced ability to erase and write to optical disks. The two classes of writeable optical disk drives are WORM (write once, read many) and erasable drives. **WORM technology** allows you to write to the medium only once. You cannot erase data on a WORM disk and reuse the medium. This can make the cost of backups expensive because the cost of cartridges for many such drives on microcomputers is more than $100. An advantage of WORM technology is that the data cannot be changed, so the backup cannot be accidentally destroyed. The newest optical disk technology allows data to be rewritten. **Rewritable optical drives** are more expensive than WORM drives, but you can expect these prices to come down. The capacities of optical drives range from 300 MB to 1 GB or more. Writable optical drives is a rapidly improving technology. Drives are available for less than $1,000 with media costs for 650 MB under $20.

LAN ADAPTERS

LAN adapters also known as network interface cards (NICs) provide the connection between the medium and the bus of the workstation or server. LAN adapters are designed to support a specific data link or media access control (MAC) protocol using a specific medium, although some can support two or three different medium types. One type of Ethernet card supports twisted-pair wires, another type supports coaxial cable, and a combination card might support both connection types. After you match medium and protocol, there are additional alternatives regarding vendor and architecture. We discuss MAC protocols in the next chapter.

The choice of a LAN adapter vendor determines the support, quality, and price of the LAN adapter. Just as you should be careful when selecting a LAN vendor, you should also be careful regarding the vendor of individual components such as a LAN adapter. The LAN adapter that is initially the least expensive may prove to be more costly in the long term if it is of inferior quality, if it does not have a good vendor-support policy, or if replacement LAN adapters are difficult to obtain should the vendor go out of business.

LAN adapters are installed in each workstation and server. Naturally the LAN adapter must be compatible with the hardware architecture of the computer into which it is installed. You also need to ensure that compatible LAN adapters are available for each type of network node you anticipate having. Certain combinations of equipment may not be supported. You may have difficulty finding ARCnet cards for each node in a network consisting of a Digital Equipment Corporation VAX server and Apple Macintosh, Sun, and IBM workstations. LAN adapters also must be compatible with the bus of the host computer. For IBM and Apple microcomputer-based LANs, you may need ISA-, EISA-, MCA-, Personal Computer Memory Card International Association-(PCMCIA), and NuBus-compatible cards.

LAN adapters also have their own architecture. LAN adapters for IBM or compatible systems often come in 8-bit, 16-bit, and 32-bit architectures. The 32-bit adapters are almost always more expensive and faster than the corresponding 16-bit and 8-bit adapters. By faster we mean that a 32-bit adapter can transfer data between the computer and the medium faster than a 16-bit adapter, which is faster than an 8-bit adapter; the bus architecture does not affect the speed at which data is transferred over the network medium. A 32-bit adapter is faster than a 16-bit adapter because it transfers data between the adapter and memory 32 bits at a time, whereas the 16-bit adapter transfers data in 16-bit groups.

PRINTERS

One major factor that affects the success of a LAN is printer support. You must be concerned not only with the number of printers but also with printer accessibility, the type of printers supported and the way in which they are supported. A **printer driver** is a software module that determines how to format data for proper printing on a specific type of printer. The printers you intend to use must be supported by the software drivers provided by the vendor. You may find that a laser printer you attach to the LAN can operate in text mode but is restricted in its graphic mode operation or in its ability to download fonts. Be sure to consider interoperability of hardware and software components to ensure that your needs are realized. Some LAN systems provide a utility program that allows you to tailor a generic printer driver to meet the needs of a specific printer you want to use. This utility allows you to define printer functions and the command sequences essential to invoking those functions. Because new printer technologies are constantly appearing, this utility is quite useful.

ADDITIONAL LAN HARDWARE

Earlier we discussed the principle of disk caching. Most efficient network operating systems use this to enhance performance. A disadvantage to using disk caching is that several disk updates can be lost if the server experiences a power failure. The lost updates result because they have been written into cache and have not yet been flushed to the disk; furthermore, high performance network operating systems usually keep data like updated end-of-file markers and user attributes memory resident. To reduce the risk of this memory resident data being lost due to a server failure, many companies protect their servers with an **uninterruptible power supply (UPS).** A UPS uses batteries to provide power to a connected computer in the event of blackout or reduced power conditions. Some UPSs also provide protection against power spikes and momentary power loss. For many business applications a UPS that costs several hundred dollars is a good investment.

UPSs come in different sizes. The size of a UPS is given in watts, which is a measure of power. It is important to select a UPS that matches or exceeds the power demands of the computer it is protecting. Each computer has a power supply rated in the number of watts it delivers to the system. The easiest way to select the proper UPS size is to meet or exceed the wattage of the power supplies for all computers protected by the UPS. A more precise but time-consuming method is to sum the power requirements of all components serviced by the UPS.

MAKING CONNECTIONS

Thus far we have discussed the medium, the network nodes, and the LAN adapter. All that remains is to connect the nodes to the medium. Connections can be made in a variety of ways. You have already learned that you must pick a LAN adapter that is compatible with the medium you choose. Therefore it is the medium that primarily influences the way physical connections are made. Let us look at the problem from a generic perspective.

The objective of network connection—connecting a computer to the LAN medium—is to provide a data path between the medium and the computer's memory. To accomplish this there must be a connection to the medium and a connection to the computer's bus or channel. The interface or connection to the medium is referred to as the **communications interface unit (CIU),** and the interface or connection to the computer's bus is referred to as the **bus interface unit (BIU).** These functions, illustrated in Figure 4-4, are provided by the LAN adapter.

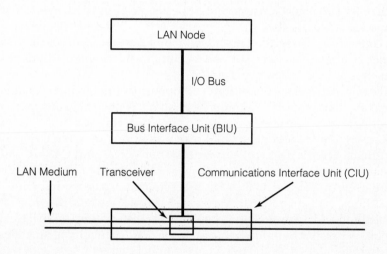

Figure 4-4

Bus/Communications Interface Units and Transceiver

A key component of the network connection is a **transceiver,** which establishes the connection to the medium and implements the transmit and receive portion of the protocol. In a few Ethernet LANs, the transceiver is connected directly to the medium. Most of today's Ethernet implementations have a transceiver that is located on the LAN adapter, as illustrated in Figure 4-5.

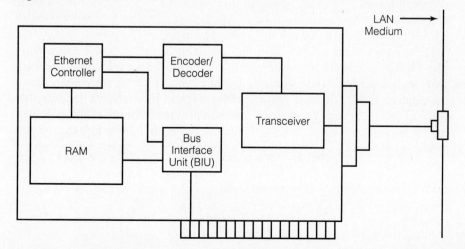

Figure 4-5

A Transceiver on a LAN Adapter

The physical connection between the computer and the medium is established through connectors. Many different types of connectors are used, but the principal ones are:

- BNC-, TNC-, or N-type connectors for coaxial cable
- RJ-11, RJ-45, or DB-nn (DB-25 or DB-15) connectors for wires
- SMA connectors for fiber optic cable

The type of connector you need is determined by your LAN adapter. A wide variety of connector adapters allow you to change connector types. One adapter can change a bayonet nut connector (BNC) to a TNC-type connector. **Baluns** are adapters that change coaxial cable connectors to twisted-pair wire connectors. These adapters allow you to transfer from one medium to another or from a connector for one medium to a different medium. Several connectors are illustrated in Figure 4-6.

In some networks, connecting a computer to the medium is sufficient for making that computer active on the network. Some LAN implementations use wiring hubs to provide node-to-node connection. Several kinds of connection hubs are commonly used. In an IBM token-ring LAN, individual stations are connected to a wiring hub called a **multistation access unit (MAU).** The ring is established via internal connections within the MAU as illustrated in Figure 4-7. An ARCnet LAN may use active and passive hubs for node connections, as illustrated in Figure 4-8. An **active hub** provides signal regeneration and allows nodes to be located at distances up to 2000 feet from the hub. A **passive hub** does not provide signal regeneration, so nodes can be located no more than 100 feet from the hub. Ethernet LANs with twisted-pair medium use wiring hubs similar to the token-ring MAU configuration.

A variety of other hardware components are sometimes needed to make the network function. On bus networks or networks using wiring hubs, terminators are often needed to prevent signal loss. **Terminators** are used at the ends of a bus to prevent echo and are required on unused passive hub ports in an ARCnet network for the same reason. The location of terminators in a LAN configuration is shown in Figure 4-6.

Sometimes LAN connections go further than simply connecting a node to the medium. You may also need to connect one LAN to another or connect a LAN to a WAN. We discuss this subject in detail in Chapter 8.

When you build a LAN, you will probably investigate the capabilities provided by a variety of vendors. You will discover several ways in which you can build a LAN, and you also might hear conflicting statements about the relative merits of each. We will now discuss the network layouts that vendors most commonly propose. You will also read about LAN topologies, media access control protocols, common ways in which topologies and media access control protocols are combined, and the strengths and weaknesses of several LAN configurations.

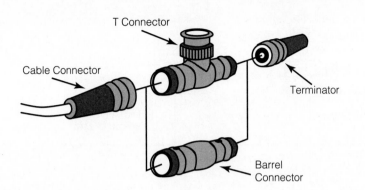

T Connector

Cable Connector

Terminator

Barrel
Connector

Figure 4-6

Use of Connectors and a
Terminator

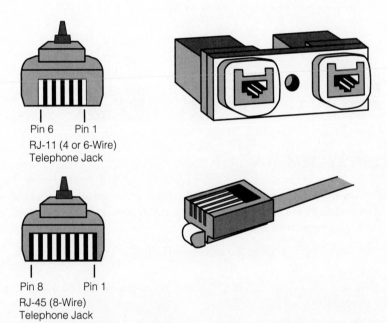

Pin 6   Pin 1
RJ-11 (4 or 6-Wire)
Telephone Jack

Pin 8   Pin 1
RJ-45 (8-Wire)
Telephone Jack

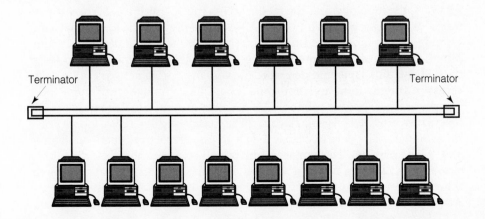

Terminator

Terminator

Figure 4-7

A Multistation Access
Unit (MAU)

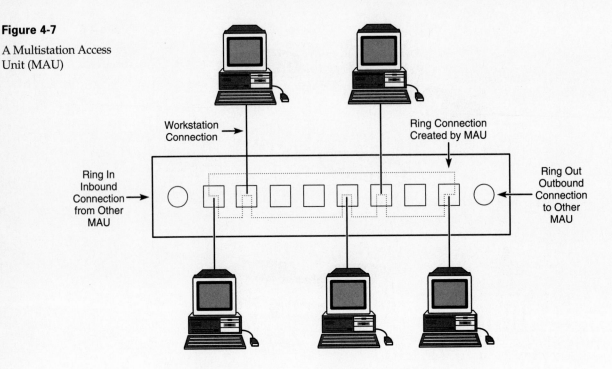

THE LAN SYSTEM

If you evaluate vendor responses to a LAN selection process, you may first
read statements intended to give you a general idea of the type of solution
proposed. Here are some examples:

- "We are happy to propose a Novell IEEE 802.3 network for your
  consideration."
- "We believe a Banyan Vines token-ring network will best suit your
  purposes."
- "Our solution uses Microsoft's Windows NT software and Ethernet."

These statements encapsulate three major LAN components: the LAN
software, the topology, and the media access control protocol. LAN software
provides the user interface to the LAN and enables its services. A **network
topology** is the model used to lay out the LAN medium and connect computers to the medium. A **media access control (MAC) protocol** operates at
the OSI data link layer and describes the way in which a network node gains
access to the medium and transmits data. The combination of these three
components is what we call the LAN architecture and provides much of the
uniqueness of a LAN. In general, you will be considering three basic topologies—
ring, bus, and star—and two basic media access control protocols—contention
and token passing. The major distinctions between one token ring, contention bus, or token bus and another are in the network operating system,
the hardware, and the medium. A number of vendors, such as Apple,
Artisoft, Banyan, IBM, Microsoft, and Novell, provide networking software.

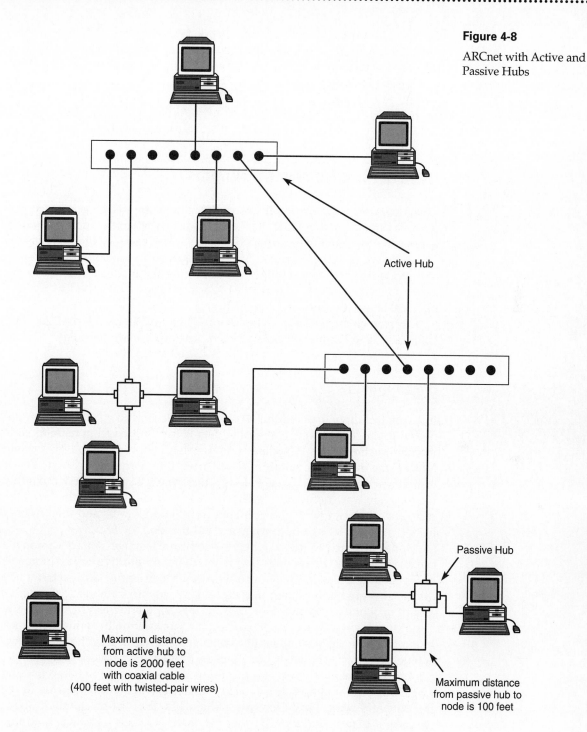

Figure 4-8

ARCnet with Active and
Passive Hubs

Active Hub

Passive Hub

Maximum distance
from active hub to
node is 2000 feet
with coaxial cable
(400 feet with twisted-pair wires)

Maximum distance
from passive hub to
node is 100 feet

When selecting a LAN you must keep one idea paramount: You are
selecting a system. The system has many components, and the overall success
of the LAN is how well these components can be integrated to form a system.
Interoperability is the key, not the efficiency of a single component. For

example, you must be able to attach workstations to the LAN and support each workstation's operating systems. The LAN might consist of IBM or IBM-compatible workstations together with Apple Macintosh or compatible systems, all with a variety of operating systems and printers. In this case the system you choose must support all of these components; some network operating systems cannot do this.

LAN TOPOLOGIES AND STANDARDS

What do we mean when we talk about a LAN topology? First, the term *topology* derives from a mathematics field that deals with points and surfaces in space—that is, with the layout of objects in space. Thus, LAN topology is the physical layout of the network. Another way you can look at a topology is as a model for the way in which you configure the medium and attach the nodes to that medium. In general, LAN topologies correspond to the OSI physical layer described in Chapter 1.

LANs have three basic topologies: ring, bus, and star. Each configuration is illustrated in Figure 4-9. Let's take a closer look at each topology.

Ring Topology

In a **ring topology** the medium forms a closed loop, and all stations are connected to the loop or ring. On a ring, data is transmitted from node to node in one direction. Thus if Node A in Figure 4-10 wants to send a message to Node F, the message is sent from A to B, from B to C, from C to D, and so on, until it reaches Node F. Usually Node F then sends an acknowledgment that the message was successfully received back to Node A, the originator of the message. The acknowledgment is sent from Node F to G, and then from G back to A, completing one journey around the loop.

Nodes attached to the ring may be active or inactive. An **active node** is capable of sending or receiving network messages. An **inactive node** is incapable of sending or receiving network messages; for example, an inactive node may be powered down. Naturally, nodes may go both from inactive to active and from active to inactive. For example, when a worker leaves at night, she might turn her workstation off, placing the workstation in an inactive state. In the morning she powers up her system and brings it into the active state. A failed or inactive network node must not cause the network to fail.

The most frequently used microcomputer ring network is a **token-passing ring.** IBM's LAN approach has been widely adopted and conforms to the Institute of Electrical and Electronics Engineers (IEEE) 802.5 standard, so we describe it here and in the CBT module "Media Access". Realize, however, that we are only discussing the topology and media access control. The token-passing ring we are describing can be implemented using a variety of different network operating systems to include Novell NetWare, Banyan Vines, and IBM's LAN Server.

Figure 4-9

Basic LAN Topologies

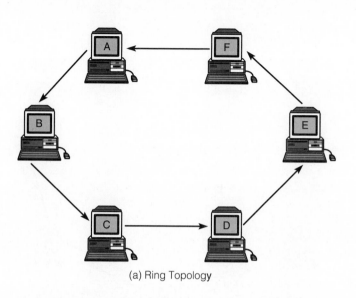

(a) Ring Topology

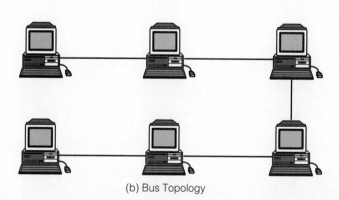

(b) Bus Topology

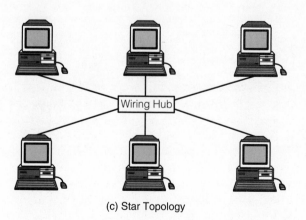

(c) Star Topology

Figure 4-10

A Token-Passing Ring
Configuration

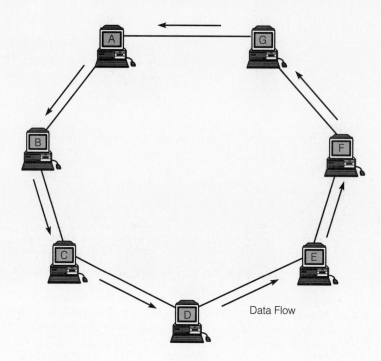

Data Flow

Figure 4-11

Backbone Network
Connecting Local
Area Networks

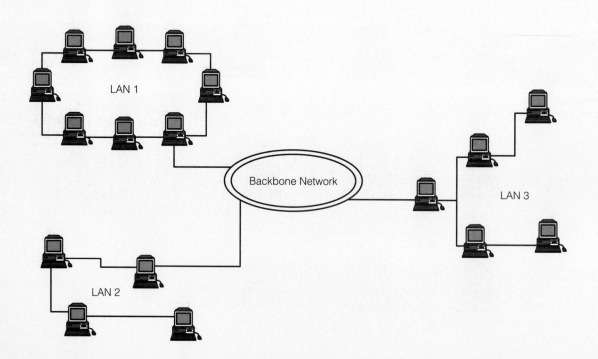

LAN 1

LAN 2

LAN 3

Backbone Network

Another network that uses a ring topology is a high-speed **metropolitan area LAN (MAN),** which is designed to cover a wider geographical area than a typical LAN. The ANSI standard for this type of network is called the **fiber distributed data interface (FDDI)** standard. It uses fiber optics for the medium and spans distances of up to 200 kilometers at a speed of 100 Mbps. An alternative to FDDI is the **copper distributed data interface (CDDI),** which uses shielded or unshielded twisted-pair wires as the medium. As LAN workstations become more powerful and the volume of data transmission increases (perhaps due to the transmission of graphic and video images), high-speed LANs may be used to connect microcomputers in one department within a company. Currently one use for an FDDI LAN is as a **backbone network** connecting microcomputer LANs within a company complex or within a metropolitan area. A backbone network, illustrated in Figure 4-11, is used to interconnect other networks or to connect a cluster of network nodes.

Bus Topology

In a **bus topology,** illustrated in Figure 4-12(a), the medium consists of a single wire or cable to which nodes are attached. Unlike with a ring, the ends of the bus are not connected. Instead the ends are terminated by a hardware device called a terminator. A variation of a bus topology, illustrated in Figure 4-12(b), has spurs to the primary bus formed by interconnected minibuses. This variation of the bus topology is quite common.

As with ring topologies, several standards describe a bus implementation. The most common of these is an implementation originally known as **Ethernet.** Ethernet LAN specifications were originally proposed by Xerox Corporation in 1972. Soon thereafter Xerox was joined in establishing the Ethernet standard by Digital Equipment Corporation (DEC) and Intel Corporation. The IEEE 802 Committee then developed the IEEE 802.3 standard, which encompasses most of the premises of the original Ethernet specification. Thus, the IEEE 802.3 standard is sometimes referred to as an Ethernet implementation. The IEEE 802.4 standard also proposes a bus technology. The primary difference between the two is the media access control protocol. The IEEE 802.3 standard specifies a contention protocol, and the 802.4 standard uses a token-passing protocol. Again, these protocols are covered later in this chapter.

Star Topology

Figure 4-13 shows true **star topology,** which consists of a central computing node to which all other nodes are directly connected. This type of topology, however, is rare in microcomputer networks. A variation called a star-wired LAN has gained wide acceptance. In a **star-wired LAN,** a **wiring hub** is used to form the connection between network nodes. Two common star-wired LANs are known as ARCnet and StarLAN.

Figure 4-12

A Bus Topology

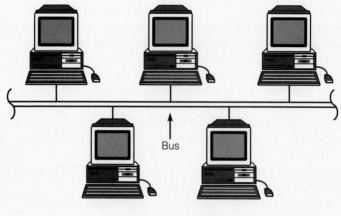

(a) A Bus Topology

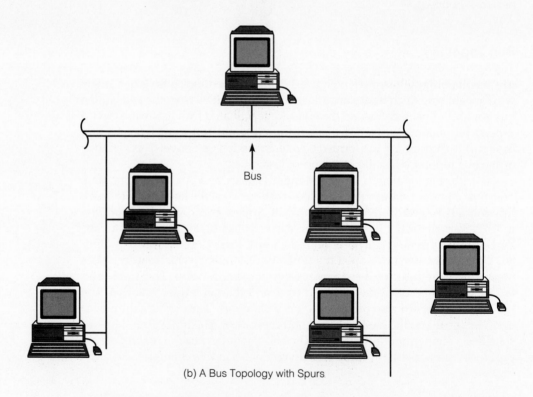

(b) A Bus Topology with Spurs

ARCnet technology was developed in the 1970s by Datapoint Corporation to form networks of their minicomputers. The technology was well developed when microcomputer LANs were evolving, and the technology was readily adopted. Because it has been so widely used, ARCnet has become a de facto microcomputer LAN standard and also has been submitted to the American National Standards Institute (ANSI) for formal standardization. An ARCnet configuration is a token-passing bus but does not conform to the IEEE 802.4 standard. ARCnet uses both active and passive hubs to connect network nodes. ARCnet speeds are 2.5 Mbps, 20 Mbps, and 100 Mbps. ARCnet

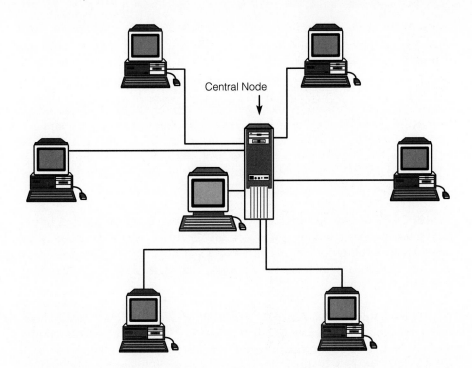

Figure 4-13
A Star Topology

media are usually either twisted-pair wires or coaxial cables. Fiber optic cables are also used for ARCnet LANs, primarily in higher-speed implementations.

StarLAN technology was developed by American Telephone and Telegraph (AT&T) Corporation. The topology was also adopted and marketed by several other companies and has been included as a low-cost, low-speed option in the IEEE 802.3 standard. Originally the StarLAN speed was 1 Mbps, but today 10 Mbps implementations are also available. A StarLAN configuration is similar to the basic star topology (Figure 4-13) in that each workstation is connected to a wiring hub. Note that the configuration is also similar to that of the ARCnet configuration (Figure 4-8). The primary medium used for StarLAN implementations is twisted-pair wires.

Media Access (Token Passing and CSMA/CD)

At this point, you should be ready to delve into some of the details of token-passing ring and CSMA/CD bus LANs; therefore, you should now shift to the CBT module entitled "Media Access (Token Passing and CSMA/CD)".

IEEE Project 802 Subcommittees

The LANs you just learned about in the CBT represent the majority of LAN architectures. In today's LANs, we often see a mixture of hardware and software from a variety of vendors. In general, it is the existence of standards that make this interoperability possible. Standards define the way in which network components should be implemented, and if hardware and software manufacturers adhere to these standards, their products should work together in the same LAN. The token ring and Ethernet LANs covered in the CBT are covered by standards developed by the IEEE, and FDDI LANs are covered by standards from the ANSI. In addition to the IEEE standards covered in the CBT, other IEEE standards exist. Many of the LAN standards are formulated by an IEEE committee designated by the number 802. The 802 Committee is broken down into subcommittees, each of which focuses on specific areas of LAN development. The subcommittees and their objectives are described below.

802.1—High-Level Interface. The high-level interface subcommittee addresses matters relating to network architecture; network management; network interconnection; and all other issues related to the OSI layers above the data link layer, which are the network, transport, session, presentation, and application layers.

802.2—Logical Link Control. IEEE has divided the OSI data link layer into two sublayers: **logical link control (LLC)** and media access control (MAC). The MAC sublayer implements protocols such as token passing or CSMA/CD. Figure 4-14 illustrates the relationship between the LLC and the MAC sublayers. The objective of the LLC is to provide a consistent, transparent interface to the MAC layer, so the network layers above the data link layer are able to function correctly regardless of the MAC protocol.

802.3—CSMA/CD. The IEEE 802.3 standard covers a variety of CSMA/CD architectures that are generally based on Ethernet. Several alternatives are available under this standard. Some of these are:

- 1Base5 is a 1-Mbps baseband medium with a maximum segment length of 500 meters (a baseband medium is one that carries only one signal at a time as opposed to a broadband medium that can carry multiple signals simultaneously). The segment length is the length of cable that can be used without repeaters to amplify the signal. This standard encompasses implementations commonly known as StarLAN.

- 10Base5 is a 10-Mbps baseband medium with a maximum segment length of 500 meters.

- 10Base2 is a 10-Mbps baseband medium with a maximum segment length of 200 meters. The cable used in this implementation is commonly called Thinnet or Cheapernet.

- 10BaseT is a 10-Mbps baseband medium with twisted-pair wires as the medium.

- 10Broad36 is a 10-Mbps broadband medium with a 3600-meter segment length.

- 100BaseT is a 100-Mbps baseband medium with twisted-pair wires as the medium.

- 100VG-AnyLAN is a specification of the IEEE 802.12 Subcommittee. This specification competes with 100BaseT for the 100 Mbps Ethernet market. The specification calls for twisted-pair wires and can support either CSMA/CD or token passing technologies.

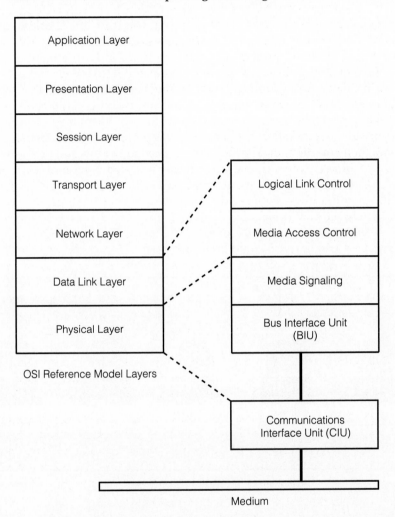

Figure 4-14

LLC and MAC Sublayers of the OSI Data Link Layer

You may infer from this nomenclature that, in general, the initial number represents the speed of the medium in millions of bits per second. The "base" or "broad" designator represents baseband or broadband, respectively. With three exceptions, 10BaseT, 100BaseT, and 100VG-AnyLAN, the last number represents the segment length of the medium in hundreds of meters.

802.4—Token Bus. The IEEE 802.4 Standard Subcommittee sets standards for token bus networks. The standard describes how the network is initialized, how new stations can insert themselves into the set of nodes receiving the token, how to recover if the token is lost, and how node priority can be established. The standard also describes the format of the message frames.

802.5—Token Ring.   The IEEE 802.5 Standard Subcommittee sets standards for token-ring networks. The standard describes essentially the same functions as those described by the token bus network.

802.6—Metropolitan Area Networks (MANs).   The FDDI family of technologies is not the only MAN proposal. The IEEE 802 LAN Standards Committee has also developed specifications, IEEE 802.6, for a MAN. The IEEE 802.6 standard has also been adopted by ANSI. The standard is also referred to as the **distributed queue dual bus (DQDB)** standard.

As the name **DQDB** indicates, the architecture uses two buses. Each bus is unidirectional, meaning that data is transmitted in one direction on one bus and in the other direction on the second bus, as illustrated in Figure 4-15. Each node must therefore be attached to both buses. The specification also allows for a variation called a looped bus. The **looped bus** still uses two one-direction buses; however, each bus forms a closed loop as illustrated in Figure 4-16. Several speeds are defined in the standard. Speeds are dependent on the medium used. With coaxial cable the speed is 45 Mbps; the speed is 156 Mbps over fiber optic cable. Distances up to 200 miles are supported.

Figure 4-15

IEEE Distributed Queue
Dual Bus LAN

Bus A, Unidirectional

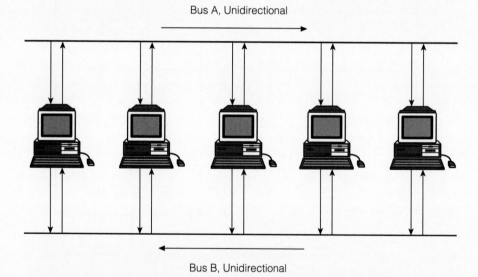

Bus B, Unidirectional

802.7—Broadband Technical Advisory Group.   This group provides guidance and technical expertise to other groups that are establishing broadband LAN standards, such as the 802.3 subcommittee for 10Broad36.

802.8—Fiber Optic Technical Advisory Group.   This group provides guidance and technical expertise to other groups that are establishing standards for LANs using fiber optic cable.

802.9—Integrated Data and Voice Networks.   This committee sets standards for networks that carry both voice and data. Specifically, it is setting standards for interfaces to integrated services digital networks (ISDNs).

Figure 4-16

IEEE Looped Bus LAN

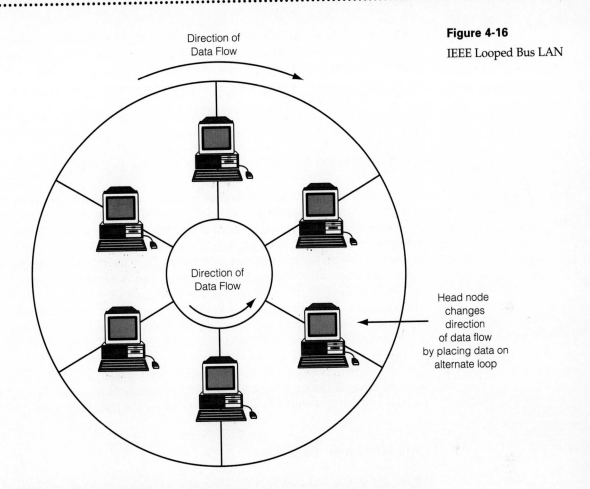

802.10—LAN Security.   This committee addresses the implementation of security capabilities such as encryption, network management, and the transfer of data.

802.11—Wireless LANs.   This committee addresses multiple transmission methods to include infrared light, as well as a variety of broadcast frequencies to include spread spectrum radio waves and microwaves. Many of the existing wireless implementations will be covered under these standards.

802.12—Demand Priority Access Method.   This subgroup is developing the specifications for the 100VG-AnyLAN protocol. The protocol specifies 100-Mbps speeds over twisted-pair wires.

The ANSI Fiber Distributed Data Interface Standard

Two major uses have been suggested for high-speed LANs. The obvious one is the high-speed exchange of data among computers located within a large urban area. Frequently, companies have several offices distributed throughout a large metropolitan area, and a MAN will allow computers in these locations to exchange large amounts of data almost instantly. The second purpose is as a backbone network to interconnect distributed LANs. This is illustrated in Figure 4-11. In the Media Access CBT you learned about how this LAN implementation works.

DATA LINK AND MEDIA ACCESS CONTROL PROTOCOLS

The physical layer of the OSI reference model describes the medium, the connectors required to attach workstations and servers to the medium, and the representation of signals using the medium, such as voltage levels for baseband transmission or frequencies for broadband transmission.

Once connected to the medium, a network node must have the ability to send and receive network messages. This function is described by the data link layer of the OSI reference model. A convention, or protocol, must exist to define how this function is accomplished. The method by which a LAN workstation is able to gain control of the medium and transmit a message is called a media access control (MAC) protocol. The MAC protocol is implemented in LANs as one of two sublayers of the OSI reference model's data link layer. MAC protocols were described in the CBT Access Control module. The other sublayer is called the logical link control (LLC) sublayer. Let us take a closer look at the functions provided by the data link layer.

Data Link Layer Functions

In general, a data link protocol establishes the rules for gaining access to the medium and for exchanging messages. To do this the protocol describes several aspects of the message-exchange process. Five of the most important aspects are:

- Delineation of data
- Error control
- Addressing
- Transparency
- Code independence

Delineation of Data.   A data link protocol must define or delineate where the data portion of the transmitted message begins and ends. You may recall from the discussion of the OSI reference model in Chapter 1 that each layer may add data to the message it receives from the layers above it. The data link layer is no exception to this. Some of the characters or bits it adds to the message may include line control information, error-detection data, and so on. When these fields are added, a data link protocol must provide a way to distinguish among the various pieces of data. This can be accomplished in two basic ways: by framing the data with certain control characters or by using a standard message format wherein a data segment is identified by its position within the message.

The framing technique is used in two types of data link protocols: asynchronous transmission and binary synchronous transmission. These protocols are common to WANs and are discussed in Chapter 6.

Many of today's LANs use a standard message format for sending data. For example, an Ethernet message has several distinct parts, as illustrated in Figure 4-17. The message frame begins with a 64-bit synchronization pattern. The synchronization bits give the receiving node an opportunity to sense the incoming message and establish time or synchronization with the sending node. The message is a stream of continuous bits, so it is important that the receiving node is able to clock the bits in as they arrive. The IEEE 802.3 standard uses a 64-bit synchronization pattern; however, the standard divides this into a 56-bit group and an 8-bit group. The first 56 bits are for synchronization, and the 8 bits that follow signal the start of the frame and thus indicate where the first bit of the remaining frame can be found. The next two fields are the addresses of the destination node and the sending node. Each address is 48 bits long.

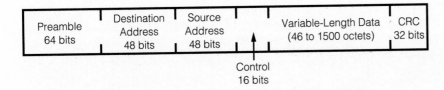

Figure 4-17

The Ethernet Message Format

The 16-bit field type is a control field. In the IEEE 802.3 standard, this represents the length of the data field that follows. The length is expressed as the number of octets of data. An **octet** is a group of 8 bits. If the message is short, extra bits may be added to make the entire message long enough to allow the message to clear the length of the network before the sending node stops transmitting. This is essential to ensure correct transmission. The frame check sequence, a 32-bit cyclic redundancy check (CRC) field as illustrated in Figure 4-17, provides for error detection.

Error Control. Error control is used to detect transmission errors. Common error-detection techniques are parity and cyclic redundancy checks. These techniques are discussed in Chapter 2.

Addressing. Communication between two network nodes is accomplished through an addressing scheme. Network addressing is similar to the addressing we use for postal mail. A postal address is a hierarchical addressing scheme, with the hierarchy being individual recipient, street address, city, state, country, and zip code. Networks also use a hierarchical addressing scheme, with the hierarchy being application, network node, and network. Like postal addresses, network addresses must be unique; otherwise, ambiguity arises as to which node is the recipient. At this point, we are concerned only with network node addressing, not network or application addressing. Each network has a specific way in which it forms station addresses. In Ethernet and the IBM token ring, each node address is 48 bits long. Each Ethernet or IBM token-ring LAN adapter card has its address set by the manufacturer. This ensures that all nodes, regardless of location, have a unique address. In ARCnet a node address is an 8-bit entity, and the LAN administrator typically sets the node address through switches on the LAN adapter (note that this limits the number of nodes on an ARCnet network to 256. On a LAN, node source and destination addresses typically are included in the headers of messages being transmitted.

Transparency. When concerned with data link protocols, **transparency** refers to the ability of the data link to transmit any bit combination. In the binary synchronous data link protocol (shown in Figure 4-18), the start-of-text and end-of-text framing characters have special meaning. These characters can be sent as part of the data only when special considerations are made. Without these special considerations, the protocol is not transparent. We want protocols to be transparent because they can be used to transfer binary data such as object programs as well as text data. The Ethernet message illustrated in Figure 4-17 does provide transparency: No bit patterns in the data field can cause confusion in the message.

Figure 4-18

Framing in the Binary Synchronous Data Link Protocol

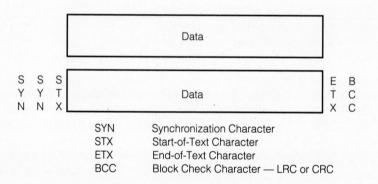

Code Independence. **Code independence** means that any data code, such as ASCII or EBCDIC, can be transmitted. These codes use different bit patterns to represent many of the characters. Code independence is important because often you must communicate with or through computers having a data code different from that of your computer. In the Ethernet protocol this is accomplished by sending data in groups of 8 bits called octets. The 8 bits are not tied to any particular code, and thus any code can be used. If your computer uses a 7-bit code, such as one of the two ASCII codes, the only requirement is that the total number of bits transmitted be divisible by 8. Thus, if you are sending 100 7-bit characters, the total number of bits in the data portion must be 704. The last 4 bits are added to pad out to an integral number of octets (700/8 = 87.5, and an integral number of octets must be transmitted; thus 704 bits are necessary because 704 is a multiple of 8).

MAC Protocols

LAN technology adheres to two primary data link protocols: token passing and contention. Both of these were explained in the Media Access CBT. In the IEEE 802 standards, the data link layer is divided into the two sublayers of logical link control (LLC) and MAC. The LLC provides the functions of flow control, message sequencing, message acknowledgment, and error checking. The MAC layer describes token passing and contention.

MAKING THE DECISIONS

Without even considering the network operating system software alternatives, the number of alternatives available in choosing a LAN can be overwhelming. You have three basic conducted media choices or three choices in the new wireless medium technology, three major topology choices, two primary media access control choices, and a wide variety of vendor choices. The issue then becomes which is the best configuration for your company and applications. If one clear option were superior for all applications and for all users, the choice would be easy. However, applications vary significantly with respect to the number of nodes, number of concurrent users, data access needs, distance spanned, and budget. Next, we explore tradeoffs you can consider when making LAN choices.

Token Passing and CSMA/CD Compared

The pros and cons of the token-passing and CSMA/CD protocols are summarized in Table 4-2. Note that each protocol has advantages and disadvantages. In practice both have been noted to have good performance.

Topology and Protocol Tradeoffs

We consider the three primary combinations of topology and protocol: CSMA/CD bus, token bus, and token ring. The StarLAN model LAN is covered under the IEEE 802.3 standard, and its characteristics are similar to that of the CSMA/CD bus. As of this writing, wireless LANs are so new that tradeoff data regarding their use is not readily available. When specifics are required, we will use popular implementations as examples: Ethernet or an IEEE 802.3 implementation for CSMA/CD buses, ARCnet for token buses, and IEEE 802.5 for token ring. Table 4-3 summarizes the topologies and protocols, which are described in the following sections.

TABLE 4-2   MAC Protocol Comparison

Token Passing	CSMA/CD
Equal access for all nodes	Equal access for all nodes
Predictable access window	Access window can be unpredictable
Maximum wait time to transmit is token circulation time	Maximum wait time to transmit is unpredictable and depends on collisions
Average wait time to transmit is predictable—half the maximum circulation time	Average wait time to transmit is unpredictable
Network congestion does not adversely affect network efficiency	Network congestion may result in collisions and reduce network efficiency
A node needs to wait for the token before being able to transmit	A node may be able to transmit immediately
One node cannot monopolize the network	One node may be able to monopolize the network
Large rings can result in long delays before a node obtains a token	A node can transmit when the network is quiet
Consistent performance for large, busy networks	Upredictable performance for large, busy networks due to possibility of collisions

CSMA/CD Buses

Most CSMA/CD bus implementations use either twisted-pair wires or coaxial cable. Less frequently, fiber optic cable and microwave radio are used. As previously stated, the IEEE 802.3 standard has not yet set the standard for using fiber optic cable. Common speeds for these LANs are 1, 10, and 100 Mbps, with 10 Mbps being the most common. The distances spanned by these networks vary, but the IEEE 802.3 standard, which covers several implementations, specifies 925, 2500, and 3600 meters. The number of supported nodes also varies. In the IEEE standard, one implementation allows 150 nodes and another allows 500. The number of nodes allowed is a hardware-based limit and addresses the issue of connectivity. The network operating system and performance needs also may limit the number of network nodes. Some network operating systems restrict the number of network nodes. We discuss network operating systems in Chapter 5. A network's performance is a critical factor in its productivity. Performance depends on both the hardware and the software. There are many different combinations of hardware and software, so we consider the general outlook for CSMA/CD bus systems.

The major concern people have voiced regarding CSMA/CD bus performance is its capacity under load. As the number of users and the number of messages being sent increase, so does the probability of collisions. If the collision rate is high, the effectiveness of the LAN decreases. When the LAN is busy, the efficiency may drop, and you might lose effectiveness just when you need it most. LAN vendors and researchers have run numerous tests to

TABLE 4-3   LAN Topology and Protocol Summary

	IEEE 802.3 or Ethernet	IEEE 802.5 or IBM's Token Ring	ARCnet	StarLAN
Speed	10 or 100 Mbps	4, 16, or 100 Mbps	2.5, 20, or 100 Mbps	1 Mbps
Medium	Twisted-pair wires, coaxial cable, or fiber optic cable	Twisted-pair wires	Twisted-pair wires or coaxial cable	Twisted-pair wires
Distance	500 meters for thick cable, 185 meters for thinnet cable segments; 5 segments can be connected with repeaters to give maximum lengths of 2500 and 925 meters	366 meters for the main ring; can be extended to 750 meters with repeaters and to 4000 meters with fiber optic cable	6110 meters; maximum distance between active hubs is 62 meters and between passive hubs is 31 meters	500 meters
Number of stations	802.3-100 per thick cable segment, 30 per thinnet sgment Ethernet-1024	260	255	Not stated by 1 Base5 standard (early StarLANs set limit at 50)
Standards	IEEE 802.3	IEEE 802.5	De facto (submitted for approval as an ANSI standard)	IEEE 802.3 1Base5
Cost for NIC and Connectors Only	Low (approx. $50 per station)	High (approx. $100 per station	Low (approx. $30 per station)	Low (approx. $50 per station)

gauge the effect of high collision rates. Under these tests the performance characteristics did not drop appreciably. However, the true test of performance comes from actual use. Under light load conditions, access to the medium and the ability to transmit are good; there is little waiting time to transmit. Performance under heavy loads can be unpredictable.

Token Buses and Token Rings

We discuss these two implementations together because their media access control characteristics are similar. ARCnet can be implemented in a bus or a star-wired topology. ARCnet operates at speeds of 2.5 Mbps on twisted-pair wires, coaxial cable, or fiber optic cable. Both 20-Mbps and 100-Mbps capabilities have been introduced. The maximum distance that can be spanned by ARCnet is 20,000 feet (6110 meters). An example of an ARCnet configuration is shown in Figure 4-8.

IBM's token ring operates at 4, 16, or 100 Mbps. Stations on the LAN connect to a multistation access unit (MAU). A typical MAU contains ports for eight workstations plus an input and output connector to another MAU. Like all LANs, a token-passing ring has limitations on distance and number of stations. The maximum distance spanned by a ring is 770 meters and the maximum number of nodes allowed is 260. These limitations can be extended by setting up two or more token-ring LANs and connecting them with a device called a bridge. When LANs are connected in this way, a user on one ring can communicate with users or devices on another connected ring; from the user's perspective the interconnected rings appear as a single LAN.

Predictability is the key of token LAN performance. Because the medium is accessed through the possession of a token, and because each station is assured of receiving the token, you can predict the maximum and average times needed for a station to transmit its message. The problem of collision, inherent in contention LANs, does not exist in a token-passing LAN. When network traffic is light, a station may need to wait longer than a station on a contention bus; however, when network traffic is heavy, the token-passing station may wait less time. Regardless of the wait time, a station is assured that it can transmit in a predictable amount of time. The maximum time a station must wait is given by

TMax = (number of stations −1) * (message transmit time + token-passing time)

Thus, a station that has just passed the token to its neighbor may become ready to send a message. That station must wait until the token comes back around. The worst-case scenario would be that every other station has a message to transmit. Thus, the station must wait on all other stations in the ring to transmit their messages and pass the token. On average, a station ready to transmit must wait for half the other stations.

Of the common microcomputer LAN implementations, token-passing solutions provide both the lowest and the highest cost solutions. In general, ARCnet LANs have a lower per-station cost than Ethernet LANs, and Ethernet LANs have a lower per-station cost than token rings. This statement is based on the cost of the hardware—LAN adapters, MAUs, wiring hubs, cables, connectors, and wiring. Because prices fluctuate over time and from one vendor to another, you should verify these costs.

SUMMARY

LAN hardware mainly consists of server platforms, workstations, LAN adapters, printers, a medium, and connectors. The hardware combines with software to provide the LAN services. LAN adapters are protocol- and medium-oriented. One LAN adapter supports **carrier sense with multiple access/collision detection (CSMA/CD)** on twisted-pair wires, another supports CSMA/CD on coaxial cable, and a different LAN adapter is necessary for token passing using fiber optic cable. Servers must be properly configured to provide the performance and backup services required by an efficient LAN. The keys to meeting this requirement are having sufficient memory, a powerful processor, high-performance disk drives, and a file backup unit. Naturally the software also must be available to exploit the hardware configuration.

You can choose from many combinations of hardware and software when you are building a LAN. The key to success is combining the alternatives so the hardware and the software form an effective team.

A LAN topology is the pattern used to lay out the LAN. The main LAN topologies are a bus, a ring, and a star. The media access control protocol is the way in which a station interfaces with the medium. The main media access control protocols for LANs are CSMA/CD and token passing. CSMA/CD is used on bus topologies and star topologies. Token passing is used on bus and ring topologies.

A variety of standards covering media access control, LAN topology, medium distances, and the maximum number of LAN nodes have been developed. The two principal standards organizations for LANs are IEEE and ANSI. Standards have resulted in open architectures. With open architectures, a variety of manufacturers can develop products that will interoperate on a LAN. As a consequence LAN administrators usually have several product choices, and competition among product developers leads to product innovation and lower prices.

KEY TERMS

active hub   104
active node   108
backbone network   111
backup   99
balun   104
bus interface unit (BIU)   103
bus topology   111
cache hit   94
cache memory   94

carrier sense with multiple access and
   collision detection (CSMA/CD)   CBT
code independence   120
communications interface unit
   (CIU)   103
copper distributed data interface
   (CDDI)   111
database server   91
disk caching   94

REVIEW QUESTIONS

1. What are the generic functions of a server?

2. Distinguish between file and SQL server technology.

3. What must you take into consideration when you select a server disk drive?

4. How do servers use memory to improve performance?

5. Explain how disk caching works. What is its benefit?

6. Why should servers have high processor speeds?

7. How do diskless systems work? What advantages do they have over disk systems? What are the disadvantages of a diskless system?

8. What is data backup? What devices are used to effect backup?

9. Why are floppy disks usually ineffective as a backup device?

10. What options need to be considered when selecting a LAN adapter?

11. What does an uninterruptible power supply (UPS) do?

12. What is a topology?

13. What are the primary LAN topologies?

14. What is a media access control protocol?

15. What are the primary LAN media access control protocols?

16. What are the IEEE 802.3, 802.4, and 802.5 standards?

17. What is the ANSI fiber distributed data interface (FDDI)? How does it differ from the CDDI?

18. What function is performed by a multistation access unit (MAU)?

19. List four items that are specified in the IEEE LAN standards.

20. Compare token passing and CSMA/CD media access control protocols.

5

LAN SYSTEM SOFTWARE
AND LAN CONSIDERATIONS

CHAPTER OBJECTIVES

After studying this chapter you should be able to:

- Describe the functions of LAN system software
- Discuss the functions performed by LAN workstation software
- Describe how spooler software works
- Explain the importance of making backups
- List backup options and elements of backup procedures
- Discuss the software requirements for shared data and application usage
- Describe several types of software licenses
- List several LAN selection criteria
- Discuss how a specific selection criterion influences the selection process

*I*n Chapter 4 you examined the details of the LAN hardware system. In this chapter you will learn about the software system that drives the hardware. We separate LAN software into two classes: workstation system software and server system software. The success of the LAN depends on how these two software classes, the application software, and the hardware interact in setting up the computing environment.

GENERIC FUNCTIONS OF LAN SYSTEM SOFTWARE

System software is designed to insulate applications from hardware details such as input/output (I/O) and memory management. System software provides an interface through which the applications can request hardware services. The applications make requests for services, and system software contains the logic to carry out those requests for a specific type of hardware. For example, an application makes disk access requests independent of the type of disk drive being used. A disk driver is a component of the operating system that fulfills the request for a specific type of disk drive.

Consider a DOS workstation on a LAN in which the server provides file and printer services. The workstation has local disk drives A, B, and C. The file server's disk drives are known to the workstation as drives F and G. The workstation's local printer ports are LPT1 and LPT2. A local dot-matrix printer is attached to LPT1; output to LPT2 is directed to a network laser printer. The key to making this environment work is transparent access to all devices. From the user's perspective, printing to a network printer and accessing a network disk drive are transparent. Thus, the workstation user accesses remote drives F and G in exactly the same way as he or she accesses local drives A, B, and C. The user also prints to the laser printer as though it were locally attached. This transparency is accomplished by the LAN system software.

LAN system software resides both in the application's workstation and in the server(s), as illustrated in Figure 5-1. The workstation's LAN system software provides two primary functions: (1) interfacing to the medium via the LAN adapter and (2) formatting and routing application I/O requests to the LAN interface software. The software module that provides the latter function is sometimes referred to as the **redirector.**

Figure 5-1

LAN System
Software
in Server and
Workstation

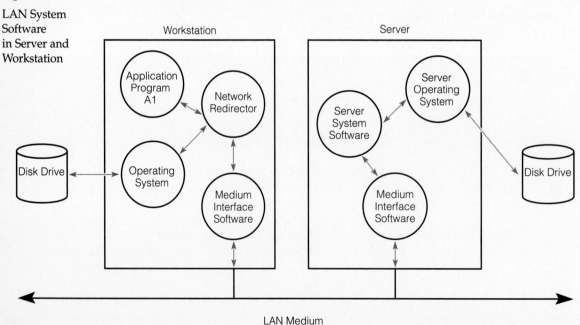

> **Network Operating System Overview**
>
> To see how the LAN system software carries out these functions, you should now switch to the CBT module entitled "Network Operating System Overview". At the conclusion of this CBT, you should be able to describe how a workstation and a server interact for file and printing services.

LAN OS IMPLEMENTATIONS

A few operating systems (OS) are designed specifically to carry out LAN server tasks and have these functions integrated with other OS tasks such as the user interface and job, file, and memory management. Other LAN system software implementations operate in partnership with a general-purpose OS such as UNIX or OS/2. The general-purpose OS is responsible for providing much of the user interface and job, file, and memory management. The LAN extensions are responsible for implementing the LAN-oriented tasks such as the LAN interface and the file and printer server functions.

Novell's **NetWare** and Microsoft's **Windows NT** Server are leading examples of the **integrated software approach.** The primary advantage of this approach is that the designers can optimize the software for LAN operation. The system is designed specifically to provide server functions and can be tailored for that purpose. The disadvantage is that this approach requires writing complex software that may already be provided by an existing operating system. This makes the development effort longer and the maintenance more complex.

Creating LAN software that runs under an existing operating system overcomes the disadvantages cited for the integrated approach. Examples of LAN software packages that run under an existing OS are **Banyan Vines,** which runs under UNIX, and IBM's **LAN Server,** which runs under OS/2. The disadvantages are that a general-purpose operating system may be less efficient than one designed to carry out only the special functions required for LAN services.

Some operating systems, such as MS-DOS, are not well suited for hosting a LAN, primarily because of their inherent memory limitations, single-user orientation, and lack of security provisions. Despite these limitations, some LAN software packages run under DOS and successfully support LANs with few workstations or with limited server requirements. The operating systems that most frequently host LAN software are UNIX and OS/2.

In the CBT module "Network Operating System Overview," you learned about the essential features of LAN OSs. Many LAN OSs extend these basic capabilities with others that enhance performance or improve reliability. In this section we first look at some extended functions you might find in a LAN OS. Then we look briefly at specific LAN operating systems by Novell, IBM, and Banyan. The other LAN OSs listed in Table 5-1 are competitive with the systems we discuss below.

TABLE 5-1   **Leading LAN Operating Systems**

LAN Name	Vendor Name	Topology	Protocol
NetWare	Novell, Inc.	Ring or bus (Ethernet, Token Rings, ARCnet)	CSMA/CD or Token Passing
LAN Server	IBM Corporation	Ring or bus	Token Passing or CSMA/CD
Windows NT	Micorsoft, Inc.	Bus or Ring	CSMA/CD or Token Passing
Apple Talk	Apple Computers, Inc.	Bus	CSMA/CA
PC Network	IBM Corporation	Bus	CSMA/CD
LANtastic	Artisoft, Inc.	Bus	CSMA/CD
TOPS	Sun Microsystems, Inc.	Bus, Star	CSMA/CD
StarLAN	AT & T Corporation	Star	CSMA/CD
Nexos	DSC Communications Corporation	Bus, Ring	CSMA/CD or Token Passing
VMS	Digital Equipment Corp.	Bus	CSMA/CD
PC/NOS	Corvus Systems, Inc.	Bus (The PC/NOS OS will also support Ethernet, IBM token ring, and ARCNET)	CSMA/CD or Token passing
Vines	Banyan Systems, Inc.	LAN OS Supporting Ethernet, IBM Token Ring, and ARCNET	CSMA/CD or Token Passing

Additional LAN Operating System Functions

Two LAN OS extended capabilities are I/O optimization and fault tolerance.

Optimized I/O. As you saw in the CBT module, a primary service provided by a server is file access. Optimizing this task, or **I/O optimization,** increases the performance of the server. Some optimization methods are hardware oriented and some are software oriented. One frequently used technique is called disk caching, which we discussed in Chapter 4.

Another I/O optimization technique is **disk seek enhancement.** A disk read requires that the read/write heads be positioned to the proper disk location. The act of moving the read/write heads is called a **seek.** The place to which the heads are moved is called a **cylinder** or **track.** Disk requests typically arrive in random order. Disk seek enhancement arranges the requests in order so the read/write heads move methodically over the disk, reading data from the nearest location. This is illustrated in Table 5-2. In Table 5-2(a) you can see the order in which several disk requests are received. Table 5-2(b) shows the optimum way to access those records and the savings in number of cylinders when processing the requests in the optimum order. Reducing the number of seeks improves performance.

TABLES 5.2   Disk Seek Enhancement

(a)

Disk Read Requests (cylinder or track) in order of arrival	Number of Cylinders Moved (assume a starting position of cylinder 0)	
50, 250, 25, 300, 250, 50, 300	$50 + 200 + 225 + 275 + 50$ $+ 200 + 250 = 1250$	

(b)

Disk Read Request (cylinder or track) in optimal order		
25, 50, 50, 250, 250, 300, 300	$25 + 25 + 0 + 200 + 0$ $+ 50 + 0 = 300$	Savings = 950 Cylinders

Fault Tolerance.   Some network operating systems provide increased reliability through a feature called **fault tolerance.** If you have only one server and it fails, the network is down. A LAN with fault tolerance allows the server to survive some failures that ordinarily would be disabling. Fault tolerance is usually provided by a combination of backup hardware components and software capable of using the backup hardware.

The lowest level of fault tolerance is the ability to recover quickly from a failure. This means that if a failure shuts the server down, the system can quickly be recovered to an operational state. One technique that makes this possible involves writing backup copies of critical disk information—disk directories, file allocation tables, and so on—to an alternate disk drive. Another helpful technique is called **read-after-write.** After writing data to a disk, the system reads the data again to ensure that no disk-write errors occurred. If the data cannot be read again, the area of the disk containing that data is removed from future use and the data is written to a good area of the disk.

Fault tolerance can also be provided by **mirrored disks,** which are two disks that contain the same data. Whenever a disk write occurs, the data is written to both disk drives. If one disk fails, the other is available and processing continues. Mirrored disks have an additional benefit: Because two disk drives are available, both disks can work simultaneously on behalf of two different requests. For added support, some LAN servers also allow duplexed disk controllers. In this configuration, if a controller fails, another is available to continue working. Thus you can survive a controller failure and a disk failure.

Mirrored disk reliability can be extended using **redundant arrays of independent disks (RAID).** RAID technology spreads data over three or more disk drives. The stored data consists of the actual data plus **parity data,** which is additional data that provides the ability to reconstruct data that has been corrupted. If one drive fails, the data stored on that drive can be reconstructed from data stored on the remaining drives. Parity data can be reconstructed because the remaining parts of the file are still available. If a section of the file is lost, it can be reconstructed from the parity data and the remaining parts of the file. The advantage of RAID over mirroring is that fewer disk drives are required for redundancy. With mirroring, two drives of data require four disk drives; with RAID, the same information can be stored on three drives with the same level of reliability. Disk mirroring and RAID technology, illustrated in Figure 5-2, can provide more efficient data access because multiple disk drives are available for reading and writing.

Figure 5-2

Mirrored Disk Drives
and RAID Technology

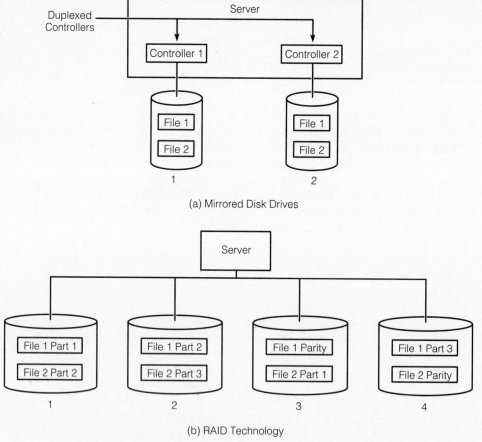

(a) Mirrored Disk Drives

(b) RAID Technology

The best fault tolerance is provided by **duplexed servers.** With this configuration one server can fail and another is available to continue working. Even though it appears that this fault tolerance capability is primarily hardware oriented, software must exist that takes advantage of the duplexed hardware.

Duplexed servers are illustrated in Figure 5-3. Fault tolerance has been provided commercially by large systems since 1977. Fault tolerance features are currently available in most leading network operating systems.

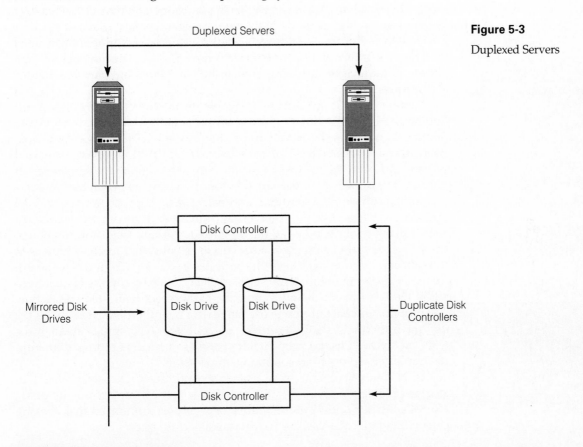

Duplexed Servers

Figure 5-3

Duplexed Servers

Novell Operating Systems

Over time Novell has offered several versions of network operating systems. Novell now offers three basic systems, with a variety of configuration options for two of the versions. For very small networks using peer-to-peer workstations, Novell offers Personal NetWare. A **peer-to-peer network** is one that has no dedicated servers, and the network administrator can make the resources of each network node accessible to other network nodes. This technique is most suitable for networks with few nodes.

For high-end networks, Novell offers NetWare 3.x and NetWare 4.x. Fault tolerance capabilities are available with each version. NetWare 4.x is Novell's newest network operating system. It is designed for companies with very large networks and for companies having several networks. NetWare 4.x supports up to 1000 nodes per LAN; simultaneous connection to multiple servers; and a network naming directory, which helps users locate local and remote network resources. NetWare 3.x and 4.x run on server hardware based on the 80386, 80486, Pentium, and later model processors only. NetWare 3.x can be purchased for networks ranging from five users to several hundred users, and NetWare 4.x fills the need for larger networks. The cost of the operating system is scaled according to the maximum number of supported users. Thus small networks can realize the same operating system technology as that used on very large LANs but at a much lower cost (the cost per user for the LAN software remains somewhat constant). An important feature of NetWare 4.x is the availablity of system messages and documentation in a variety of languages including French, Italian, German, Spanish, Chinese, and Japanese.

Another significant feature available from Novell is **System Fault Tolerance (SFT),** which provides an environment in which certain hardware failures do not cause network failures. For example, SFT supports mirrored disk drives. A higher level of fault tolerance, SFT III, supports duplexed servers and protects the LAN against most hardware and software server failures. The duplexed servers are mirrors of one another. Each has the same memory and disk configurations, and each runs a copy of NetWare STF III operating system. One of the servers is primary and the other is secondary. The primary server handles all the server requests and sends information to the backup thereby allowing the backup to remain in synchronization with the primary. If the primary fails, the backup can continue from where the primary failed and maintain LAN services. The duplexed servers are connected by the LAN medium and a separate, high-speed, dedicated connection. The primary and backup server exchange data over this dedicated link. If the dedicated link fails, the two servers can continue to communicate over the LAN medium. Thus, no single point of server or media failure will disrupt the duplexed servers from continuous processing.

All Novell OS versions are designed to optimize LAN performance. An efficient file server must be able to quickly retrieve data from its disks. Novell provides optimized disk directory support, optimized disk seeking capabilities, and disk caching to maximize performance.

Microsoft's Windows NT

For several years Microsoft has provided LAN server OS support via its LAN Manager product that runs under the OS/2 operating system. LAN Manager has been replaced by a new, more powerful product, Windows NT (which stands for *new technology*). Public and press reaction to Windows NT has been generally favorable and it is expected to become a network OS that will provide strong competition to Novell's NetWare and other leading LAN OSs.

Windows NT is one of a family of Microsoft products that span a wide range of user needs and hardware platforms. The low-end product is Windows 3.x, and Windows NT provides the high-end operating environment. Between these two products are Windows for Workgroups (WFW) and Windows 95. Windows NT has two versions: NT for client workstations and NT Advanced Server (NTAS) for LAN servers. A typical NTAS-based LAN might have client workstations using a variety of operating environments including DOS, Windows and UNIX.

NT is a 32-bit operating system that provides multitasking and multi-threading, both of which are essential to efficient server operation. On client workstations these services are needed primarily by power users who need to run multiple tasks on powerful desktop systems.

On server platforms, NTAS hardware and software costs are comparable to those of its competitive network OSs. NTAS's ability to support systems with multiple processors also makes it well suited for use with the most powerful servers. NTAS supports the two most common LAN architectures, Ethernet and token-passing rings. It also supports interfaces to WANs and has the ability to make WAN resources appear as local LAN resources. These interfaces are available because NTAS supports a wide variety of internet-working protocols, such as the TCP/IP protocols discussed in Chapter 8.

IBM's LAN Server and OS/2 Operating System

OS/2 is the second generation of operating systems for IBM and IBM-compatible microcomputers. It incorporates several data communications capabilities, including both LAN interfaces and terminal emulation features. The OS/2 operating system provides multitasking, presentation services, and data communications capabilities similar to those of the original IBM PC operating system, DOS. Communications products that run under OS/2 provide several enhanced data communications capabilities via IBM's **LAN Server** and a communications manager and a database manager, as illustrated in Table 5-3.

TABLE 5-3   LAN Server Configuragation

	Services Sofware	
Printer	Communications	SQL Server
	OS/2 Operating System	

The communications manager provides terminal and gateway support. Terminal support includes asynchronous terminal emulation, IBM 3270 terminal emulation, X.25 services, and a program-to-program gateway to an IBM host system. Other capabilities include a variety of interfaces to IBM's Systems Network Architecture (SNA), which is discussed in Chapter 7. Some of these communications manager functions also exist under DOS; however, OS/2 provides these functions in one comprehensive package rather than as a variety of individual packages from various vendors. OS/2's multitasking capabilities also allow more terminal sessions to be active than in the DOS environment. Connections to multiple hosts as well as to a LAN can be supported concurrently. The LAN Server software provides file and printer sharing services; an interface to IBM's network management system, NetView; and support for Apple Macintosh computers. Because of these interfaces, LAN Server is well suited for companies with SNA networks that need to interface to the LAN.

Banyan Vines

Banyan **Vines** is recognized for its support for large networks and network interconnections. Banyan Vines runs on UNIX-based servers—a distinct advantage because many WANs contain nodes running the UNIX operating system. This makes it easier for Vines systems to connect to those nodes. A server based on UNIX also can be used effectively as an application system in addition to providing LAN services, which means the server platform can function not only as a server but also as a platform for running application programs. OS/2 operating systems allow multitasking but not multiuser capabilities and thus cannot match UNIX-based machines, which allow several users to run applications.

One major strength of Vines is a global naming strategy called StreetTalk. **StreetTalk** is a database that provides network directory services such as identifying network resources, including users, files, hardware, and so on. This database is replicated on each server in the network, providing a measure of fault tolerance as well as making resource lookup more efficient. Applications use StreetTalk to locate needed resources: A mail application can use it to find the location of mail recipients. LAN managers use StreetTalk to assist in controlling the network and network users: The access rights of each user can be placed in the StreetTalk database. A feature of StreetTalk that makes it more effective for international networks is the ability to store information such as status and error messages in several languages.

Interoperability of Server Software

A large LAN may need more than one file server (the point at which a second server is needed varies according to the number of active, concurrent users and their server access profiles). If two or more servers are required, you must ensure that they operate correctly. If all servers are using the same hardware and software platforms, they often can operate correctly in concert. It is not always true, however, that two different server software packages can interoperate correctly.

Interoperability basically means the ability of all network components to connect to the network and to communicate with shared network resources. With a global view, this means the ability to interconnect different networks so nodes on one network are able to communicate with nodes on the same network or on another network. On a single network, it means any node can use resources to which it has appropriate security access. Interoperability is usually easy in a homogeneous network, in which only one network operating system version is used and the workstations are all the same type and use the same operating system. Networks using a mixture of network operating systems and workstation platforms make interoperability more complex.

We now look at interoperability in a single network. Consider a network that has two servers with different network operating systems, such as Novell NetWare and Banyan Vines. If users were to use only one or the other server, it would probably be easier to divide the network into a Novell network and a Banyan Vines network. If both servers are available on one network, we may assume that some users must have access to both servers. Table 5-4 lists complications that may exist as a result. How well the server operating systems handle these issues affects the interoperability of the network.

TABLE 5-4   Possible Complications of Having Two Network Operating Systems in One LAN

Compatibility of user identifiers and passwords

Synchronization of user identifiers and passwords across servers

Ability to simutaneously access data on two servers

Ability to access data on one server and print to spooler on another

Applications that can run from both servers

Support for common appplication program interfaces (APIs)

Supppport for common protocols at the OSI network and transport layers

Ability to use/have two redirector processes

BACKUP SOFTWARE

In Chapter 4 we discussed backup hardware. The software used to perform the backups is as important as the hardware. **Backup software** is responsible for reading the files being backed up and writing them to the backup device. During recovery, a **restoration module** reads the backup medium and writes the data back to disk. Several backup software options are available. They all provide the basic functions of backing up and restoring data. However, they differ with respect to backup and restoration procedure, including the options they provide, the devices they support, and their ease of use. Backup devices frequently come with backup and restore programs and most LAN system software includes basic backup and restore modules. Some LAN administrators choose to purchase a separate, more functional backup/restore system than the basic software provided with the LAN OS or backup hardware. Table 5-5 lists some features supported by backup software.

TABLE 5-5   Backup Software Capabilities

Back up all files

Back up all files modified since a particular date

Back up by directory

Back up by list of files

Back up all but a list of files to be excluded

Maintain cross-reference of tape serial numbers and backup

Automatic backup by time or calendar

Start backup from workstation or server

Data compression

Multivolume backup

Generate reports

SOFTWARE ISSUES FOR SHARED USAGE

Most early microcomputer applications were written for single-user systems, which means the software developers could make certain simplifying design decisions. To use these applications in a shared LAN system, accommodations must be made by the LAN administrators, by the LAN system software, or by the application itself. We now consider the required changes.

Hardware Configuration

Software written for a single user need not be concerned with problems of computer configuration. You are probably aware that microcomputers may be configured with a variety of options. The primary variations are in memory, disk configurations, printer configuration, and monitor support. In a stand-alone system the application software is set up to match the configuration of that system. However, a LAN might have many different workstation configurations, and application software should support each configuration as much as possible.

Some older applications that were not designed for network sharing support only one configuration. The hardware settings of such applications are stored in a single file. One way to use this type of application is to configure the application for the lowest common denominator of hardware and have each user get essentially the same configuration. Users with high-resolution color graphics monitors might have images displayed in monochrome at low resolution, or a user with a hard disk drive might have to use a floppy disk drive rather than the hard disk drive for some files. Usually LAN administrators can avoid this type of configuration by storing multiple versions of the application in different disk directories. Users can then use the configuration that most closely matches their computer's profile.

Some applications allow several configuration files and decide which to use by a run-time parameter or by making a default choice if the startup parameter is not specified. LAN administrators can provide each user with a tailored environment by virtue of a batch startup file.

Applications designed for LAN use usually have a user-oriented configuration file. Each LAN user has his or her personal configuration that is tailored for the specific user and the specific hardware. This provides users with the most flexibility and requires little or no customization by the LAN administrator. These options are listed in Table 5-6.

TABLE 5-6   User Configuration Options

Default disk drive

Default disk directory

Disk drive mappings

Disk drive/directory search paths

Printer mappings

Initial program/menu

Application Settings

Application settings are the software equivalent to hardware configurations. Ideally, users tailor application settings to meet personal preferences. One user may prefer his or her word processor application to display green characters on a black background with tabs at every five character positions. Another user might prefer white characters on a blue background with tabs at every four character positions. Each user should receive these settings as the default. Application settings can be defined in a way similar to setting hardware options.

Contention

Whenever two users are capable of accessing the same resource at the same time, **contention** for that resource can occur. Contention resloution like a spooler for printer contention is necessary to avoid errors that can result from conflicts. Similar problems occur when accessing files. A classic file contention problem is illustrated by two users updating one document at the same time. Suppose user A and user B are simultaneously updating the same document. Eventually, user A saves the document and subsequently user B saves it. User B's document replace user A's and all traces of user A's updates are lost. The same type of problem can occur when two users access and update the same database record. A primitive way to handle contention is simply to avoid it by scheduling user activities so they do not interfere with each other. On small LANs this may be possible, but as the number of concurrent users increases, this method becomes clumsy. Rather than avoiding contention, an application or LAN software package should prevent contention problems by exerting controls over files or records.

One prevention mechanism is activated when an application opens a file. The three basic file open modes are exclusive, protected, and shared. In **exclusive open mode,** an open request is granted only if no other user already has the file open. File open requests from other users also are denied until the application having an exclusive open closes the file. This is a common open mode for word processing software. This open mode would have prevented user A and user B's contention problem described earlier.

Exclusive opens may be too restrictive for some applications. Suppose two users, Alice and Tom, are both working on the same word processing document. Alice needs to update the document, and Tom only needs to read it. In this case Tom will not interfere with Alice's work. A protected open mode can satisfy both users' needs. **Protected open mode** grants an open request only if no other user has already been granted exclusive or protected mode. Once a file is open in protected mode, only the application with protected open can update the document. **Shared open mode** allows several users to have the file open concurrently. In **shared update mode,** all users can update the file. In **shared read-only mode,** all users can read the file but cannot write to it. If Alice opens the document in protected mode and Tom opens the document in shared read-only mode, Alice can read and update the document but Tom can only read it. Furthermore, Tom cannot open the document in exclusive, protected, or shared update mode while a protected open exists.

Sometimes a read-only application must be protected against file updates. An application that is doing a trial balance of an accounting file must prohibit updates during the reading and calculations. If another application makes changes while the file is being read, the figures may not balance. The trial-balance application can protect against this by opening the accounts file in protected read-only mode. This prevents other processes from opening the file in update mode while allowing processes to open the file in shared read-only mode. Table 5-7 shows the combinations of exclusive, protected, and shared open modes.

TABLE 5-7   Comparison of Open Modes

Open Mode Requested	Currently Opened As			
	Exclusive	Protected	Shared Update	Shared Read-Only
Exclusive	Denied	Denied	Denied	Denied
Protected	Denied	Denied	Denied	Granted
Shared update	Denied	Denied	Granted	Granted
Shared read-only	Denied	Granted	Granted	Granted

Exclusive and protected open modes are sufficient for meeting some contention problems, such as our word processing example. However, they are overly restrictive for other applications, such as database processing. One objective of database applications is to allow several users to share data. Exclusive opens allow only one user at a time to use the data. The problem with file-open contention resolution is overcome by exerting controls at a lower level, the record level. Record-level controls are called **locks.**

Suppose Alice and Tom want to update a database. So long as they are using different records, they will not interfere with each other. However, suppose that at some time both Alice and Tom need to access and update the same record, leading to contention problems. If Alice locks the record when accessing it, Tom's read request will be denied until Alice unlocks the record. This process is illustrated in Figure 5-4. Note that Tom must wait until the record has been unlocked before he is allowed to proceed.

Record locking can, however, cause another problem: **deadlock,** or **deadly embrace.** Suppose Alice and Tom are accessing the database. Alice's application reads and locks Record A and, at nearly the same time, Tom's application reads and locks Record B. After reading Record A, Alice attempts to read Record B and, of course, waits because the record is locked. If Tom then attempts to read Record A, deadlock occurs: Alice and Tom are waiting for each other, and neither can continue until the record they are waiting for is unlocked, which can never happen because there is a circular chain of users waiting on each other. Three or more users can also be involved in this circular chain of events. The deadlock problem is illustrated in Figure 5-5. Deadlock avoidance or resolution methods exist but are beyond the scope of this text. You can read about these methods in many database texts.

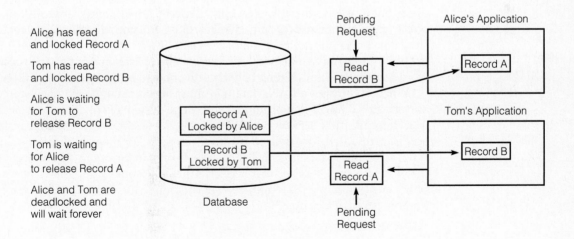

Figure 5-4

Record Locking
and Accessibility

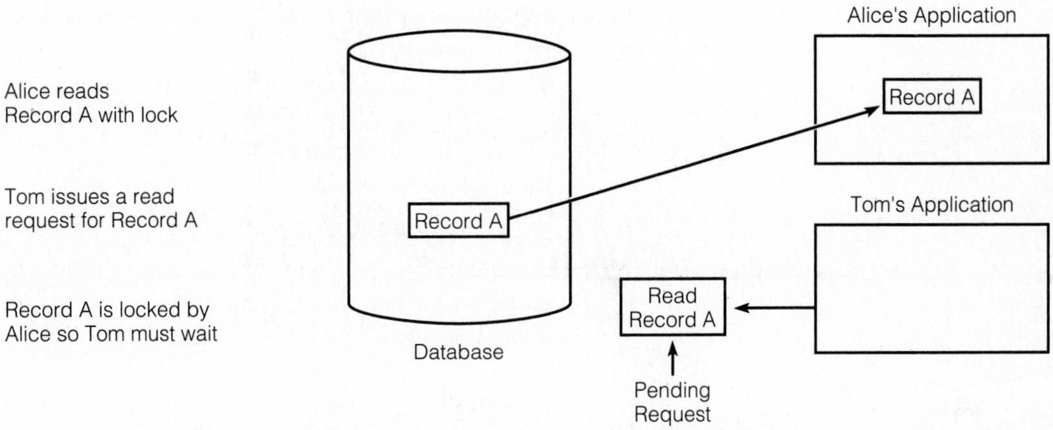

Alice reads
Record A with lock

Tom issues a read
request for Record A

Record A is locked by
Alice so Tom must wait

Alice's Application

Record A

Database

Tom's Application

Read
Record A

Pending
Request

Figure 5-5

The Problem of Deadlock

Alice has read
and locked Record A

Tom has read
and locked Record B

Alice is waiting
for Tom to
release Record B

Tom is waiting
for Alice
to release Record A

Alice and Tom are
deadlocked and
will wait forever

Pending
Request

Alice's Application

Read
Record B

Record A

Record A
Locked by Alice

Tom's Application

Record B
Locked by Tom

Record B

Read
Record A

Database

Pending
Request

Some database systems take care of contention for users. These systems recognize when contention is occurring and prevent the problems associated with it. One convention used to do this is outlined as follows:

1. User A reads Record X.
2. User B reads Record X (and the read is allowed).
3. User A updates Record X (and the update is allowed).
4. User B attempts to update Record X.
5. The database management system recognizes that the record has been changed since User B read it.
6. The database management system sends the revised copy of Record X to User B and notifies the user that the update was rejected because the record was changed by another user.
7. User B reissues the update or takes another course of action.

In selecting LAN software, it is critical that you understand the problems of configuration and contention. If these issues are not resolved the effectiveness of the system is reduced or, worse yet, the data becomes corrupted. Sharing data has another side effect that must be addressed: security.

Access Security

Early operating systems, and many current systems for stand-alone micro-computers, do not provide file security. Even though only one user can use a microcomputer at one time, several users might use one system. Without **access security** these users not only have access to another user's sensitive data, but also might accidentally (or intentionally) remove another user's files. Access to the computer essentially provides access to all data stored on that computer. Users might store sensitive data on a stand-alone microcomputer's disks, but those users are limited with respect to their ability to protect that data from unauthorized reading, changes, or destruction. Instead, a user could store data on a removable disk and store that disk in a secure place when it is not being used. Another alternative is buying an application that provides pass-word security or allows hiding or encrypting data to protect data from misuse.

When you install a LAN, data that must be shared and was once stored as "private" data on one or more stand-alone systems is likely to be placed in a database on a server. Without security, all data on the servers can be accessed, updated, and deleted by any LAN user. For most applications this is not acceptable. Therefore, the LAN system software must provide protection through security. Other security concerns include protecting against software piracy and preventing the introduction of computer viruses. We discuss security in more detail in Chapter 10.

SOFTWARE LICENSE AGREEMENTS

One of the most important things to know about your software is its license agreement. Virtually all software you buy is covered by a license agreement. This is true for both system and applications software. The **license agreement** covers the rules under which you are allowed to use the product. It is a way of protecting both the manufacturer and the user. To better understand the need for license agreements, we first look at an analogy.

Consider the books you purchased for school, which probably were rather expensive. Of course, the publisher does not pay nearly that much just to print the book. Part of your book price goes to profit, but the publisher also incurs other expenses. One or more authors worked many hours to write the material; editors worked many hours with the authors to develop the format and content; designers laid out the style (graphics and page formats); marketing analysts determined a marketing strategy and created advertising brochures; and the sales force were told about the book, its target markets, and key selling points. All this activity required a considerable investment. Some books never become popular and the publishing company actually loses money on them. Others become very popular and the publishing company makes a profit. Some of that profit is used to offset losses on other projects. Now, suppose someone decides to illegally reprint a text and sell the successful books. With today's technology, it does not cost much just to print these copies. This person can sell the copies for much less than the publisher because he or she has not had to make the investment of developing the work, paying the salaries of editors and production workers, the royalties to the developers, and so on.

Patent and copyright laws are intended to protect the investments of designers, artists, filmmakers, authors, publishing companies, and so on. Software companies also make a sizable investment in creating applications or system software. Systems analysts design the product, programmers write and debug the code, marketing analysts create a marketing plan, advertising campaigns are developed and implemented, manuals are created, a support organization is staffed and trained, and the product is brought to market.

Several years probably elapsed from the time the product was conceived to the point at which it was ready to sell and make a profit. Thousands of dollars were probably expended before there was any opportunity to sell the software. In addition, once a software product is released, expenses continue. Support staff must be paid and new enhancements designed. Similar to the situation with illegal book printing, the gain from all this effort can be eroded by illegal software copying. To give you an idea of the magnitude of this problem, at the end of the 1980s several software piracy shops in Hong Kong were raided. Some estimated that the annual loss of revenues to software companies resulting from software piracy in one building alone to be hundreds of millions of dollars.

Software vendors must therefore take steps to protect their investment. Like books, pictures, films, and fashion designs, software can be illegally copied and sold. Software is protected in six basic ways:

1. The code is kept secret so other software houses cannot use special algorithms—developed by the original company—to write a competing system.

2. The code is copyrighted to prevent another company from copying the code and writing a competing system.

3. The software is copy protected to deter the making of illegal copies.

4. The software requires a special hardware device to run.

5. License agreements are used to establish the terms of ownership and use.

6. Legislation penalizing those who do not adhere to the copyright and license restrictions is applied.

The first two measures protect the source code from being used by someone else. During development, it is common to keep the source code of software secret. However, after the product has been released, it is always possible to derive the source code, even if the software is released only in object code format. Deriving the source code from object code is done through reverse engineering. To protect themselves from reverse engineering, software manufacturers usually copyright their software. Copyright laws, originally intended to cover writing, films, and works of art, have been extended to include software. New legislation also has been enacted to further define the restrictions and penalties for unauthorized software copying.

Each of these first two measures is rather clear; most people understand and observe the rules. However, three issues—copy protection, the use of a hardware device, and license agreements—are less standard and directly involve how the software is used. **Software piracy** has always been a problem, even before the introduction of microcomputers. With minicomputers and mainframe systems, software piracy is easier to detect and hence its incidence is negligible relative to its occurrence on microcomputers. There are two good reasons for easier detection of large system software piracy. First, large computers are used by large organizations with professional data processing departments. Software piracy is difficult to hide in such organizations, and ordinarily anyone found using pirated software is subject to dismissal and the company is subject to lawsuits. Second, large computer sites typically work closely with the software vendor's personnel. The vendor's employees are aware of the software its customers are authorized to use, and it is easy to detect the presence of unauthorized software. Easy piracy detection is not the case with microcomputer software.

A few software companies protect their software by requiring the use of a special hardware device that attaches to a serial or parallel port. The device and an application work together to provide application security. When started, the application attempts to read data encoded in the device. If the device is not attached, the application terminates. One disadvantage to this approach is having several applications, each of which need a different device. Because the number of serial or parallel ports is limited, changing from one application to another may require changing the device. Other companies have accomplished somewhat the same effect by requiring a "key disk." The **key disk** is usually a flexible disk that must be in a disk drive when the application is run. The application uses the key disk only to verify the disk's presence. This technique is seldom used today and, of course, cannot be used with diskless systems.

Originally many microcomputer software vendors used **copy protection** to deter software piracy. The software disk was encoded to prevent copying using standard operating system copy facilities such as DOS's COPY or

DISKCOPY commands. In general, copy protection only gave rise to a new software industry: software to allow copying of copy-protected software. Of course, vendors of such software were careful to point out that the sole purpose of their software was to make a legitimate backup copy and not to make illegal duplicate copies. Many companies that once copy protected their software have abandoned that means because it proved relatively ineffective. Instead of or in addition to copy protection, software vendors now rely on copyright protection together with software license agreements.

When you buy software, both applications software and LAN system software, often the disks that hold the software are sealed in an envelope. Written on or attached to the envelope is text regarding the license agreement and a message that opening and using the software is a commitment to adhere to the stipulations of that license agreement. The license agreement states the conditions under which you are allowed to use the product.

In essence, when you buy software, you do not get ownership of that product; you are simply given the right to use the product. An attorney might quibble with this statement, but the basic premise is correct. Some license agreements explicitly state that you own the disk but not the contents of the disk. This means you cannot make copies of the software to give to your friends, you may not be able to run it on several workstations at the same time, you may not reverse-engineer it to produce source code for modification or resale, and so on. Your rights to the software are limited to using the software in the intended manner. You can, if you like, destroy the software, cease to use it, sell it, or give it as a gift. In the last two cases you also transfer the license agreement to the recipient. Some software vendors go so far as to state that transferring the software must be approved by the software vendor. In some cases the software license covers the use of the accompanying documentation as well.

One problem with license agreements is that there are no standards. If you buy two different applications, you are liable to find two different license agreements. To protect yourself and your organization from civil and criminal suits, you must understand the provisions of each agreement. Several companies including a major state university have been investigated for illegally copying software, found guilty of the offense, and heavily fined. It is important that a company and individuals respect license agreements. We now consider some general licensing provisions:

- Single user, single workstation
- Single user, multiple workstations
- Restricted number of concurrent users
- Server license
- Site license
- Corporate license

Single User, Single Workstation. Single-user, single-workstation license agreements are the most restrictive. They specify that the software is to be used on only one workstation and by only one person at a time. If you have a multiuser microcomputer, only one user can be running the software at any time. In most instances, restricting the software to only one machine also implies a single user.

This license agreement also means that if an office has two or more computers, a separate copy of the software must be purchased for each machine on which the software is to be used. If you have two employees, one on a day shift and one on a night shift, using the same software but on different workstations, each needs an individual copy of the software. In this situation, the software is never used concurrently, yet two copies are required.

One way that software vendors enforce this policy is through the software installation procedure. The install process counts the number of installations. When you install the product the counter is decremented to zero and you are not able to install the program on another system. To move the software to another system you must uninstall the software on the first system. The uninstall process removes the application from the computer's disks and increments the installation count. Another method used to enforce a single-user, single-workstation license is the requirement for a key disk, described earlier.

Single User, Multiple Workstations.   This type of license agreement relaxes the constraints of the single-user, single-workstation agreement. It usually also relies on the honor system for enforcement. Software vendors that use this agreement recognize that different people may want to use the software and at different workstations, such as in the office and on a portable computer. The purchase of a single copy of the software allows the owner to install it on several systems. However, the license restricts use of the software to one user at a time per software copy.

Suppose an office with ten workstations must do word processing. Each of ten employees can use the word processor, but only five employees need to use the product concurrently. With a five user license agreement, the company can buy five copies of the software and install them on ten different systems. So long as five or fewer employees use the word processing application at any one time, the company has lived up to the license provisions. Note that it is possible for six users to inadvertently use the application at the same time, in violation of the license agreement.

Restricted Number of Concurrent Users.   On a LAN it is common for several users to run an application concurrently. Three employees may be doing word processing, 10 may be using the spreadsheet software, and 25 may be using the database software. With file or database server technology, only 1 copy of each application is on the server's disks. Most LAN-compatible software is inherently designed for multiple users; however, some software vendors place restrictions on the number of concurrent users. The main idea behind this strategy is to charge by the number of users.

Consider the database needs of the company just mentioned, where the maximum number of concurrent database users is 25. The database vendor has a license agreement that allows 10 concurrent users for a certain fee. The vendor also has an expansion policy that allows concurrent users to be added in groups of 10 with an additional fee for each such group. In this case the company must purchase three modules to satisfy its need of 25 concurrent users. This type of license is typically enforced by a meter program that controls the concurrent use of the application. When a user starts the application, the meter program increments a counter by 1. When a user exits the application, the counter is decremented by 1. If the license agreement is for 30 users, a user can run the application so long as the counter is 29 or fewer. If the counter is 30, a user requesting the application receives an error message indicating that the file is not available.

Server License.   A **server license** allows an application to be installed on one server. All users attached to that server may use the application. If a company has three servers and wants to use the application on each of them, the company must purchase three licenses or three copies of the software.

Site License.   A **site license** gives the user unlimited rights to use the software at a given site. The site may be a single LAN or multiple LANs at one location.

Corporate License.   A **corporate license** gives a corporation unlimited use of the software at all locations. Some companies restrict a corporate license to all locations within one country. Sometimes the right to reproduce documentation is also granted.

The license agreement is intended primarily to protect the rights of the manufacturer. However, the holder of a license agreement also has certain rights. Among these rights may be:

- The owner can transfer or assign the license to another user.
- The owner can get a refund if the product is defective or does not work as stated.
- Legal rights may be granted by certain states or countries regarding the exclusion of liability for losses or damage resulting from the use of the software.
- The user can terminate the license by destroying the software and documentation.

When selecting your application and system software, take care to understand fully all the conditions of the license agreements. You want each user to have available the necessary software services. Different license and pricing policies among competing products can result in substantial differences in availability to you or cost to your company.

Although originally designed to connect minicomputers, mainframes, and supercomputers, most LANs being installed today are used to link microcomputers. In the next section, you will learn about the selection, implementation, and use of microcomputer-oriented LANs.

LAN IMPLEMENTATION ALTERNATIVES

LAN system software provides several alternatives for implementing a LAN. In the "Network Operating System Overview" CBT module you saw two basic configurations: server based and peer-to-peer. Let us look more closely at these implementation alternatives. A LAN can be implemented using dedicated servers, using nondedicated servers, and using a peer-to-peer configuration.

Dedicated Servers

In a **dedicated server** LAN, one or more computers are designated as file or database servers and these computers serve only in that capacity. They do not double as user computers. Many current LANs use client/server technology with dedicated server nodes. This is certainly true of most large LANs. However, one vendor study showed the average number of nodes per microcomputer LAN is 6.3. This implies that many LANs have six or fewer nodes. For these small LANs, dedicating an expensive server machine (which will probably be underutilized) reduces the cost-effectiveness of the network. Two other technologies, nondedicated servers and peer-to-peer LANs, provide alternatives.

Nondedicated Servers

A few LAN operating systems allow nondedicated servers. A **nondedicated server** works as both a server and a workstation. A nondedicated server usually is the workstation with the most resources. For example, it is hard to imagine four users in a typical office keeping a dedicated server busy most of the time. If the server is allowed to also function as a workstation, it can be used more effectively.

The advantage of nondedicated servers is more effective use of resources. There are also some disadvantages. A nondedicated server must divide its workload between its application work and its server work. Sometimes it might be very busy in both roles. In these instances, both those using the server as a server and the person(s) using the server as a workstation will experience service degradation. If these conflicts occur too often, the LAN administrator should think of making the server dedicated.

Another disadvantage of nondedicated servers is the increased likelihood of server failures. Simply running both applications and server software increases the possibility of failures because the server is doing more and the environment is more complicated. However, the most probable source of a nondedicated server failure is the user's application or the user him- or herself. If the application gets locked, the server may be unable to attend to its server duties. If the user powers the server down or unintentionally formats the server disk, the server function will also be disrupted.

Peer-to-Peer LANs

Taking nondedicated servers one step further leads to peer-to-peer LANs. In a peer-to-peer LAN, any or all nodes can operate as servers. If five microcomputers are networked in a peer-to-peer LAN, the network administrator can designate which computer resources are shareable and which are not. On one computer, a laser printer may be shared, but a dot-matrix printer may be private to the user of that system. The computer's hard disk drive and one floppy disk drive may be shared, but a second floppy disk drive may be private.

All the computers in this network are primary workstations for a user. Thus, the activities of one user can directly affect other users. If a user powers down the computer, its resources are not available to other users, and if a user's program gets caught in a loop, that computer's resources will not be available to other users. Some peer-to-peer network operating systems allow you to designate each node as client only, server only, or both. A peer-to-peer LAN is primarily used when there are few LAN workstations. The main benefit of peer-to-peer networks is the low cost per node—usually less than $200 for both hardware and software. Two disadvantages of peer-to-peer LANs are (1) centralized network management is more difficult and (2) fewer capabilities are provided for linking to other networks than are typically found in server-based LANs.

LAN SELECTION CRITERIA

The material in Chapter 4, this chapter, and the associated CBT modules provides the foundation for evaluating a company's LAN needs and for selecting the components necessary to build an effective LAN system. We now look at the major factors influencing LAN selection. These criteria are summarized in Table 5-8.

TABLE 5-8   Major Factors Influencing LAN Selection

Cost	Device Connectivity
Number of Concurrent Users	Vendor
Medium and Distance	Manageability
Expandability	Type of Workstations
LAN Software and Hardware	Number of Printers
Vendor Support	Applications
Number of Workstations	Connectivity with Other Networks
Type of Use	Adherence to Established Standards
Speed	Security

Cost

If cost were not a consideration, LAN selection would be easier. You could buy the fastest, biggest workstations and servers available and use the most comprehensive LAN software available. Deciding which hardware and software modules fit this description would not be simple, but lack of price constraints would make selection much easier. However, cost often is an overriding constraint, and you must choose the best solution within your budget. In the final analysis the LAN must be a cost-effective solution for your situation.

Hardware and software are not the only costs you will incur. Other costs you must plan for include the immediate and recurring costs shown in Table 5-9. **Immediate costs** are those you incur when installing a LAN. **Recurring costs** are the costs of operating and updating the LAN and training LAN users and administrators.

TABLE 5-9   Immediate and Recurring LAN Costs

Immediate Costs

Equipment upgrades	Training—users, operators administrators
Documentation	
Installation of cabling	Site preparation
System software installation	Hardware installation
Creating user environments	Installing applications
Space required for new equipment	Testing
	Supplies and spares

Recurring Costs

LAN management—personnel costs	Hardware and software maintenance
Consumable supplies	Training—new users, administrators

Number of Workstations

The effect the number of workstations has on the immediate costs of attaching a LAN has already been discussed. The number of workstations is also a key factor in network configuration. Each LAN is physically capable of supporting a specific maximum number of workstations. If you exceed that maximum, you must make some provision for extending the maximum number. Various techniques exist for doing this, and each increases the cost of the LAN. Other workstation costs can be incurred as well. If you intend to use existing microcomputers on the LAN, they may need to be upgraded. For example, because LAN software will be resident in each workstation, the amount of memory available to applications will be reduced. You therefore may need to add memory to some workstations.

Type of Workstations

The type of workstations you use will be a significant influence in your LAN alternatives. If your LAN will consist of Apple Macintoshes, a number of DOS-oriented LAN systems will be eliminated. If your workstations are IBM-compatible systems, Apple LANs will be eliminated. The same logic applies if your LAN consists of any of the other possible workstation platforms, such as those of Sun Microsystems. The LAN hardware and software must be compatible with the workstations used. If you need to mix the types of workstations on the LAN to allow both Apple and IBM-compatible workstations, you will again eliminate a number of LAN options and, perhaps, increase the cost.

Number of Concurrent Users

The number of concurrent users may differ from the number of workstations. Some networks have restrictions regarding the number of active users. One network operating system allows four concurrent users, but more than four workstations can be attached. An increase in the number of concurrent users also increases the LAN workload. As the LAN workload increases, you have two basic choices: You can allow system responsiveness to decrease, or you can increase the work potential of the system to maintain or improve the responsiveness. Naturally the second option involves higher costs. Some ways to improve LAN responsiveness are to select a faster LAN (one with higher transmission speeds), to use additional or more powerful servers (which means more expensive computers), or to use more efficient (and typically more costly) LAN software. The number of concurrent users of an application also has an impact on the cost of the application. Software vendors vary in their user license provisions; in general, application costs are directly proportional to the number of concurrent users. As the number of concurrent users goes up, so do software costs.

Type of Use

The impression you may have gained from the preceding paragraph is that having more concurrent users increases the LAN workload. However, you need to understand more about the effect of concurrent users on LAN performance. To do so, we look at two very different ways of using a LAN.

Suppose the primary LAN application is word processing, and the operating mode is as follows: LAN users access the word processing software on the file server at the beginning of their work shift, they save their documents on a local disk drive, and they periodically print documents. What demands are there on the LAN? The demand is heavy when a user starts the word processing program. The program must be downloaded, or transferred from the server to the workstation. The user does not need LAN services again until he or she prints a document or, in some cases, requires an overlay module for the word processor.

An example of an **overlay module** is a spelling checker. Current microcomputer software is so rich in capabilities that all the functions cannot always be included in one memory-resident module. An overlay module overcomes this constraint by sharing memory with other overlay modules. LAN requests are therefore infrequent, but the amount of data transferred is large. Adding users may not significantly increase the LAN workload if there is a considerable amount of idle time. If you have used a LAN in a classroom situation, you probably have experienced this type of usage. At the beginning of the class, LAN response is slow because many students are starting an application at nearly the same time, and the demand for LAN resources is high. After that, however, LAN responsiveness improves because the LAN usage becomes intermittent.

Suppose instead that the primary LAN activity is database access, with users continually accessing and updating a database. In this case the LAN is constantly busy transferring large and small amounts of data. Adding users in this instance can have a noticeable impact on LAN performance.

Number and Type of Printers

The number and distribution of printers can affect your LAN decision as well. Some LAN operating systems require that network printers be attached to file servers, and each file server can support only so many printers. With such systems, if you have a need for a large number of printers, you may need to add server hardware and software simply to provide printing services. You also must be sure that the LAN you select is capable of supporting the types of printers you will be using. Each printer requires printer driver software to direct its operation. The driver software knows how to activate the particular printer features needed to print special typefaces, underlining, graphics, and so on. **Spooler software** is responsible for writing printed output to shared printers. It follows that there must be an interface between the spooler and the printer drivers. Drivers are often included as part of the server software. When selecting a LAN you must ensure both that the printers you plan to use are supported and that they are supported in the manner in which you plan to use them. For example, a certain printer may be supported for printing text but not for printing graphics.

Distance and Medium

LANs serve a limited geographical area at high speeds. Distance and speed are related. Attaining high speed over long distances can be very expensive, and each LAN has a maximum distance it can cover. Different types of LANs also have different distance limitations. The distance is measured in wiring length. If you snake a cable back and forth through an office complex, you may not cover a wide geographical area, but the cable distance can be quite long. In general, as the distance your LAN needs to cover increases, your LAN options decrease. Distances for popular microcomputer LANs range from a few hundred meters to several thousand meters.

The type of medium also influences the selection process. If your facility already has wiring installed, you may select a LAN that can use that type of wiring. Each medium has speed and error characteristics. Earlier you read that twisted-pair wires support lower speeds and are more susceptible to errors than either coaxial cable or fiber optic cable. If your LAN wiring needs to pass through areas that can induce transmission errors (such as areas that produce electrical or magnetic interference), you may need to select a LAN that can use a more noise-resistant medium such as coaxial cable or fiber optic cable. One company came to this realization the hard way. In wiring the building with unshielded twisted-pair wires, the company ran the wiring through the shaft of a freight elevator. The freight elevator was seldom used; however, every time it was operated, the motor interfered with the data being transmitted on the LAN, causing numerous transmission errors. Replacing the cabling in the elevator shaft with more error-resistant wiring eliminated the periodic failures.

Speed

LAN speeds can be somewhat deceptive. A LAN speed quoted by the vendor is the speed at which data is transmitted over the medium. You cannot expect the LAN to sustain this speed at all times. Time is required to place data onto the medium and to clear data from the medium. This is done in a variety of ways, which you learned about in Chapter 4. It is important that you select a LAN capable of meeting your performance goals. If you expect access to data on your LAN's file server to have a transfer rate comparable to that of a hard disk, such as 5 Mbps, this requirement eliminates a number of low-speed LANs. Common LAN speeds available for microcomputers are 1, 2.5, 4, 10, 16, 20, and 100 Mbps. The trend is toward higher speeds because of greater LAN use and because of the types of data now being used in LAN applications. Applications using graphics, audio, and full-motion video are becoming more common. These applications require the transfer of large amounts of data and place a heavy load on the media and servers.

Applications

Most major application software packages are now available in LAN-compatible versions. This does not mean all applications can run on all LANs. Applications communicate with the network through interfaces called **application program interfaces (APIs),** and a variety of APIs are in use. If the application uses an interface not supported by a particular LAN, then the application probably will not work on that network. Some software simply is not LAN compatible. Either it cannot run on a LAN at all or it does not support sharing on a LAN but can be used by one user at a time. Custom-written applications also may not be LAN compatible. It is important to determine whether software you need to use will work on the LAN you are considering.

Expandability

After installing a LAN you probably will need to add workstations to it or move workstations from one location to another. The ease of doing this varies among implementations. The ease may depend on the medium used and on the way the medium was installed. Adding nodes to some systems using twisted-pair wires or coaxial cable is relatively easy. Adding a node to a fiber optic cable may require cable splicing, which means you must cut the cable, add the connectors, and rejoin the cable so the light pulses can continue along the cable. Fiber optic cable splicing technology has improved and is not difficult; however, adding a node is still more difficult than for twisted-pair wires or coaxial cable.

Device Connectivity

Some organizations need to attach special devices to the LAN, such as an optical disk drive. LAN interfaces for such devices may not be available on some LANs or LAN file servers. This, of course, reduces your options to the LANs and servers that support the interface.

Connectivity to Other Networks

A LAN is often only one part of an organization's computing resources. Other facets may be a WAN, a large stand-alone computer, or other LANs. If there are other LANs, they may be of different types. When various computing resources are available, it is frequently desirable to connect these resources. This allows a node on the LAN to communicate with a node on a WAN or to access data on a central mainframe system. Various connection capabilities exist, but a given LAN may not support all of them. If you have immediate connectivity needs or anticipate them in the future, you need to select a LAN that will support the connection protocols you expect to use.

LAN Software and Hardware

If you already have microcomputers and associated software and hardware, you probably want to preserve your investment in them. That means you need to select LAN software and hardware that will be compatible with your existing equipment. Notable differences between capabilities of LAN software and hardware also may be important in making your LAN selection.

Adherence to Established Standards

Some LANs conform to the standards for LAN implementation, whereas others do not. Several nonstandard LANs have been adopted by many users and have thus become de facto standards. Other LANs are neither covered by standards nor very widely adopted. A LAN's adherence to a standard does not necessarily mean it is superior to nonstandard LANs. However, there are benefits to choosing a LAN that conforms to a standard. Because standards are published, any company is able to design components that work on the LAN. This creates competition, gives users alternative sources of equipment, and usually drives down the cost of components. Adopting a standardized LAN also is often regarded as a "safe" decision because the community of users is frequently large. This generates a body of expertise that new users can tap for either information or personnel. On the other hand, a nonstandard LAN may provide innovative features that are not yet covered by standards. Adopting such a LAN can place an organization ahead of competition that is using a more conventional system. You can read about more LAN standards in Chapter 4.

Vendors and Support

When you select a LAN, you are selecting much more than hardware and software. You also are selecting a vendor or vendors with whom you expect to have a long-term relationship. Your vendors ought to be available to help you in times of problems; provide maintenance and support; and supply spare parts, hardware and software upgrades, and new equipment. You can be more successful with a good vendor and a less capable LAN than with a poor vendor and a superior LAN, especially if your vendor can quickly resolve problems, obtain needed equipment, and so on. Evaluate prospective vendors and their support policies as carefully as you evaluate the equipment itself.

Manageability

Do not underestimate the time and effort required to operate and manage a LAN. Even a small, static LAN requires some management once it has been installed and set up. Occasionally a user might be added or deleted, applications may be added or updated, and so on. The major ongoing activities will be backing up files, taking care of printer problems, and solving occasional user problems. In a large LAN, management can be a full-time job—perhaps for more than one person. In Chapter 9 you will learn about network management. During the selection process you must ensure that your LAN will have the necessary management tools or that third-party tools are available. **Third-party tools** are those written by someone other than the LAN vendor. The tools you need will depend on the size of the LAN and the complexity of the users and applications involved. As a minimum you should be able to easily accomplish the tasks listed in Table 5-10.

TABLE 5-10   LAN Management Tasks

User/Group Oriented

Add, delete users and groups	Set user/group security
Set user environment	Solve user problems

Printer Oriented

Install/remove printers	Setup user/printer environment
Maintain printers	

Hardware/Software Oriented

Add/change/delete software	Add/change/delete hardware
Diagnose problems	Establish connections with other networks
Plan and implement changes	

General

Make backups	Maintain operating procedures
Carry out recovery as necessary	Educate users
Plan capacity needs	Monitor the network
Serve as liaison with other network administrators	

Security

With stand-alone microcomputers, security generally is not an issue because stand-alone systems are usually single-user systems and, thus, no security provisions were built into the operating systems or applications software. As a result, access to the system is tantamount to access to all data stored on that system. By contrast, data in a LAN is shared. This does not imply that all users have unlimited access to all data. The LAN software must have the ability to control access to data. For each user you should at least be able to establish read, write, create, and purge rights for each file. Chapter 10 gives more comprehensive coverage of LAN security.

SUMMARY

LAN software can be separated into system software and applications software. LAN system software in the servers and workstations is responsible for carrying out the LAN functions. Applications software solves business problems. LAN system software is found on servers and workstations.

Workstation system software is responsible for intercepting application I/O requests and deciding whether the request is local or network. If the request is local, the workstation LAN software passes it along to the workstation operating system. If the request is for a network resource, the workstation LAN software formats a network message and sends the request over the network for processing. The workstation LAN software also is responsible for accepting LAN messages and passing them along to the proper application. Because LAN workstation software must remain resident in the workstation memory, a stand-alone workstation may need a memory upgrade to run some LAN applications.

LAN server software is more complex than workstation software. Some functions it may provide are:

- I/O optimization
- Fault tolerance
- Printer services
- Utility and administrative support
- Access security
- File backup and restoration
- Contention resolution

These functions help to make performance better, to improve reliability, or to protect data from accidental or intentional damage.

When choosing LAN software, you need to consider how that software will interoperate with other software, other networks, and your hardware. Poor interoperability increases the complexity of using a LAN and decreases its usability.

A major difference between stand-alone microcomputers and microcomputers attached to a LAN is resource sharing. Sharing hardware and data may lead to contention problems, and mechanisms must be available to arbitrate resource contention. Spoolers manage contention for network printers. Open modes and file or record locks are commonly used to resolve data contention. These forms of data-contention resolution may lead to another problem called deadlock. If two or more processes are involved in a deadlock, none of the processes is able to proceed until one of them releases the resources it has locked. Resolving contention and deadlock problems is essential to preserving the integrity of data and ensuring the progress of applications.

Purchased software is covered by a license agreement that describes the manner in which the software may be used. In using the software, an organization agrees to abide by the licensing provisions, which typically limit the number of concurrent users and the hardware platforms on which the software may be installed. License agreements protect the software vendor's investment in developing, manufacturing, and distributing the software and give the user rights to use and upgrade a product. System administrators must ensure that the licensing provisions are adhered to. Numerous organizations that have ignored licensing provisions have been assessed large fines and were required to pay for additional licenses to cover the way the software was being used.

Various factors must be considered when selecting a LAN. First, you should decide whether a LAN is required or whether a LAN alternative will suffice. If a LAN is required, factors to consider include cost-effectiveness, available system and applications software, security, compatibility with existing hardware and software, LAN organization (dedicated server, nondedicated server, or peer-to-peer), adherence to established standards, number of concurrent users supported, ability to interconnect with other networks and computers, and vendor support and expertise. The weight associated with each selection criterion may differ among organizations. In making the right selections, you need to evaluate the alternatives from the perspective of your organization's immediate and future communications objectives.

KEY TERMS

access security 144

application program interface (API)   155

application settings 141

backup software 139

contention 141

copy protection 146

corporate license 149

cylinder 133

deadlock 142

deadly embrace 142

dedicated server 150

disk seek enhancement 132

duplexed servers 134

exclusive open mode 141

fault tolerance 133

I/O optimization 132

immediate costs 152

integrated software approach 131

interoperability 138

key disk 146

LAN Server (IBM) 131

license agreement 144

lock 142

mirrored disks 133

NetWare (Novell) 131

nondedicated server 150

OS/2 137

overlay module 153

parity data 134

peer-to-peer network 135

protected open mode 141

read-after-write 133

recurring costs 152

redirector 130

redundant arrays of independent disks (RAID) 134

restoration module 139

seek 132

server license 149

shared open mode 141

shared read-only mode 141

shared update module 141

site license 149

software piracy 146

spooler software 154

StreetTalk (Banyan) 138

system fault tolerance (SFT) 136

system software 130

third-party tools 157

track 133

Vines (Banyan) 138

Windows NT (Microsoft) 131

REVIEW QUESTIONS

1. Explain how an application's network request is processed by both the workstation and the server.

2. Why may a stand-alone workstation need a memory upgrade when added to a LAN?

3. What is a client/server or requester server protocol? Give an example (see CBT module).

4. What is an application program interface (API)?

5. What is the purpose of I/O optimization? Give two examples.

6. What is the benefit of fault-tolerant servers?

7. Describe three fault tolerance capabilities.

8. Explain how a print spooler works.

9. Explain two ways applications software can be tailored to individual users.

10. Describe two ways data contention can be avoided.

11. What is deadlock? Give an example.

12. What is a software license? Why are software licenses necessary?

13. Compare and contrast a dedicated and nondedicated server.

14. Describe a peer-to-peer LAN. How does it differ from a dedicated server LAN?

15. A network operating system (NOS) extends the capabilities of a standard operating system. What are the extended functions a NOS offers?

16. Compare server-based and peer-to-peer network operating systems. Which is more generally favored for LANs with large numbers of users?

17. Describe the functions of a LAN print server.

6

WAN HARDWARE AND
DATA LINK CONTROL

....

CHAPTER OBJECTIVES

After studying this chapter you should be able to:

- Trace the evolution of enterprise networks
- Discuss a variety of terminal attributes
- Explain what *ergonomics* means and the importance of ergonomic design
- Describe how multiplexers work
- Compare and contrast WAN and LAN network topologies
- Describe the workings of the asynchronous transmission protocol
- Describe the workings of character-oriented and bit-oriented synchronous transmission protocols
- Compare and contrast asynchronous and synchronous protocols
- Compare and contrast WAN and LAN data link protocols

WIDE AREA NETWORK CONFIGURATIONS

*I*n the preceding chapters you had the opportunity to learn about local area networks (LANs), and through the accompanying software tutorials you also experienced the types of media used in LANs, how data is represented on those media, the way in which LAN nodes gain access to the medium and exchange messages, and the fundamental workings of a network operating system. We began our discussion of networks with LANs because you probably had some prior knowledge of them, as LANs are the focus of most of today's network publicity, and it is likely that you have used a LAN at work or at school. However, another type of network, a wide area network (WAN), pre-dates LANs and continues to be the basis for many networks in large enterprises. To see how these networks evolved and are used in today's computing systems, shift to the CBT tutorial module entitled "Enterprise Network Evolution." As you step through this tutorial, take note of the hardware components used to implement WANs, and mentally compare these components to those used in setting up a LAN. Later in this chapter, we expand on the hardware and software technologies presented in the tutorial. Note also the layout or topology of the network components and the use of network protocols. We also discuss these topics later in this chapter. The protocols you will see are equivalent to the CSMA/CD and token-passing protocols you learned about in Chapter 4 and through the "Media Access" tutorial.

Enterprise Network Evolution

At this point, through the CBT tutorial module entitled "Enterprise Network Evolution" you see how these networks evolved and are used in today's computing systems. As you step through this tutorial, take note of the hardware components used to implement WANs, and mentally compare these components to those used in setting up a LAN. Note also the layout or topology of the network components and the use of network protocols. The protocols you will see are equivalent to the CSMA/CD and token passing protocols you learned about in Chapter 4 and through the "Media Access" tutorial.

In the tutorial "Enterprise Network Evolution" you saw several WAN configurations. The configuration shown in Figure 6-1(a) illustrates one of these, a single host computer connected to a variety of terminals. In this type of network, all the processing is done by the host, and the terminals simply act as input and output devices. The WAN illustrated in Figure 6-1(b) combines two or more nodes like the one in Figure 6-1(a) into a network of computers. The nodes in Figure 6-1(b) may be concentrated in a small area such as a computer facility within one building, or they might be distributed around the world. In Figure 6-1(c) we have taken the next logical step and combined several distinct networks into one large enterprise network. The joining of several networks is called an **internet,** and the networks that are connected in an internet can be WANs, or LANs, or a mixture of both. Perhaps you have heard about or even used once such internet called *the* Internet, a network implementation described in Chapter 7. Regardless of the network type or configuration, all networks use one or more types of media to connect one computer to another computer or to connect a terminal to a computer. Between the connections of terminals and computers the network designers may place devices that make the use of a medium more efficient, more cost-effective, or both. We now look at the main WAN hardware components. In discussing WAN hardware, we refer primarily to the network illustrated in Figure 6-1(a).

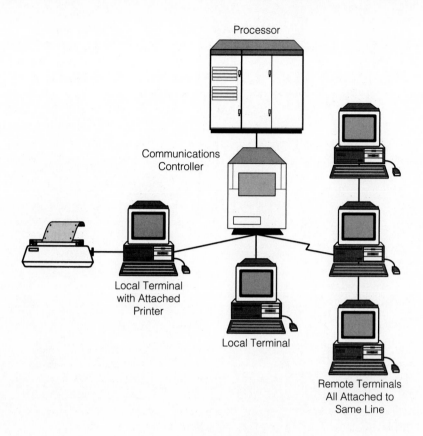

Processor

Communications
Controller

Local Terminal
with Attached
Printer

Local Terminal

Remote Terminals
All Attached to
Same Line

Figure 6-1 (a)

Various Network
Configurations

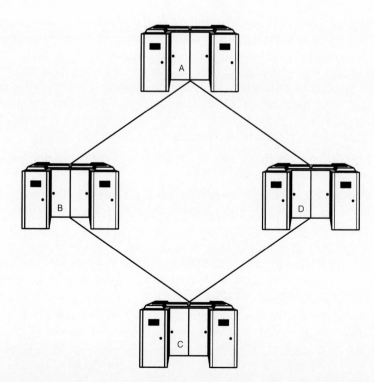

Figure 6-1 (b)

Various Network
Configurations

Figure 6-1 (c)

Various Network
Configurations

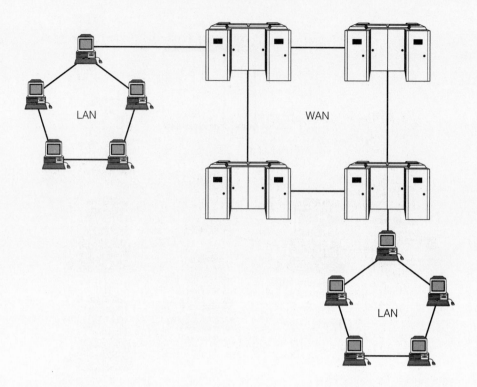

TERMINALS

We define a **terminal** as an input and/or output device that is connected to
a local or remote computer, called a **host computer.** The terminal is at certain
times dependent on the host for computation, data access, or both. There is
a wide variety of terminals and you are likely familiar with several that are
commonly used in businesses. For example, you may have used a bank's
automatic teller machine (ATM) or a gas station's automated gas pump, or
you may have had your purchases entered on a terminal at a grocery store,
department store, or restaurant. Other types of terminals include:

- Microcomputers that may augment duties of the host by doing a
  portion of the processing.

- Remote job entry (RJE) terminals that can be used to forward batches
  of record images to a host system and receive printed reports back
  from the host.

- A **video display unit (VDU),** (see Figure 6-2) or a hard-copy device
  such as a teletypewriter (TTY) that provides data entry and display.
  (A VDU is also sometimes referred to as a **video display terminal
  (VDT)** or a **cathode ray tube (CRT).**)

- Sensor devices used in laboratory, hospital, or data collection
  applications.

- Display-only devices such as ticker-tape monitors in stock markets.

- Point-of-sale (POS) terminals used to help maintain inventory, record receipts, and—in some instances—participate in money transfers from a buyer's account to a merchant's account.

- Touch-tone telephones when used to pay bills or to register students in classes.

Terminal Capabilities

From the list of terminal types just listed you might correctly surmise that there is a large variety of terminal features and abilities. We can separate terminals into three classes—dumb, smart, and intelligent—according to their basic capabilities.

Some terminals are classified as "dumb" because they function only as simple input/output devices. **Dumb terminals** typically operate in a conversational mode in which a host prompts for data and the user enters responses. **"Smart" terminals,** on the other hand, have memory and are able to hold several screenfuls of data, can be controlled by a host computer, and allow full-page editing of documents and forms. Examples of host control include the ability to lock the terminal's keyboard, and thus to disable operator entry, and specifying areas of the screen as display only, and thus preventing the operator from changing certain data. Smart terminals usually have an address used by the host. The address allows the host to specify which terminal should send or receive data. This capability, called polling, is discussed later. Polling allows several terminals to share a single communications line and thereby reduces transmission costs. Smart terminals may also support auxiliary data entry devices such as light pens, mice, and touch-screens. Many smart terminals have an attached printer for printing a displayed page and for automatic logging of data received by the terminal, and most smart terminals have additional keys known as function keys, or program attention keys, that transmit specific character sequences to the host. Function keys allow the operator to indicate to the application what function is to be performed on the data provided.

An **"intelligent" terminal,** typified by a microcomputer, has memory, a processor, and, typically, locally attached devices such as a printer and disk drives. An intelligent terminal can assist the host by performing some of the processing and data formatting. In this terminal hierarchy, a smart terminal generally includes all the capabilities of a dumb terminal, and an intelligent terminal includes the capabilities found in smart terminals. Moreover, an intelligent terminal may use software programs called **terminal emulators** that allow the intelligent terminal to assume the characteristics of a variety of other terminal types.

In addition to the capabilities that distinguish a terminal as dumb, smart, or intelligent, you might choose a terminal based on criteria such as cost, output capabilities (such as printed output versus a video display), the protocol(s) it supports (such as the asynchronous or synchronous protocols covered later in this chapter), and the speeds at which it operates. Several terminal attributes are listed in Table 6-1.

TABLE 6-1   Some Terminal Attributes

Cost	Synchronous	Auxiliary storage	EBCDIC
Conversational	Batch	Protected fields	Protocol support
Block mode	Point-to-point	Graphics	Attached devices
TTY-compatible	Multipoint	Formatting	Duplex
Dumb	Function keys	Character sets	Screen size
Smart	Editing	Keyboard	Character size
Intelligent	Cursor control	Blink	Modified data tags
Printer	Host control	Half intensity	CPU
Speed	Color	Reverse video	Interface
Asynchronous	Programmable	ASCII	Portability

One of the attributes listed in Table 6-1, ergonomics, deserves special mention. **Ergonomics,** also called human engineering, is the science of designing equipment to maximize worker productivity by reducing operator fatigue and discomfort and by improving worker safety. Ergonomics is important because poorly-designed terminals have ostensibly caused health problems in users. Reported issues include radiation-related problems, carpal tunnel syndrome (a hand malady), severe headaches, neck aches, and eyestrain. When selecting a terminal device that will be used extensively by people, some of the ergonomic considerations you should make include:

- Low radiation emissions
- Monitor (a non-glare surface without flickering screens and without sharply contrasting colors—green or amber characters on a black background is better than white characters on a black background)
- Monitor position (monitor should tilt and swivel to avoid neck aches)

- Keyboard (well-sculpted, easily accessed keys with adjustable, audible key click)
- Keyboard position (be able to be located at comfortable hand positions)

Terminal Configurations

On any communications channel, the two options for attaching terminals to a host are point-to-point and multipoint. **Point-to-point connections** use a communications line to connect one terminal to the host computer. **Multipoint connections** have a computer on one end of the line and multiple terminals on the other end. Point-to-point connections are common in computer-to-computer communications, local connections between a host and a terminal where the cost of the line is negligible, and remote locations having only one remote terminal. Multipoint connections are common whenever multiple terminals are located near each other either locally or remotely. Multipoint connections help reduce the cost of communications lines to the terminals' locations. Whether point-to-point or multipoint, terminals and hosts need a convention, a line discipline, for gaining access to the medium.

In point-to-point connections the line discipline is typically contention. In **contention mode,** the host and the terminal contend for control of the medium much like nodes on a CSMA/CD LAN. The terminal and the host are considered to have an equal right to transmit. To transmit, one station issues a bid for the channel, asking the other party for control. If the other station is ready to receive data, control is granted to the requester. Upon completion of the transfer, control is relinquished and the link goes into an idle state, awaiting the next bid for control. A collision can occur when both stations simultaneously bid for the line. If this occurs, either one station is granted the request based on some predetermined priority scheme or each station waits awhile and then reattempts the bid. With the latter approach, the time-out intervals must not be the same, or another collision would occur. Conflicts for the use of the channel in a point-to-point configuration typically are few, because only the host and the terminal are candidates for transmission.

In a multipoint connection, several terminals share one communications link. The number of terminals allowed to share the medium depends on the speed of the medium and the aggregate transmission rate of the terminals. As the number of terminals on the line increases, the average time each terminal has access to the link decreases. With multipoint terminals, the most common line discipline is polling.

Polling is the process of asking terminals whether they have data to transmit. In polling, one station, usually the host computer, is designated as the supervisor or **primary station.** There is only one primary station per multipoint link; all other stations (terminals) are referred to as **secondary stations.** The primary station is in complete control of the link. Secondary stations may transmit data only when given permission by the primary station. Each secondary station on a line has a unique address. Although there are several distinct methods of polling, essentially the process works as follows. The primary is provided a list of addresses for terminals on a particular line.

The primary picks an address from the list and sends a poll message across the line using that address. All secondary stations receive the poll message, but only the addressee responds. The poll message asks the secondary station whether it has any data to transmit to the primary. If the terminal has data to transmit, it responds with the data or with a positive acknowledgment and then the data. If the secondary station has no data to send, it responds with a negative acknowledgment. On receiving the station's response, the primary moves to the next address in the polling list.

Polling is used to gather data from terminals. A similar convention, **selection,** is used to send data to terminals. When the primary has data to send to one or more secondary stations, it selects the station in much the same manner as polling. In the selection process, the primary sends a selection message to the terminal. A selection message consists of the terminal's selection address and an inquiry to determine whether the terminal is ready to accept data. After a positive acknowledgment to the selection message, the primary transmits the data to the terminal.

Advantages and Disadvantages of Multipoint Connections

The advantages of multipoint connections are reduced costs. Communication line costs are less because several terminals share the same line, and modem costs are reduced because there are fewer communications lines. There are also disadvantages to the multipoint configuration. First, terminals used in this environment must have some intelligence, making them more expensive than terminals using a point-to-point connection. This higher cost is usually negligible, however, when compared with the savings in medium and modem costs. Because the medium is shared among several terminals, a terminal may have to wait to transmit its information. If messages are short, the wait time should not be long; on the other hand, if messages are lengthy, such as when a microcomputer transfers a file, the other terminals may be required to wait an inordinate amount of time.

Multiplexers

Polling requires the use of smart terminals that are addressable and have memory. Another line-sharing technique, multiplexing, does not require the use of smart terminals. **Multiplexing technology** allows signals for several terminals to be transmitted over a single data link without relying on terminal addresses or special terminal capabilities. Figure 6-3 presents a general multiplexer configuration. Several communication lines enter the multiplexer from the host side. The multiplexer, or mux, combines the data from all incoming lines and transmits it over one line to a multiplexer at the receiving end. The receiving multiplexer separates the data and properly distributes it among the outgoing terminal lines. The number of lines going into the multiplexer on the host side is the same as the number going out to terminals (or other multiplexers) on the remote side. To the user, the multiplexer appears to function as though there were several physical lines, one between the host and each terminal, as opposed to just one. The configuration of one high-speed link and a pair of multiplexers costs less than that of several lower-speed links with a pair of modems for each. The multiplexer makes the line sharing transparent to the user, because the application essentially sees a point-to-point line.

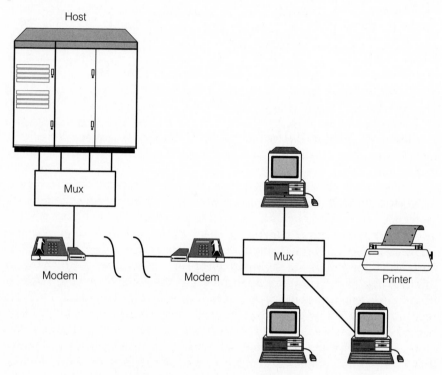

Host

Mux

Modem

Modem

Mux

Printer

Figure 6-3

General Multiplexer Configuration

Four host lines combined with one long distance line.
A modem is not required by all types of multiplexers.

Types of Multiplexers

Multiplexers work in three basic ways. The first technique, known as **frequency division multiplexing (FDM),** separates the link by frequencies. The second technique, known as **time division multiplexing (TDM),** separates the link into transmission time slots, and the third technique, **statistical time division multiplexing (STDM),** is a TDM enhancement.

In frequency division multiplexing the available bandwidth of the circuit is broken into subchannels as illustrated in Figure 6-4. For example, suppose a communications line has a bandwidth (frequency range) of 10,000 hertz (Hz). We could represent four different subchannels on this line by dividing the frequency range into four parts. One subchannel could use frequencies between 500 and 2500 Hz; the second, from 3000 to 5000 Hz; the third, from 5500 to 7500; and the last, from 8000 to 10,000 Hz. Note that we have left a 500-Hz separation between each subchannel. These separations, called **guardbands,** help prevent signal interference between adjacent subchannels.

Figure 6-4

A Frequency Division
Multiplexer Configuration

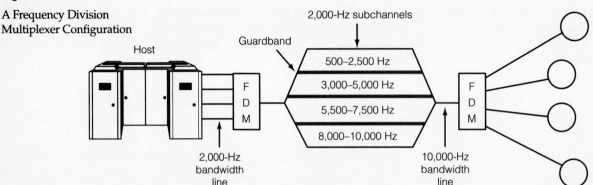

Instead of splitting the frequency range, TDM shares time. With TDM, each line is given a time slot for transmitting, which is accomplished by interleaving either bits or characters. Bit interleaving is more common for synchronous (block at a time) transmissions and character interleaving is more common with asynchronous (character at a time) transmissions. To understand how TDM operates, look at the four-port TDM in Figure 6-5. The multiplexer in the figure combines signals from the four lines on the host end onto a single communications circuit. Data entering the TDM from the ports on either end of the multiplexer is placed in a buffer. With **character interleaving,** first a character from Line 1 is transmitted, then a character from Line 2, one from Line 3, one from Line 4, and back again to Line 1 to repeat the cycle. **Bit interleaving** works in the same manner except that a bit instead of a character is taken from each port in turn to form a transmission block. The multiplexer at the other end breaks the data back out and places it on the appropriate line.

STDMs (also known as stat muxes) improve on the efficiency of TDM by transmitting data only for those lines with data to send. Idle terminals do not take up any carrying capacity of the communications circuit. Figure 6-6 illustrates STDM. Because neither time slot nor frequency is allocated to a specific terminal, an STDM must also transmit a terminal identifier along with the data block. When all devices have data to transmit, an STDM looks just like a TDM; when only one device has data to send, the entire line capacity is devoted to that line, giving improved efficiency.

Multiplexer Configurations

In addition to attaching terminals to multiplexers, other multiplexers can be added in daisy-chain fashion, a configuration illustrated in Figure 6-7. **Daisy chaining,** also referred to as **cascading,** allows some circuits to be extended to another remote point. This is useful in a situation with two areas for data entry. With eight terminals in each area, a 16-port stat mux could provide linkage between the host and Area A, and eight lines from Area A could travel via an eight-port multiplexer to Area B. The number of ports on a multiplexer varies. Commonly, multiplexers have 4, 8, 16, 32, 48, or 64 ports.

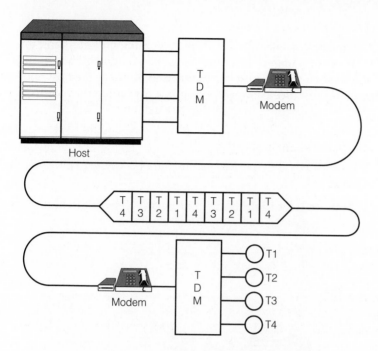

Figure 6-5

A Time Division
Multiplexer Configuration

*A modem is not required for all TDMs; for example,
an in-house digital TDM may not require modems.

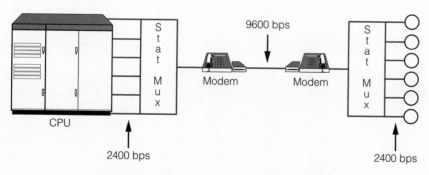

Figure 6-6

Statistical Time Division
Multiplexing

One 9600-bps line supporting six 2400-bps devices

CONCENTRATORS

In the "Enterprise Network Evolution" tutorial you should have noticed two
other line-sharing devices, a cluster controller and a remotely located minicomputer. Both are examples of what is generically called a **concentrator.** A
concentrator's functions are similar to those of a multiplexer, allowing multiple
devices to share communications circuits. Because a concentrator is a computer,
it can participate more actively than a multiplexer. The principal differences
between a multiplexer and a concentrator are:

- Concentrators are used one at a time; multiplexers are used in pairs.
- A concentrator may have multiple incoming and outgoing lines, with a different number of incoming lines than outgoing lines; a multiplexer condenses a certain number of incoming lines at the host end onto one long-distance communication line and converts back to the same number of outgoing lines at the terminal end.
- A concentrator is a computer and may have auxiliary storage for use in support of an application.
- A concentrator may perform some data processing functions, such as polling.

You may want to refer back to the "Enterprise Network Evolution" tutorial for a review of concentrator configurations.

Figure 6-7

Cascading Multiplexers

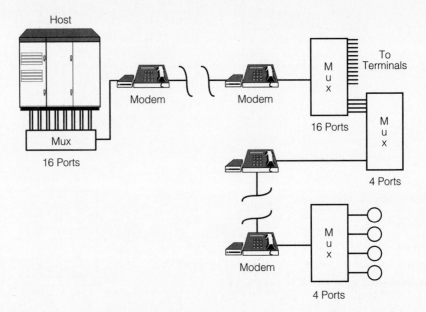

FRONT-END PROCESSORS

Recall from the "Enterprise Network Evolution" tutorial that a **front-end processor (FEP),** sometimes referred to as a communications controller or message switch, is employed at the host end of the communications circuit much like a concentrator is used at the remote end. The FEP takes over much of the line management work from the host; in many respects, FEPs and concentrators serve the same function. An FEP interface with a host system uses one or more high-speed links. The FEP is responsible for controlling the more numerous low-speed circuits. All functions of a concentrator can also be performed by an FEP, except, of course, concentrating message traffic for multiple remote terminals onto one communications line. FEPs may be either special purpose or general purpose. Special-purpose FEPs, such as the IBM 3745 communications controller, are designed specifically for handling data communications; their operating system and software are solely communications-oriented. General-purpose computers, such as minicomputers, are also used as FEPs.

WAN TOPOLOGIES AND TRANSMISSION SERVICES

One objective you had when looking at the "Enterprise Network Evolution" tutorial was to observe the ways in which the networks are configured. You might want to review parts of the tutorial to refresh your recollection of these configurations. Also, recall from the LAN section of the text that the way in which the hardware and media are laid out is called a topology. LANs use star, bus, or ring topologies. The primary WAN topologies are star, hierarchy, plex or interconnected, and hybrid. The star topology was covered in the LAN section, so you may wish to go back to Chapter 4 and refresh your knowledge on that topology. Most WANs use either a hierarchical, plex, or hybrid topology.

Hierarchical Network

The **hierarchical topology,** shown in Figure 6-8, is also referred to as a tree structure. Directly connected to the single root node (Node A) are several nodes at the second level. Each of these can have several cascaded nodes attached. This type of topology, often found in corporate computer networks, closely resembles corporate organization charts. With a corporate computer as root node, division systems are attached directly to the root, regional systems to divisional systems, districts to regions, and so on. Corporate reports from a lower level are easily consolidated at the next higher level, and the network generally mirrors the information flow pattern in the corporation. Information flowing from a district in one division to a district in a different division would need to go through the root, or corporate, node.

Plex (Interconnected) Network

A **plex,** or **interconnected, network** is illustrated in Figures 6-9. Plex networks allow any node to be connected to any other node. This affords the maximum flexibility in network configuration and allows the network designer to minimize the costs of communications media while providing connections between nodes that need to communicate frequently. The flexibility of this topology is demonstrated by its ability to form star, ring, bus, and hierarchical networks. A plex network or hybrid topologies are the most common WAN topologies.

Figure 6-8

A Hierarchical Topology

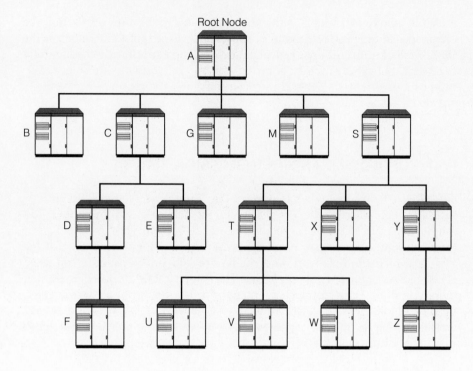

Figure 6-9

A Plex or Interconnected
Configuration

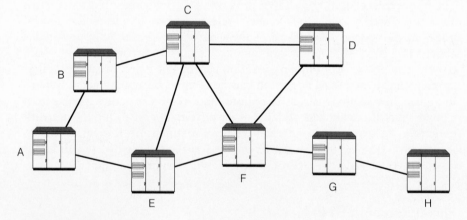

Hybrid Networks

Combinations of the above topologies are sometimes integrated into one
hybrid network. One such combination is a backbone network—such as a
ring—with spurs attached, as illustrated in Figure 6-10. The backbone nodes
can be dedicated to message transfer and data communications while the
other nodes are used for both data processing and data communications. In
widely distributed systems with many nodes, a backbone network helps
reduce the number of nodes on the path between sender and receiver and

helps reduce network congestion problems. If the backbone is implemented as a ring, multiple paths are available and reliability is also improved. Table 6-2 summarizes the different types of topology with respect to cost, control, number of hops (speed), reliability, and expandability.

Figure 6-10

A Backbone Network

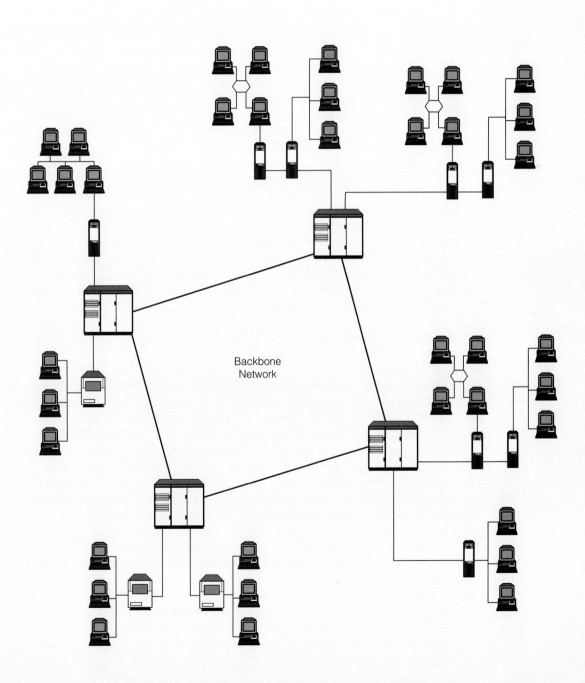

TABLE 6-2   **Network Topology Characteristics**

Topology Type	Cost	Control	Number of Hops	Reliability	Expandability
Star	Can be high	Very good	Maximum of two	Poor	Good
Hierarchical	Can be high	Good	Can be many	Fair	Fair to good
Interconnected					
Full	Highest	Distributed	One only	Good	Very poor
Other	Can be lowest	Distributed	Can be many	Good	Good
Ring	Good	Distributed	Can be many	Good	Good
Bus	Good	Distributed	N/A	Good	Good

WAN DATA LINK PROTOCOLS

In the CSMA/CD and token-passing tutorial you learned that most LANs use contention and token passing for data link control. WAN data link protocols are typically either asynchronous or a form of synchronous protocols. Unlike LANs, many WANs use several different data link protocols within a network. One link may use a synchronous protocol, another link may use a different type of synchronous protocol, and a terminal may communicate with a host via an asynchronous protocol. Asynchronous is most often used to connect hosts with terminals. Synchronous protocols are used between computers as well as between computers and terminals.

Asynchronous Transmission

Asynchronous transmission (async) is the oldest and one of the most common data link protocols. In asynchronous transmission, data is transmitted one character at a time, and sender and receiver are not synchronized with each other. The sender is thus able to transmit a character at any time. The receiver must be prepared to recognize that information is arriving; accept the data; possibly check for errors; and print, display, or store the data in memory. Individual characters also can be separated over different time intervals, meaning no synchronization exists between individual transmitted characters. Asynchronous transmission is also referred to as a start-stop protocol because each character is framed by a start bit and a stop bit, as illustrated in Figure 6-11.

When an asynchronous link is set up, sender and receiver are configured to agree on transmission parameters, including the number of bits per character, parity, the number of stop bits, line speed, and the conditions that terminate the transmission. A message terminator usually is a defined set of characters called **interrupt characters,** a count of a specific number of characters, or a time-out interval. The characters transmitted when the user presses the Enter key are commonly used as interrupt characters. An asynchronous communications link is either idling or transmitting data. In the idle state, an asynchronous protocol transmits a continuous stream of 1 bits. For the following discussion we assume that sending and receiving stations are configured the same with respect to the number of bits sent per character, parity, message termination, and maximum speed of the link (as detected by the receiving modem). We assume that the line is in the idle state, that there are seven data bits and one parity bit, and that odd parity will be checked.

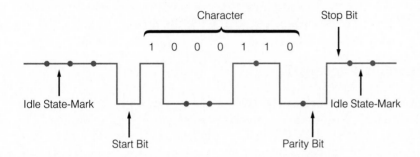

Figure 6-11

Asynchronous Transmission of the Letter F

Transmitting a Character. A character's arrival is signaled by a **start bit,** which is a change in the state of the line from a 1 bit to a 0 bit. The start bit is followed by seven data bits, one parity bit, and a **stop bit,** which is a return to a 1 bit. If parity does not check or if the tenth bit is not a 1, it is assumed that an error has occurred. The ASCII representation for the character *F* is 1000110; the asynchronous representation for transmitting this character is given in Figure 6-11. After a character is transmitted, the line goes back to the idle state until the next start bit is encountered.

Buffer overflow, or **overrun,** can arise when the data block being transmitted is larger than the receiving buffer area or when data from a subsequent block is received before the previous block's data has been emptied from the buffer. In such cases there is no place to store the arriving characters, and they are lost. Frequently in such instances the data link protocol uses a technique known as double buffering to avoid losing characters. **Double buffering** means there are two input buffers capable of receiving data. The buffers are alternated: When one buffer is filled, new incoming characters are stored in the alternate buffer. While an alternate buffer is being used, data in the full buffer can be passed to the application, which makes that buffer available for receiving new data. Double buffering might be used when transmitting data from a microcomputer's disk to the host. Such data may form a continuous character stream that can arrive at nearly maximum data link speed and in variable-length blocks. A receiving computer with single buffering may not be fast enough to empty its buffer and be ready to accept the next arriving characters.

Why Asynchronous Transmission Is So Popular. Although it is the oldest data link protocol, asynchronous transmission remains commonly used for several reasons. Because it was the only way to transmit data for several years, many terminals and controller boards were designed for asynchronous operation. Thus, asynchronous technology is well developed, and a wide variety of hardware options are available at a relatively low price. Asynchronous also is very well suited to many types of applications. People performing data entry in a conversational mode or even in block mode operate at speeds compatible with asynchronous protocol. Furthermore, asynchronous transmission was somewhat revived with microcomputers. A microcomputer's serial port is an asynchronous device and, as you are probably aware, the serial port is used for most microcomputer communications connections. The primary penalty paid with asynchronous is its inefficient use of the circuit.

Synchronous Transmission

Synchronous transmission can be divided into two groups: character oriented and bit oriented. Bit-oriented protocols are the newer technology and the basis for most modern WAN data link protocols. With asynchronous transmission, the sender and receiver are not synchronized with respect to data transmission. A sender can transmit at any time, and there is no set interval between the arrival of characters. Moreover, data is transmitted one character at a time. Synchronous transmission requires that sender and receiver be synchronized. Synchronous modems have clocks that are set in time with each other by a bit pattern transmitted at the beginning of a message. Unlike asynchronous transmissions, synchronous transmissions involve sending a block of characters at a time. Figure 6-12 illustrates the differences between asynchronous and synchronous transmission.

Figure 6-12

Asynchronous vs.
Synchronous Transmission

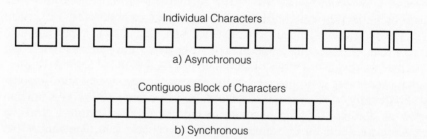

Character Synchronous Protocols.   Both corporate and national standards specify how **character synchronous protocols** are to be implemented. National standards include American National Standards Institute (ANSI) standards X3.1, X3.24, X3.28, and X3.36, all of which pertain to various aspects of character synchronous transmission. The IBM **Binary Synchronous Communications (BISYNC or BSC) protocol** has become a de facto industry-standard communications protocol supported by many manufacturers. Because it is so common, BISYNC is used as a model of character synchronous protocols in the following discussion.

BISYNC was introduced by IBM in 1967 as the data link protocol for remote job entry. In BISYNC, special characters are used to denote message parts and control functions. For example, one character is used to establish synchronization, another to denote the presence of a message header, one to denote the start of data, one to signal the end of data, and so on. To start the transmission, one or more synchronization characters are placed at the beginning of each transmission block to synchronize the modems. To maintain timing for long transmission blocks, additional sync characters are inserted at regular intervals. Figure 6-13 shows a message with BISYNC control characters for synchronization (SYN), the start of text (STX), and the end of text (ETX). BISYNC supports both point-to-point and multipoint configurations.

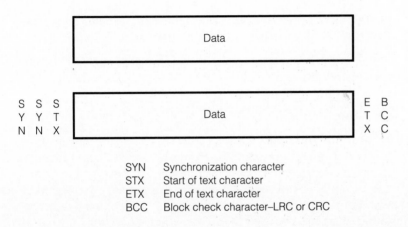

Figure 6-13

BISYNC Control Characters

SYN	Synchronization character
STX	Start of text character
ETX	End of text character
BCC	Block check character–LRC or CRC

Each transmitted block can have an optional header field for message control that designates such items as routing information, priority, and message type. The beginning and end of text are identified by framing the data with control characters. An STX character signals that the data portion of the text is starting. One of several characters—such as ETX, ETB, or EOT—can be used to identify the end of a block of data, depending on whether an intermediate or final block is being transmitted. The ETB control character designates the end of the transmission block, ETX signals the end of the text, and EOT means end of transmission. Lengthy messages are ordinarily broken down into segments or blocks. If a message were broken into four different transmission blocks, the first three blocks would terminate with the ETB control character and the last would terminate with the EOT character.

One limitation of BISYNC is that it is essentially a half-duplex protocol, so each message transmitted must be acknowledged by the receiver before the next message can be sent. This is not a major concern for some applications, especially those involving terminal data entry, for which the amount of time required to acknowledge is short compared with the speed of data submission. For host-to-host communications, on the other hand, half duplex can be quite restrictive. Consider a file transmitted between two processors: It would be more efficient if the sender could transmit several blocks before receiving an acknowledgment and if the acknowledgment could be transmitted in parallel with the data, as would occur in full-duplex mode.

Bit Synchronous Protocols.   **Bit-oriented synchronous data link protocols** use bits rather than bytes to delineate data and provide message control. The first bit-oriented synchronous data link protocol, **Synchronous Data Link Control (SDLC),** was introduced by IBM in 1972. Since then, numerous other bit-oriented data link controls have surfaced. Three other major bit synchronous protocols are:

• **HDLC, High-level Data Link Control,** a standard of the International Standards Organization (ISO)

• **ADCCP, Advanced Data Communications Control Procedure,** an ANSI standard data link protocol (ADCCP is frequently pronounced "addcap")

• **LAPB, Link Access Procedure, Balanced,** designated as the data link protocol for X.25 packet distribution networks

All of these bit synchronous protocols operate similarly. Although there are both national and international standards, SDLC is used in the following discussion as the model for bit-oriented data link protocols because it is representative of many of the bit synchronous implementations.

Synchronous Data Link Control (SDLC).   The basic unit of transmission in SDLC is the **frame,** presented in Figure 6-14. SDLC uses three types of frames: information, supervisory, and unnumbered. **Information frames** carry data and provide for message sequencing. **Supervisory frames** are used to acknowledge receipt of data and to designate the readiness to accept data. **Unnumbered frames** are used to provide control functions, such as disconnecting or initializing a station, and to send data that does not need to be acknowledged, such as a broadcast message.

Figure 6-14

An SDLC Frame Format

8 bits	8 bits	8 bits	Variable	16 bits	8 bits
Flag 01111110	Address	Control	Data (Optional Octets)	Frame Check Sequence	Flag 01111110

A **flag field** is used to indicate the beginning and end of a frame. The bit pattern for the flag—01111110—is the only bit pattern in the protocol that is specifically reserved; all other bit patterns are acceptable. The second field within the frame, the **address field,** has eight bits. A maximum of 256 unique addresses is possible. Other data link protocols, such as ADCCP and HDLC, allow the address field to be expanded in multiples of eight bits, significantly increasing the number of addressable stations per link. The **control field,** also eight bits wide, identifies the frame type as either unnumbered, informational, or supervisory. Only the first two of these three types are used to transmit data, with the primary data transport frame being the information frame.

The **data field,** always omitted for supervisory frames, is optional on unnumbered frames and is usually present on information frames. The only restriction on the data field is that the number of bits must be a multiple of eight, or an octet. This restriction does not mean an 8-bit code must be used;

in fact, any code is acceptable. But if necessary, the data being transmitted must be padded with additional bits to maintain an integral number of octets. If the data being transmitted consists of 5 Baudot characters, at 5 bits each, only 25 bits would be required for the data and an additional 7 bits would be required to complete the last octet. Following the optional data field is a 16-bit cyclic redundancy check (CRC) frame-check sequence for error detection. The final field of the frame is the flag that signals the end of the message. The bit pattern for the ending flag is the same as that for the beginning flag.

SDLC is a positional protocol, which means each field except the data field has a specific length and location relative to adjacent fields. No special control characters (except the flag characters) are used to delimit the data or headings in the message. For control frames, which are either unnumbered or supervisory, the control function is encoded in the control field. Unnumbered frames have 5 bits available to identify the control function, so 32 different function types are possible. The supervisory frame has only 2 bits available, so a maximum of 4 functions can be defined.

Unlike BISYNC, SDLC inherently provides full-duplex transmissions. In SDLC information frames, the control field contains two three-bit fields known as the **number sent (Ns)** and **number received (Nr) subfields.** The Ns and Nr counts, used to sequence messages, allow for full-duplex transmission. Being able to send several messages before receiving an acknowledgment or to have messages passing in both directions simultaneously can significantly improve on total amount of data passed over a link.

HDLC/SDLC

At this point, through the CBT tutorial module entitled "HDLC/SDLC", you can experience how sending and receiving stations are able to effect this full-duplexing capability. The key points you will observe are the use of the Ns and Nr fields to account for messages passing in both directions and the use of these fields in effecting recovery when necessary.

Choosing a Data Link Protocol

Although several other data link protocols exist, those described in this chapter are the most common. The question is, which one is appropriate for a specific situation? Table 6-3 compares synchronous and asynchronous protocols. When selecting the proper protocol, the network designer must first choose a protocol supported by the hardware vendor. Most vendors support some version of asynchronous, character synchronous, and bit synchronous protocols. CSMA/CD and token passing are found primarily in local area networks. Second, the type of hardware used in an application partly dictates the data link protocol. Most terminals support one or possibly two protocols; the exception is intelligent terminals, which can support a wide variety of protocols. Third, the network support provided by the vendor affects the choice of data link protocol. Many newer network systems have been designed around a bit-oriented synchronous protocol.

TABLE 6-3   Comparison of Asynchronous and Synchronous Protocols

Asynchronous	Synchronous
Character-at-a-time transmission	Block transmission
Modems are not synchronized	Modems are synchronized
Error detection commonly is parity	Error detection commonly is CRC or parity plus LRC
Fixed overhead per character	Fixed overhead per block (may be less efficient for small messages but more efficient for large ones)
Less efficient use of communications link	More efficient use of communications link
Lower-cost devices	Higher-cost devices

In practice, do not select a protocol and then gather the equipment to support it. Instead select a network design, a hardware vendor, and associated hardware, all of which determine a particular protocol. There are several bit-oriented implementations, and several standards exist. The industry trend is toward higher-speed transmission and efficient use of the data link, both factors that definitely favor synchronous transmission protocols.

THE OSI NETWORK LAYER

The OSI network layer performs four major functions: routing, network control, congestion control, and collection of accounting data. Whereas the data link layer is concerned with moving data between two adjacent nodes, the network layer is concerned with end-to-end **routing**, or getting data from the originating node to its ultimate destination. Data may take a variety of paths from the originating node to the destination node. The network layer must be aware of alternative paths in the network and must choose the best one. Selection of the best path depends on several factors, including congestion, number of intervening nodes, speed of links, and so on.

Network control involves sending node status information to other nodes and receiving status information from other nodes to determine the best routing for messages. The network layer must enforce the priority scheme when priorities are associated with messages. **Congestion control** means reducing transmission delays that might result from overuse of some circuits or because a particular node in the network is busy and unable to process messages in a timely fashion. The network layer should adapt to these transient conditions and attempt to route messages around such points of congestion. Not all systems can adapt to the changing characteristics of the communications links. Finding the best route is similar to our attempts to control automobile traffic congestion. In traffic control we try to route vehicles around congested or closed streets so the vehicles can arrive at their destinations sooner. In some instances, such attempts at congestion avoidance lead to congestion on other streets. In some network layer software, attempts are made to identify and avoid links and nodes that are experiencing heavy loads, and as with traffic routing, such schemes can create congestion in other portions of the network.

Message routing is achievable through several algorithms used to direct messages from the point of origination to final destination. Determination of message routing can be either centralized or distributed. Routing itself can be either static, adaptive, or broadcast and is governed by a network routing table resident at each node. The **network routing table** is a matrix of node identifiers and the link or path to that node; some routing tables may contain additional information such as alternate routes or the relative merits of several existing routes. If a message destined for Node X arrives at Node K, Node K's routing table is consulted for the next node on the path from K to X. The following discussion covers several routing techniques.

Centralized Routing Determination:
The Network Routing Manager

In **centralized routing determination,** one node is designated as the **network routing manager** to which all nodes periodically forward such status information as the number of inbound and outbound messages and the number of messages processed within the most recent interval. The routing manager is thereby provided with an overview of network functioning, location of any bottlenecks, and location of underutilized facilities. The routing manager periodically recalculates the optimal paths between nodes and constructs and distributes new routing tables to all nodes.

There are several disadvantages to this form of network routing. The routing manager's ability to receive many messages from the other nodes increases the probability of congestion, a problem that can be exacerbated if the routing manager is itself a node used to accept and forward messages. Networks are sometimes subject to transient conditions, such as when the internode transfer of a file saturates a link for a short period of time. By the time this information is relayed to the routing manager and a new routing is calculated, the activity may have already ceased, making the newly calculated paths less than optimal. Some nodes also will receive the newly calculated routing tables before others, leading to inconsistencies in how messages are to be routed. Figure 6-15 shows a change in the message path. Under the old routing mechanism the best route from Node A to Node X was A → B → D → X, whereas the new path is A → C → D → X, as indicated in Figure 6-15. Also, the new path from Node B to Node X is B → A → C → D → X. If Node B receives its new routing table while Node A is still using the old table, then for a message destined from A to X, A will route it to B and B will route it back to A, continuing until A receives the new routing table. Transmission of the routing tables themselves also may bias the statistics being gathered to compute the next routing algorithm.

Figure 6-15

A Change in the
Message Path

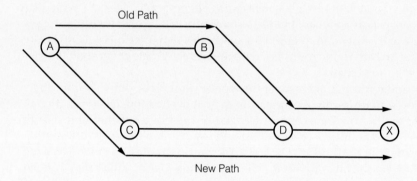

Additional problems with centralized route calculations are the amount of CPU processing power needed and the reliability of the routing manager. If this node fails, either the routing remains unchanged until the system is recovered or an alternate routing manager must be selected. The better situation is to have alternate routing managers available in case the primary routing node fails. This approach is implemented most efficiently by having the routing manager send the alternates "I'm alive" messages at predefined intervals; if the backup manager fails to receive this message within the prescribed interval, it assumes the primary manager has failed and takes over. The backup manager's first responsibility is to broadcast that network status messages should now be routed to it.

Distributed Routing Determination

Distributed routing determination relies on each node to calculate its own best routing table, which requires each node to periodically transmit its status to its neighbors. As this information ripples through the network, each node updates its tables accordingly. This technique avoids the potential bottleneck at a centralized routing manager, although it may take some time for changes to flow through the network to all nodes.

Static Routing

The purest form of **static routing** involves always using one particular path between two nodes. This means that if a link in that path is down, communication between those nodes is impossible. Fully interconnected net-works were sometimes used for this approach. The only path between any two nodes was the link between them. If that link was down, the available network software was incapable of using any alternate paths. This type of system has largely disappeared. Static routing generally now refers to the situation in which a selected path is used until some drastic condition makes that path unavailable. An alternate path is then selected and used until the route is switched manually, a failure occurs on the alternate path, or the original path is restored.

When multiple paths exist, some implementations weight each path according to perceived utilization, which is referred to as **weighted routing.** The path is then randomly selected from the weighted alternatives. Figure 6-16 shows three paths from Node A to Node X, via Nodes B, C, and D. Suppose the network designers had determined that the path through Node B would be best 50 percent of the time, the path through Node C would be best 30 percent of the time, and the path through Node D would be best 20 percent of the time. When a message is to be sent from Node A to Node X, a random number between 0 and 1 is generated. If the random number is 0.50 or less, the path through Node B is traversed; if the random number is greater than 0.50 and less than or equal to 0.80, the path through Node C is selected; otherwise, the path through Node D is selected. The path may alternate, but each path is used with the same frequency as in the routing tables. This type of routing can only be changed by altering the route weighting in the routing tables.

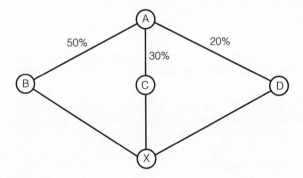

Figure 6-16

Weighted Routing

Adaptive Routing

Adaptive routing, occasionally referred to as **dynamic routing,** attempts to select the best current route for the message or session. The best route may be determined by several different parameters, such as link congestion, link speed, session type, and so on. The simplest adaptive routing algorithm is to have a node pass along the message as quickly as possible, with the only restriction being not to pass it back to the sending node. The receiving node looks at all potential outbound links, selects the one with the least amount of activity, and sends the message out on that line. There is no attempt to determine whether that path will bring the message closer to its destination. This type of algorithm is not very efficient and causes messages to be shuffled to more nodes than necessary, which adds to network congestion. The message conceivably could be shifted around the network for hours before arriving at its destination.

The more intelligent adaptive routing techniques attempt to select the best route, as determined by one or more of the following parameters: the number of required hops, the speed of the links, the type of link, and congestion. Routing of this type requires current information on the status of the network. If a node is added to the network or if one is taken off the network, that information must be relayed to the nodes doing route calculation. Knowing the speed of the links as well as the number of hops is important. For example, it is probably more efficient to pass data over two 9600-bps links than over one 2400-bps link.

SUMMARY

There is a wide variety of terminals, terminal capabilities, and terminal prices. The industry has been moving toward terminals with more intelligence, which provide functions that are simple to use and may also reduce overall communications cost and host processor work. Intelligent terminals in the form of microcomputers have replaced standard terminals in many networks. Their flexibility and local processing ability make them very effective in the modern communications network. Ergonomic features are important to consider when selecting a terminal.

If several terminals are placed near each other in a remote location, it is usually impractical to have one line for each terminal, so the terminals must share one communications line. One way in which this is done is polling, which requires addressable terminals. Line sharing is also accomplished with multiplexers and concentrators.

Many alternatives are available when configuring a data communications system. The hardware components—multiplexers, concentrators, and front-end processors—overlap in the functions they can provide. These components can reduce circuit costs significantly as well as make more efficient use of the circuits and reduce some of the processing load of the hosts.

The principal WAN topologies are the star, hierarchical, and plex (interconnected) topologies. Rings or loops and busses are also used in WANs, but are most common in LANs. The primary WAN data link protocols are asynchronous and synchronous. Asynchronous protocols were adapted from precomputer technologies such as telegraphy. Asynchronous transmission is widely used, particularly for connections between terminals and host computers and between microcomputers and other computers. The two classes of synchronous protocols are character oriented and bit oriented; furthermore, each class has several varieties of protocols. The preferred protocol today is a bit synchronous protocol such as SDLC, HDLC, LAPB, or ADCCP.

The OSI network layer performs four major functions: routing, network control, congestion control, and collection of accounting data. Several routing algorithms exist and can be classified into two broad categories: static and adaptive. Static routing algorithms choose a path and continue using that path so long as it is available. Adaptive routing algorithms may vary the path used in an attempt to always use the best path. Thus, adaptive routing may be able to avoid congestion and more effectively use all available paths between a sender and a receiver.

KEY TERMS

adaptive routing   187
address field   182
Advanced Data Communications
    Control Procedure (ADCCP)   182
asynchronous transmission (async)   178
Binary Synchronous Communications
    (BISYNC or BSC) protocol   180
bit interleaving   172
bit-oriented synchronous data link
    protocol   182
buffer overflow/overrun   179
cascading   172
cathode ray tube (CRT)   166
centralized routing determination   185
character interleaving   172
character synchronous protocol   180
concentrator   173
congestion control   185
contention mode   169
control field   182
daisy chaining   172
data field   182
distributed routing determination   186
double buffering   179
dumb terminal   167
dynamic routing   187
ergonomics   168
flag field   182
frame   182
frequency division multiplexing
    (FDM)   171
front-end processor (FEP)   174
guardbands   171
hierarchical topology   175
High-level Data Link Control
    (HDLC)   182
host computer   166
hybrid network   176

information frame   182
intelligent terminal   168
internet   164
interrupt characters   178
Link Access Procedure, Balanced
    (LAPB)   182
multiplexing technology   170
multipoint connection   169
network control   184
network routing manager   185
network routing table   185
number received (Nr) subfield   183
number sent (Ns) subfield   183
plex (interconnected) network   175
point-to-point connection   169
polling   169
primary station   169
routing   184
secondary station   169
selection   170
smart terminal   167
start bit   179
static routing   186
statistical time division multiplexing
    (STDM or stat mux)   171
stop bit   179
supervisory frame   182
Synchronous Data Link Control
    (SDLC)   182
synchronous transmission   180
terminal   166
terminal emulator   168
time division multiplexing (TDM)   171
unnumbered frame   182
video display unit or terminal (VDU or
    VDT)   166
weighted routing   187

REVIEW QUESTIONS

1. Compare and contrast dumb, smart, and intelligent terminals.

2. Why is ergonomic design an important terminal selection criterion?

3. Describe the poll/select protocol.

4. What are the advantages of multipoint connections? What are the disadvantages?

5. Why are microcomputers a good replacement for terminals?

6. In general, how does a multiplexer work?

7. Compare and contrast frequency division multiplexing (FDM), time division multiplexing (TDM), and statistical time division multiplexing (STDM).

8. Compare and contrast a multiplexer, a front-end processor, and a concentrator.

9. Why is double buffering sometimes necessary?

10. Trace the evolution of the enterprise network.

11. Describe the functions of front-end processors, minicomputers, and cluster controllers in a WAN (see CBT module "Enterprise Network Evolution").

12. Explain the popularity of asynchronous protocols.

13. How do asynchronous and synchronous protocols differ? In what respects are they the same?

14. What advantages does SDLC have over BISYNC?

15. Describe the use of Ns and Nr counts in HDLC or SDLC.

16. Give an application in which extended Ns and Nr counts are beneficial.

17. What is the purpose of the SDLC poll/final bit?

18. What is the purpose of HDLC supervisory frames?

19. What are the advantages and disadvantages of centralized routing calculations?

20. What are the advantages and disadvantages of local route determination?

21. Distinguish between static and adaptive routing.

22. What are the advantages and disadvantages of the quickest link routing algorithm?

23. Describe the weighted routing algorithm.

7

WAN SYSTEM SOFTWARE AND WAN IMPLEMENTATIONS

CHAPTER OBJECTIVES

After studying this chapter you should be able to:

- Describe the functions of the OSI session layer
- Explain the capabilities of a teleprocessing monitor
- Trace the flow of a transaction through a system
- Explain the organization and workings of the Internet network
- Discuss the components and workings of IBM's Systems Network Architecture (SNA)
- Describe the problems inherent in international networks

*I*n this chapter we discuss several major software components of a data communications network. In the OSI reference model, software exists at every layer from the data link level up. We have already looked at functions of the physical, data link, network, and transport layers. The software discussed in this chapter primarily addresses functions found in the OSI session layer. In this chapter you also learn about two wide area network (WAN) implementations—the Internet and IBM's Systems Network Architecture (SNA).

THE OSI SESSION LAYER

Whenever two entities in a network communicate, a **session** is established between them. The major objectives of the session layer are to establish the dialogue rules between two entities, to manage the exchange of data between the entities, to dissolve the session, and to aid in session recovery if the session is disrupted. The dialogue rules include the method of flow control, which can be either full duplex or half duplex.

Another aspect of the dialogue rules is establishing synchronization points. If a session is interrupted for any reason, the synchronization points help reestablish and recover the session. Other parameters that the session layer might stipulate for a session are message lengths and quality of service. Quality-of-service parameters include the ability to set priorities, security, and speed and quality of the communications link. When the entities involved in a session need to terminate the dialogue, the session must be dissolved. Dissolution may occur at the request of either session member. Prior to a session being dissolved, all data in transit must first be received and acknowledged. We now consider a generic software environment and then two WAN software systems that provide session-level services.

Before reading about the characteristics of system software in the following sections, you may wish to review the section "The Software Environment" in Chapter 1 and the Chapter 1 CBT module entitled "OSI Reference Model." Refreshing your memory on these topics will establish a framework for the ensuing discussion. Figure 7-1 represents a generic software environment. We now discuss the data communication portions of that environment.

Figure 7-1

A Generic Software Configuration

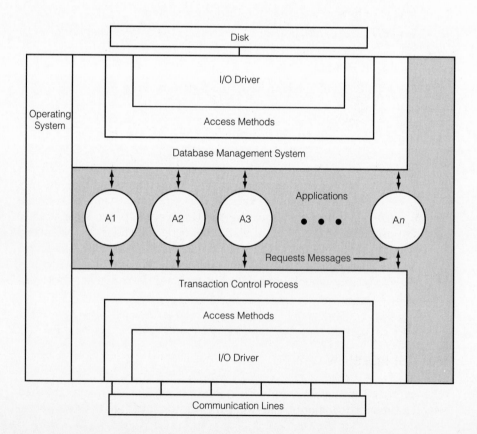

DATA COMMUNICATIONS ACCESS METHODS

Data communications **access methods** give system users easier access to terminal devices. They relieve users from the device-specific attributes of terminals and provide connection, disconnection, and data transfer services to the applications. As with transaction control processes (TCPs), the scope of access methods differs with the vendor and even within different access methods from a single vendor.

One function of an access method is to provide terminal-application connections. This may be accomplished by having a pool of applications and a pool of terminals available, as illustrated in Figure 7-2. The access method serves as a switch to connect terminal requests with the proper application(s). Because an access method separates the application program from the terminal access logic, access methods can be used with or without a TCP, depending on the environment. Figure 7-3 illustrates two situations: TCP present and TCP absent. The access method performs fewer functions when the TCP is present because some functions, such as message routing and data editing, are performed by the TCP.

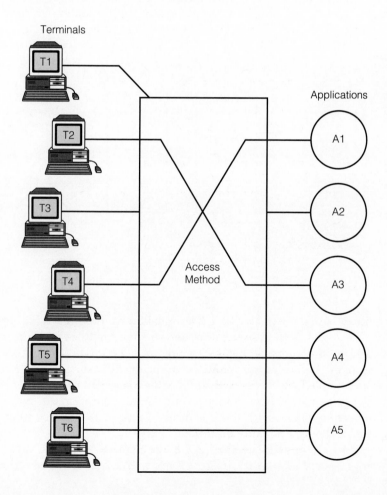

Figure 7-2

Access Method and
Pooled Application
Terminal Connections

Figure 7-3

An Access Method With
and Without a TCP

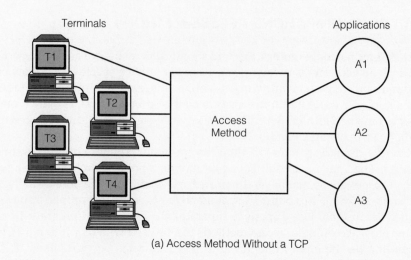

(a) Access Method Without a TCP

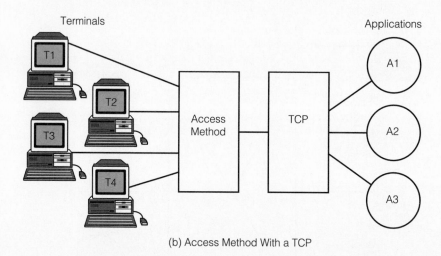

(b) Access Method With a TCP

The first requirement of accessing a terminal from a program is to connect the two. The access method serves as an intermediary in this case. Either the application initiates a connection by issuing an open or connect request to the access method or the terminal initiates the action by issuing an application logon request through the access method. Once the connection has been honored, a communication path exists, and the terminal and application can exchange data. Connection requests can be denied for security reasons or because the application or device is already occupied.

Without a TCP, the access method makes the connection between an application program and a terminal. In some implementations the connection is static: The application and terminal are attached to each other through the access method, and the terminal can run only those transactions provided by that particular application. For the terminal user to access another application process, the terminal must first be disconnected from its current access application and then reconnected to the new one. Other systems provide more flexibility in making the connection between a terminal and an application. For example, IBM's **Virtual Telecommunications Access Method (VTAM)** provides several methods for terminal-application connections.

TRANSACTION CONTROL PROCESS

TCP Configuration

The configuration of the **transaction control process (TCP)** is shown in Figure 7-4. Because the TCP serves as a switch between applications and terminals, it must be aware of the terminals attached to it, the transactions that can be submitted, and the applications responsible for processing those transactions. In this environment, any terminal can access any application known to the TCP. Implementation can be as a monolithic process, as in Figure 7-5(a), or as multiple processes, as in Figure 7-5(b).

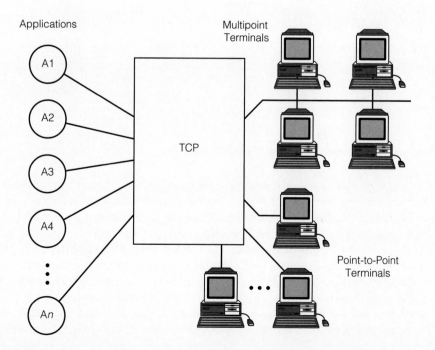

Figure 7-4

A Generic TCP Configuration

Figure 7-5

TCPs

Applications

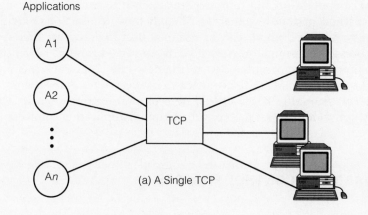

(a) A Single TCP

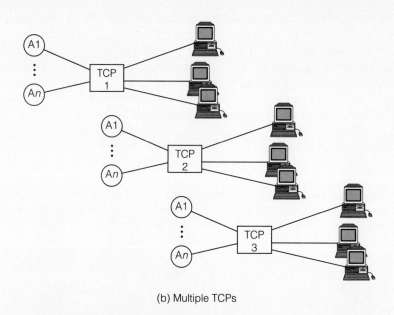

(b) Multiple TCPs

Single Threading Versus Multithreading

The efficiency of the application environment depends upon how quickly transactions can be processed. If multiple transactions can arrive at once, good performance requires that parallelism in transaction processing be provided. This means the TCP may need to process several transactions concurrently, a concept known as **multithreading.** With **single threading,** a process accepts an input, processes the input to completion, produces an output, and then is ready to accept another input for processing. A TCP operating in this manner would accept an input from one terminal, send the transaction to an application process, wait for the response, and send the result back to the terminal. Then the TCP would accept another transaction and process it. Meanwhile, other terminals may be waiting for service. This processing method will result in long delays for terminals with queued requests.

The difference between single threading and multithreading can be likened to what happens in a grocery store when people queue up at the checkout counter. The checkout clerk represents the TCP process, and the customers represent the terminals. The clerk ordinarily operates in a single-threaded manner, processing one customer and one customer only until the total order has been tabulated and the money collected before turning to the next customer. If an object does not scan correctly, everyone waits while an assistant checks the price. Looking up the price is analogous to accessing a disk, with the assistant as the DBMS. Everyone waits while the clerk scans each item, missing prices are checked, coupons are deducted, and the check is written and verified. To improve efficiency, the clerks could be multithreaded: Everyone in the line would get attention as time allows. The clerks would maintain separate totals for each customer. While a missing price was being checked, the clerk could move on to the next customer's order. While a check is being written, another customer could be served. The multithreaded clerk must, of course, be much more flexible than the single-threaded clerk. Multiple totals are accumulated, items are taken from the correct basket and placed in the proper bag, and the totals are delivered to and collected from the proper customers. Multiple application threads are simultaneously active within a multi-threaded process simultaneously. A comparison of single-threaded and multithreaded processes is presented in Figure 7-6.

Maintaining Context

An additional requirement of multithreaded processes is maintaining **context data.** Each single-threaded transaction is completely self-contained. In a multithreaded process, a transaction might be separated into several parts, and each part might be acted on by a different program. To unify this work, one program must (1) keep track of the completed parts and the parts yet to be worked on and (2) ensure that an interrupted transaction is restarted at the correct point. The action to be performed also may be contingent on a previous activity. For instance, in searching a database for an employee named Smith, an application might select and display the first ten Smiths plus additional identifying information. If none of the ten names is correct, the next ten are displayed, and so on until the proper Smith is found. The search for the next ten names is contingent on where the previous search stopped.

Like the multithreaded grocery clerk, the TCP must handle multiple customers at once. Suppose a TCP controls four terminals—T1, T2, T3, and T4—and three applications—A1, A2, and A3. At the start of the system, all three applications request to open, or connect to the TCP. The TCP records this information and issues a command to open and display the first screen, and it posts a read on each of the four terminals. At this point the TCP is awaiting input from the terminals or a process. A chronological record of the TCP's activities is outlined in Table 7-1. This type of interleaved processing continues throughout the workday.

Figure 7-6

Single Threading vs.
Multithreading

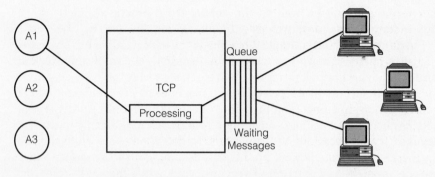

(a) Single Thread: Only One Transaction Active

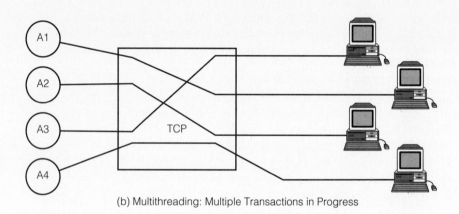

(b) Multithreading: Multiple Transactions in Progress

For the activities in Table 7-1, context was maintained in the TCP. It also could have been maintained within the application or the terminal. However, the application is not as logical a place as the TCP for maintaining context because multiple copies of one application may be used to increase efficiency, in which case the TCP would have to send the second part of a transaction to the same process that worked on the first part. Saving context in applications programs also makes those applications programs more complex. Some designers prefer to remove this type of complexity from the application. Because many TCP processes are supplied by software houses or computer vendors rather than being written by the end user, it benefits the user to have the multiuser complexity in the TCPs and not in the applications.

Memory Management

To manage context information and accept data from both terminals and applications, the TCP must provide **memory management** functions. At any time, the TCP can receive a message from either terminals or applications, and multiple messages may be queued up simultaneously. The way in which TCPs manage memory varies. Essentially, the TCP must have sufficient memory available to provide storage for terminal and application messages as well as for context data. Sometimes this requires virtual memory algorithms similar to those employed by some operating systems: The disk is treated as an extension of memory and data is swapped back and forth between real memory and disk.

TABLE 7-1   Multiple TCP Transaction Threads

Accept update transaction from T2

Write T2's transaction on audit log

Accept inquiry transaction from T4

Route T4's request to application A1

Receive *write complete* on T2's audit log write

Begin transaction for T2

Route T2's transaction to A2

Receive inquiry transaction from T3

Route T3's transaction to A1

Receive A1's return message for T4

Write response to T4

Receive A2's return message for T2

End T2's transaction

Receive inquiry transaction from T1

Receive request for next ten records from T4

Send T1's request to A3

Receive notice tht T2's transaction has ended

Send response to T2

Send T4's request together with stored context to A1

Transaction Routing

The TCP also must provide **transaction routing,** which means routing the transaction received from a terminal to one or more application programs. Several techniques are used to determine how to route a transaction. One method uses a transaction code embedded within the data message itself. The terminal operator enters the transaction code in the text of the message, as illustrated in Figure 7-7. The TCP must recognize this code and route the transaction accordingly. Another method is based on context and a signal from the terminal. The signal is usually either a transaction code or the operator pressing a designated function key. Other signals may be indicated by using a light pen, mouse, or touch-screen.

Figure 7-7

Transaction Routing
in a TCP

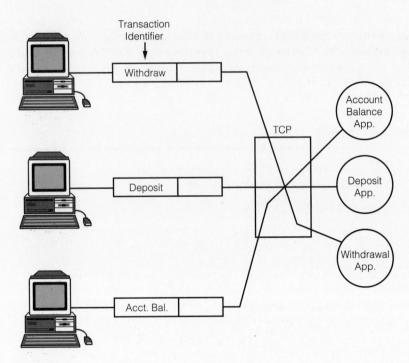

Transaction routing requires that the TCP know both which application handles a given transaction as well as the path or connection that leads to that application. Transaction routing could be table driven, in which case the TCP would look up the transaction ID in a table that provides directions to the proper application process. Alternatively, a procedural interface with a case statement or similar construct would result in a program call or a message being sent to that process.

Transaction Log

The TCP is a logical place to implement transaction logging. A **transaction log** captures the transaction inputs, usually on tape or disk. Once inputs are captured, the system can assure the user that the transaction will be processed. This does not necessarily mean the transaction will be successfully completed (errors could prevent that); it does mean the transaction will not be lost should a system failure occur. In addition to its use in recovery, transaction logging is sometimes required by auditors, especially in financial transactions. Electronic data processing (EDP) auditors will periodically check transaction sources and trace them through the system to determine whether they were correctly processed. If transaction logging is implemented, as soon as a transaction is received by the TCP, the transaction is written on the log file. Usually the TCP appends additional information to the message, such as a date-time stamp, transaction ID, or similar identifying information. Sometimes the completion of a transaction is also logged. In recovery situations this prevents a transaction from being processed twice.

In some systems the transaction log is synchronized with the database logging function to ensure that a message received by the system will be processed and that no duplicate transactions will be processed if a failure occurs. One system even guarantees that transactions requiring reprocessing in the event of a failure will be processed in the original order. This last is an important feature in banking applications. For instance, an account with an initial $100 balance may receive a $500 deposit and then a $200 withdrawal. In the time-compressed recovery situation, the transaction could possibly be processed in reverse order, meaning that the withdrawal would be rejected for insufficient funds and the account would be overdrawn.

Security and Statistics

A TCP can be a focal point for online transactions entering the system, so it is a logical place to collect statistics and provide for security. Several statistics that are necessary to effectively manage a network system can be collected in the TCP, including the total number of transactions from all terminals, types of transactions, number of characters transmitted to and from a terminal, application processing time per transaction, and number of transactions per terminal. Security at the terminal and transaction levels could be enforced at the TCP. All online transactions for terminals managed by a TCP must be routed through the TCP, making the TCP a logical place to implement security.

With these fundamental concepts of the functions provided by a TCP, let us now see how a transaction might be processed by the generic system shown in Figure 7-1. The sample transaction represents admitting a new patient in a hospital.

1. The user selects the "admit patient" transaction from the menu. This selection is transmitted to the TCP.

2. The TCP responds to the user's selection by displaying a patient identification form on the terminal and issues a read request for that terminal. The user fills in the form and transmits it to the TCP.

3. The TCP receives the transaction from the terminal, completing the read the TCP has issued for that device. For each of the other terminals, the TCP also has an outstanding read. Thus, at any time, a terminal operator may complete a task and transmit data to the TCP. The TCP must be able to accept these messages when they arrive.

4. The TCP sends the patient's ID to an application with a request to find a patient record that matches the requested ID. The objective is to determine whether this patient already has a hospital record.

5. The application issues a database read request to obtain a patient record with the ID sent to it by the TCP. If the record exists, it is returned to the application; otherwise, the application receives a message from the DBMS stating that the record does not exist.

6. The application returns the result to the TCP. In this case we assume the patient does not have a record on file.

7. The TCP displays a patient registration form on the terminal and posts a read on the terminal. The user enters data into the form and sends it back to the TCP. At this point the TCP has all the data necessary for admitting the patient.

8. Data edits are performed on all fields for which they have been specified. For example, the TCP determines whether the patient's name has been entered, whether the data entered for the patient's gender is either M or F, whether the birth date entered is valid, and so on. If any field is found to be in error, the TCP displays an error message on the terminal and highlights the field(s) to be corrected. The user then corrects the mistake and the TCP rereads the data.

9. When all data edits have been successfully completed, the TCP writes the data received to a transaction log. The transaction log is used for recovering from failures and sometimes for system auditing.

10. Because this transaction will modify the database, the TCP starts a transaction for recovery purposes. A transaction that changes data in the database must leave the database in a **consistent state,** which means the transaction must either be completed in its entirety or leave the database as it was before the transaction started. Thus, a transaction is a unit of work as well as a unit of database recovery. Starting a transaction is typically not necessary for read-only transactions because they do not change the database and do not need to be recovered. If the admissions clerk checks the database to see whether the patient already has a record on file, this activity does not require that a transaction be started.

11. The TCP examines the transaction and determines which application(s) should process it. Some transactions require the services of more than one application. In this example, one application will create a patient record, another will locate a room and calculate room charges, and still another will generate a standard patient supplies issue and build supply charge records. The TCP may send each participating application its work at the same time, or the TCP may wait until one application finishes before sending the second application its portion of the work.

12. An application receives its portion of the transaction and begins processing. We consider here only the activity performed by the application that creates the patient record. The application uses the data received from the TCP to create a database record for the patient. The application sends the record to the database management system with a request to insert the new record.

13. The DBMS receives the request from the application and acts on it. Each time a record is updated or a new record inserted, images of the records being changed are inserted into the DBMS recovery log. Images of the record before and after the changes are written to the log. This allows the transaction to be reversed if it cannot be completed and also allows it to be re-created at a later time if necessary.

14. After logging the before- and after-images, the DBMS inserts the patient record and returns a successful result status to the application.

15. When the application has performed all of its work, including the database requests, it formats a reply message and returns it to the TCP. In this case, the reply is a status code indicating the success of the transaction. If the database operation is unsuccessful, the response will be an unsuccessful result code and a message or data to be returned to the terminal. This insert might have failed because the patient file was full.

16. The TCP determines whether another application process must become involved in the transaction. The other applications are given their work to accomplish, and they respond to the TCP with the results. When all applications have successfully completed their work, the TCP posts a transaction completion message on the transaction log, formats a response, and sends the response back to the terminal.

17. The application process(es), having finished the transaction, posts another read request on the message file, which indicates its ability to accept another transaction (another transaction may already be queued on the application's input file). The TCP posts another read on the terminal, thus enabling additional transaction input.

While the above activity is being accomplished for this transaction, other transactions may also be in various states of completion. Examples of other transactions that may be in progress include:

- Another admission clerk may be admitting a different patient.

- A nurse may be reading a patient's record to find the patient's work telephone number.

- An accounting clerk may be consolidating the fees for a patient being dismissed.

- A clerk in the radiation laboratory may be entering a charge for a patient who has just been X-rayed.

In addition to the capabilities described above, a TCP may provide additional functions such as message priorities, development environments, and operations interfaces.

Message Priorities

The TCP is in an ideal position to assist with implementing message priorities within the online system. Every message received could be examined for priority, or priorities could be assigned by the TCP. Priorities could be established according to the source and type of message. Priority messages could then be given service first and routed to special server applications to expedite message processing.

Application Development

It is necessary to establish test environments consisting of terminals, access methods, TCPs, applications, and a database when designing an online system. This environment is also used to develop and test enhancements and problem fixes after a system has been placed in operation. The TCP can provide features to make testing and debugging easier, including the ability to trace or examine transactions received by the TCP, the ability to store transactions in a transaction file and pass them through the TCP as though they were entered at a terminal, and the ability to vary the rate of transaction submission. The TCP should also allow concurrent running of production applications and test applications.

Operations Interface

An **operations interface** gives a network administrator the ability to monitor and control the TCP environment. Monitoring the TCP environment includes looking at statistics such as buffer utilization; number of transactions waiting in various queues for service; and busy rates for lines, devices, and the TCP. Controlling the TCP includes activities such as adding terminals and applications, starting or stopping devices, and reconfiguring the system. This may be accomplished through an operations interface program, illustrated in Figure 7-8. The operations interface provides some or all of the following capabilities:

TCP startup	TCP shutdown
Defining lines, terminals, applications	Starting lines, terminals, applications
Stopping lines, terminals, applications	Adding lines, terminals, applications
Deleting lines, terminals, applications	Displaying statistics
Enabling/disabling statistics gathering	Moving lines, terminals, applications from one TCP to another

Figure 7-8

TCP-Operations Interface

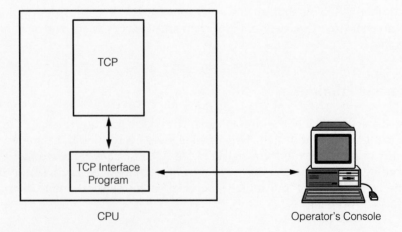

Other TCP Functions

Additional functions that a TCP might carry out include:

- If an application fails, the TCP should be able to automatically restart it. If a transaction arrives for a process that is not currently running, the TCP should be able to activate the process.
- If one application receives so many requests that response times become degraded, the TCP should be able to initiate additional copies of that process to enhance performance.
- If a process has been inactive for a long time, the TCP should be able to optionally delete that process to free the resources the process is holding.

Table 7-2 summarizes the activities of a TCP.

TABLE 7-2   TCP Activities

Provides a user interface with the TCP subsystem

Manages memory

Provides an interface between applications and terminals

Manages applications

Logs messages

Participates in recovery

Provides transaction definition

Edits data fields

Formats data for terminals and applications

Routes messages to server processes

Gathers statistics

Provides testing and debugging facilities

Assists in providing security

Assists in implementing a priority system

The hardware and software components discussed in this and the previous chapter combine to form a network implementation. You may have noted that the application environment in a WAN is quite similar to that in a LAN. A LAN file server and a TCP platform have similar functions, and the generic application model in Figure 7-1 can be transformed into a LAN client/server model with only a few simple alterations. Let us now look at two ways a network has been implemented. We start with a network you probably have heard about and perhaps even used, the Internet.

THE INTERNET

What Is the Internet?

The term *internet* is used in two contexts. In one context, an internet refers to the interconnection of two or more networks. *The* **Internet** is a specific collection of interconnected networks spanning more than 40 countries and providing services to millions of users through nodes numbering in the thousands.

The **NSFNet,** which replaced the ARPANET, serves as the backbone network that provides the interconnection of the other networks. More than 2000 different networks participate in the Internet. The member networks are both WANs and LANs and represent academic institutions, research facilities, companies, and government agencies. As you will soon read, private individuals are also subscribers to Internet services; in the future, household Internet-like service subscriptions will be as common as telephone, newspaper, and cable television services. It is even likely that all these services will be integrated into a single information and entertainment service.

Computers in the Internet's member networks fall into two basic categories. Host nodes are used to attach a network to the Internet. Nonhost nodes have access to the Internet through a host node but are not directly connected to the Internet. For example, many home computers can access the Internet through information services such as CompuServe and America Online, and these home computers are nonhost nodes. Access to the Internet is provided at three basic levels: national, regional, and local. National providers are commercial entities such as Advanced Network and Services Inc. and the Sprint Corporation, that sell access to the Internet in various cities. You also may be able to access some Internet services through providers such as CompuServe, Uunet, and AppleLink. Regional providers sell access in a region. In the United States, a region might consist of several contiguous states and would probably provide toll-free access numbers within the region. Examples of regional providers in the United States are Midwestern States Network (MIDnet), New England Academic and Research Network (NEARNET), Southwestern States Network (WestNet), Colorado SuperNet, and California Education and Research Federation Network (CERFNet). Local providers are proprietors of networks or computers attached to the Internet and provide individual access to the network. Examples are individual colleges, universities, businesses, and government facilities.

Internet Addressing and Access

To gain access to the Internet you need an access connection and a user ID. **Access connections** are issued by national, regional, and local providers. Many Internet users gain access through their place of employment or education. Private individuals can subscribe to services through a commercial provider.

Every node on the Internet has a unique address called its **internet number** or its **IP address.** Addresses are 32 bits long and are usually written as 4 separate numbers delineated by a period, or as an address name. Using the first convention, a node address might be written as 101.209.33.17. Each number in the group represents an octet, or a range of numbers from 0 to 255. The address itself does not divide conveniently into 8-bit groups, but in general the first set of numbers represents the network identification of a node's network, called the **subnet,** and the last numbers identify a specific node on the subnet. The subnet address may consist of 1, 2, or 3 octets depending on the class of the node or subnet.

Currently there are four address classes, A through D; Class E is defined but reserved for future use. With the exception of Class D, classes are based on the number of nodes on the subnet. As the number of nodes on the subnet increases, more bits of the address are needed to distinguish each subnet node. Class A addresses are used for networks with more than 2^{16} nodes. The first bit of the 32-bit address is 0, to distinguish this class from the others, which start with a 1 bit; the next 7 bits represent the network ID. There can be no more than 128 subnetworks in this class. The remaining 24 bits are used to distinguish among the subnet nodes.

Class B addresses are used for subnets with 2^8 through 2^{16} nodes. The first 2 bits in this class start with a 1 followed by a 0, and 14 bits are used to represent the subnet address, leaving 16 bits available for node addresses on the subnet. Class C addresses are used for subnets with fewer than 2^8 nodes; this class is distinguished by starting bits of 110. Class C addresses use 21 bits for the subnet address and 8 bits for subnet node addresses. Class D nodes begin with bits of 1110 and designate host nodes that want to receive broadcast messages.

In conclusion, Class A nodes use one octet to represent the subnet address, Class B nodes use two octets, and Class C nodes have three octets representing the subnet address (including the class designator with the subnet address). All network addresses are assigned by the Network Information Center to avoid address duplication.

Internet Naming Conventions

For most Internet users, the four-octet address representation, called a **dotted quad,** is too cumbersome. Therefore, most users substitute a naming convention that consists of a user name followed by what is essentially a node name. The node name includes a computer's name followed by a **domain name.** Common domain names are EDU, GOV, MIL, and COM, which stand for education, government, military, and company organizations, respectively. Domain names also may be qualified by country names. For example, AU, CA, and FR represent Australia, Canada, and France, respectively. Intercountry communications will use the country domain designator, whereas intracountry communications typically would not need the country qualification because it defaults to the host's country. Generic network addresses using the naming convention are:

user@computer.domain

einstein@physics.edu

jdoe@nasa.gov

comgen@usahq.mil

sysmgr@xyzcorp.com.AU

The @ symbol is used to denote the node name, and the period is used as a separator and to specify domain names. The *computer.domain* notation is called a **fully qualified domain name (FQDN).** Naturally, there is a correspondence between the dotted quad and the *user@FQDN* addresses. Translation between the two is automatically provided by the host node through a mapping dictionary. Thus, users are able to use names rather than a series of numbers as addresses.

Internet Connections

The Internet uses a variety of communications lines. The backbone nodes illustrated in Figure 7-9 use T1 or T3 links to provide speedy transmission from one area to another. Regional links may use T1, 56-Kbps or slower lines. The connection services are accomplished using the transmission control protocol/Internet protocol (TCP/IP) suite covered in Chapter 8.

Figure 7-9

Internet Backbone
Network

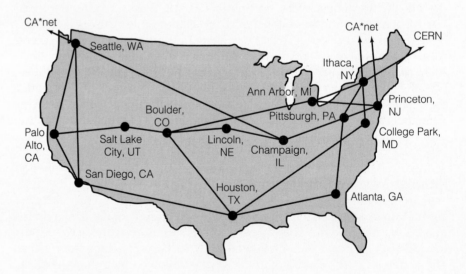

Internet Services

The Internet provides a variety of services, including:

- Electronic mail
- File transfer
- Remote login

- Access to software archives
- News reports
- News groups and the distribution of news for special-interest groups
- Bulletin boards
- Library services
- Electronic journals
- Electronic shopping

Historically, the general goal of the Internet has been to promote research and scholarly activity. Commercial use of the Internet was discouraged. Recently, the network has taken on a more commercial overtone. Now companies advertise and sell their products over the "'Net," and accusations have been raised regarding the use of the Internet as a delivery mechanism for pornographic material and as a means of communication for terrorist groups. Obviously the research and scholarly objectives are being replaced.

THE INFORMATION SUPERHIGHWAY

When the United States was primarily an industrial society, the federal government funded the building of a national highway system. This system, augmented by state and local roads, provided transportation for people, raw materials, and finished goods to needed locations. The national highway system helped establish the strength of the U.S. economy. Today the United States is primarily an information society, with more than half the workforce engaged in the business of information. We now envision a new national highway system geared to moving the raw materials (data) and finished goods (information and ideas) of information to their needed locations. This new highway system is formally called the **National Information Infrastructure (NII)**, but it is commonly and most often referred to as the **information superhighway.** We use the less formal term *information superhighway* for our discussion. If built and used correctly, the information superhighway will help maintain and extend the economic strength of the United States.

Building the Information Superhighway

The federal government was instrumental in funding and building the interstate highway system. In contrast, the information superhighway will be built largely by the private business sector. The roles of the federal government will be to provide guidance, legislation, procedures, and prototype systems and to fund research and development efforts for new technologies. After the information superhighway has been established, the federal government also may subsidize use of the system by public entities such as libraries, schools, and hospitals.

In the areas of procedures and legislation, it has already been recognized that privacy and security issues need to be addressed. Federal regulations undoubtedly will be required to help control access and set penalties for abuses, much like the Interstate Commerce Commission regulates commercial use of the interstate highways and roads. To provide this guidance the federal government has established an **Information Infrastructure Task Force (IITF)** to oversee information superhighway development.

Like the interstate highway system, the information superhighway will evolve over time. Many technologies needed for building the information superhighway are currently in place; still needed is the investment to integrate and install the technologies so they can be made available throughout the country. Different companies or consortiums may form regional segments of the information superhighway, and then the regional infrastructures will be integrated into a national or perhaps a global supernetwork. This evolution will probably be similar to that of the Internet.

The information superhighway is envisioned as an integration of communications networks, information and service providers, and computer hardware and software. To provide these components, mergers and alliances are being formed among common carriers, computer hardware and software companies, cable TV companies, and the entertainment industry. A cross-industry working team of 28 companies has been formed to design the information superhighway. The members represent communications, computer, banking, publishing, and cable TV companies. The cross-industry working team has formed four subgroups: applications, services, architecture, and portability. The role of the first three is apparent from their names. The portability subgroup will address the needs of mobile communications.

The architecture of the information superhighway will likely resemble that of the Internet in that a high-speed backbone network of fiber optic and satellite links will speed data from one region to another. Local delivery will be established by regional providers over fiber optic cable, coaxial cable, and copper media. Businesses that make heavy use of the information superhighway will likely have the data delivered to their premises by fiber optic cable. Local distribution within the company will be over fiber optic cable, coaxial cable, or twisted-pair wires.

Regarding personal use, it is unlikely that in the near future fiber optic cable will be brought into homes. Instead, fiber optic cable will bring the data to a local distribution point from which coaxial cable or twisted-pair wires will distribute the data to individual homes. There are several reasons for copper-based delivery to individual subscribers. In many locations cable TV and telephone companies have already installed this type of delivery mechanism and it can be used for the last-mile delivery system. The data speeds required for home use also will be much lower than those for many businesses, so the higher speed of fiber optic cable will not be necessary. Figure 7-10 illustrates a potential hierarchy of the information superhighway implementation.

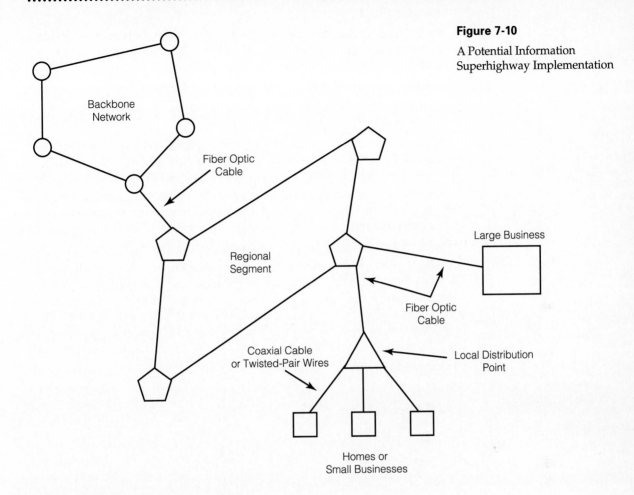

Figure 7-10

A Potential Information
Superhighway Implementation

Information Superhighway Uses

Several potential information superhighway uses are:

- A business might use the information superhighway to conduct a
  conference among employees in different locations.
- A software company might use the information superhighway to
  distribute software directly to customers.
- A publishing company might distribute books or magazines directly
  to readers or perhaps to a local outlet for on-demand printing.
- Companies and individuals could subscribe to information utilities
  such as stock market and financial news, congressional records, and
  so on.

- Companies and individuals will be able to shop for merchandise via online catalogs and to make airline, car, hotel, and entertainment reservations.

- Movies and games may be available on demand.

- Education classes at all levels may be available and allow people to learn new skills at their homes or offices.

- Health care may be delivered by patients getting advice remotely. A physician may be able to view patients at remote locations, coach paramedical personnel on procedures, and recommend cures.

- Electronic mail and video images may be exchanged. Interactive use of such technologies may give rise to online discussion groups and conferencing.

From these few suggestions it may be apparent that possible information superhighway uses are varied. The information superhighway will deliver far more that just data; it can deliver information in a variety of formats including data, voice, and video. At issue is how individuals and companies will gain access to these resources and how much it will cost to use them. For some services, costs of more than $200 per connect hour are likely. Access to the information superhighway also will require the media connections and equipment necessary to send and receive the signals.

Social Implications

The information superhighway is likely to bring a profound change in the way businesses operate and in individuals' private lives. The costs required for information superhighway connection and services may also lead to new social issues. People who cannot afford these services will have fewer opportunities than those who have the services. Consequently, publicly funded access through schools, libraries, and civic centers may be needed to ensure that all members of society have access to the opportunities the information superhighway will provide.

VENDOR WIDE AREA NETWORKS

Vendor offerings play a major role in network implementation and configuration, with almost every major computer vendor offering networking capabilities. Vendor networks compete with each other and with common carrier networks. The following section is devoted to IBM's **Systems Network Architecture (SNA),** the most common proprietary WAN implementation. Most networks currently implemented on IBM mainframe systems use SNA. If another vendor's equipment interfaces with an IBM network, it will likely do so via an SNA interface.

IBM'S SYSTEMS NETWORK ARCHITECTURE

SNA, announced by IBM in 1974, provides the framework for implementing data communications networks using IBM or IBM-compatible equipment. SNA is not a product per se but a blueprint for how hardware, software, and users interact in exchanging data on IBM systems. A network based on SNA consists of a variety of hardware and software components in a well-defined configuration.

SNA Layers

The early releases of SNA referenced either six or four functional layers. The discrepancy between a six-layer and a four-layer definition is explained by the fact that layers three through five are sometimes referred to as a single layer, known as the **half-session layer.** The lowest OSI reference model layer, the physical layer, is not usually specified in SNA, nor is the application layer included. However, both layers obviously must exist. The four-layer definition is given in Table 7-3. The six layers are identified in parentheses, where applicable. In the current version of SNA, the layering has been somewhat redefined. The presentation service layer is omitted from the earlier definition and the services manager is now referred to as the function management layer. Although the layering carries different names, the functions each performs are similar to those for the OSI reference model.

TABLE 7-3 SNA Layers

Layer 1	Data link control
Layer 2	Path control

Layer 3	Half-session layer, consisting of:
	    Transmission control (layer 3)
	    Flow control (layer 4)
	    Presentation service (layer 5)

Layer 4	Services manager (layer 6)

SNA Session Flows

To see how data is transmitted through the SNA layers, you should transition to the CBT module entitled "SNA Session Flows".

SNA also defines four distinct hardware groupings called **physical units (PUs).** The four physical units are numbered 1, 2, 4, and 5, with no PU currently assigned to number 3. These device types are listed in Table 7-4. The hardware configuration consists of IBM or IBM-compatible CPUs; communications controllers; terminal cluster controllers; and terminals, printers, or workstations. These are all connected by any of the media discussed in Chapter 2. Other vendors' equipment may also be included in the network if that equipment conforms to the SNA protocols. The preferred data link protocol is SDLC, but accommodations have been made for other protocols such as BSC and asynchronous.

TABLE 7-4   SNA Physical Units

Physical Unit	Hardware Component
Type 1	A terminal device, e.g., 3278
Type 2	A cluster controller, e.g., 3274
Type 4	A communications controller, e.g., 3745
Type 5	A host processor, e.g., System/390 or AS/400

Logical Units and Sessions

Users of SNA are represented in the system by entities known as **logical units (LUs).** An LU is usually implemented as a software function in a device with some intelligence, such as a CPU. The dialogue between two system users is known as a session. Because a logical unit is the agent of a user, when one user wants to establish a session with another user, the LUs are involved in establishing the communications path between the two. A session involves two different LUs; the activities and resources used by one LU in a session are called a **half-session.** In the SNA layering in Table 7-3, the half-session layers represent the functions that would be performed by an LU for its user.

Session Types

Many different types of sessions can be requested, such as program to terminal, program to program, or terminal to terminal. Each category can be further stratified as to terminal type (interactive, batch, or printer) and application type (batch, interactive, word processing, or the like). One logical unit also can represent several different users, and a user can have multiple sessions in progress concurrently. If a terminal (operator) desires to retrieve a record from a database, the terminal will need to use the services of an application program to obtain the record. Each user—the terminal and the database application—is represented by a logical unit. The terminal LU issues a request to enter into a session with the database application LU. The application LU can either accept or reject the session request. Rejection is typically either due to security reasons, because the requesting LU lacks authority to establish a session with the application LU, or due to congestion, because the application LU has already entered into the maximum number of sessions it can support. If the session request is granted, a communications path is established between the terminal and the application. The two users continue to communicate until one of them terminates the session. Figure 7-11 shows several sessions between users communicating through their respective logical units.

Figure 7-11

SNA Session and Logical Units

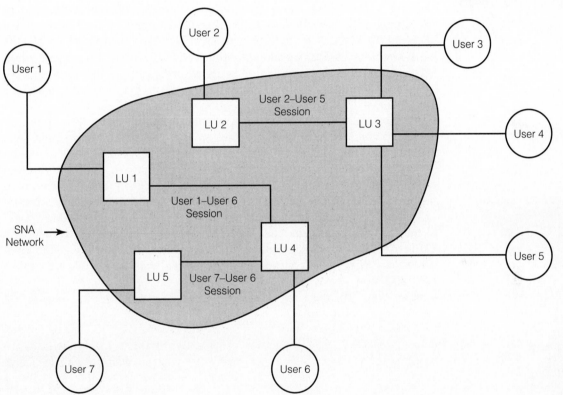

LU Types

Seven LU types have thus far been defined within SNA. These are numbered from 0 to 7, with the definition for LU Type 5 omitted. It is important to note that the LU types refer to session types and not to a specific LU. Thus, a specific LU can participate in a Type 1 LU session with one LU and a Type 4 LU session with another LU. For two LUs to communicate they must both support and use the same LU session type. Of the seven LU types all but Types 0 and 6 address sessions with hardware devices such as printers and terminals. LU Type 6 is defined for program-to-program communication. It has evolved through two definitions, LU 6.0 and LU 6.1, to its current definition, LU 6.2. **LU 6.2** is a key SNA capability.

There are several significant aspects of LU 6.2. First, LU 6.2 defines a protocol for program-to-program communication. Most of the other LU types are somewhat hardware-oriented, involving sessions between 3270 devices, printers, and so on. A program-to-program communications interface is more general and can have wider uses than hardware-oriented interfaces. Second, program-to-program sessions provide a communications path for applications distributed over multiple nodes. Two applications communicating with each other are not required to be in the same node. This capability supports transaction processing systems with multiple processing nodes. For example, an inventory inquiry can start on a network node in a sales office and communicate with a warehouse node application to determine whether stock exists to cover a pending order. Finally, and perhaps most significantly, a program-to-program interface is more generic than a session type involving specific hardware devices. This means that other vendors' equipment can enter into SNA sessions with an application process running in an IBM processor so long as the communicating program in the vendor's processor adheres to the session rules. This allows an application on Vendor A's hardware to enter into a transaction with a database application running on an IBM node.

Many vendors have implemented an LU 6.2 capability for their SNA interface because such an interface can be made device-independent. Given a configuration as illustrated in Figure 7-12, a program in Vendor X's system can interface to its terminal device on one side and to an IBM application on the other. This logically provides the ability for a non-IBM terminal to interface to an IBM application system. Without LU 6.2, Vendor X would need to appear to the IBM application as one of the supported hardware types, such as a 3270 terminal or cluster controller. The International Standards Organization (ISO) also has agreed on a transaction interface that is compatible with IBM's LU 6.2 session.

Figure 7-12

Non-IBM Vendor in an
LU 6.2 Session

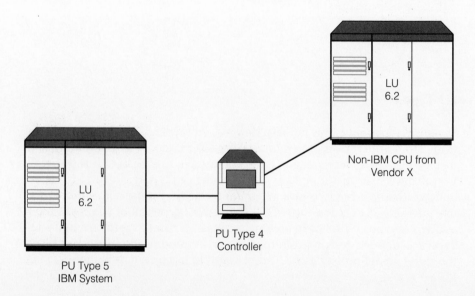

Non-IBM CPU from
Vendor X

PU Type 4
Controller

PU Type 5
IBM System

Systems Services Control Point

As mentioned above, a dialogue between two users within the SNA environment is called a session. A supervisor or intermediary is involved in establishing a session. In SNA this extremely important entity is known as the **systems services control point (SSCP);** it resides in a host processor, which is a physical unit Type 5. Not all PU Type 5 devices house an SSCP. The SSCP is the software controlling its host's portion of the network. The devices controlled by the host and its SSCP represent a domain.

Networks implemented under early versions of SNA had only one SSCP and thus only one host computer. All of the network was controlled by this host. In 1979, SNA was enhanced to allow multiple-host systems, and hence multiple domains. This became necessary because large SNA networks were being implemented. Multiple SSCPs were better able to manage many devices and sessions. A two-domain SNA configuration is shown in Figure 7-13.

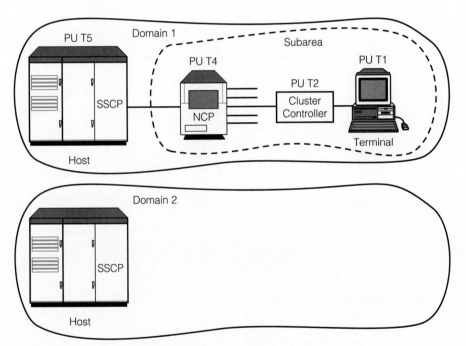

Figure 7-13

The IBM SNA Network

Within a given domain the SSCP is the controlling entity. It is responsible for the physical and logical units within its domain. In fulfilling this obligation, the SSCP manages its units, including unit initialization, maintaining the status of individual units, placing units on- and offline as necessary, and serving as mediator in the establishment of sessions. Physical units subordinate to an SSCP must be able to carry on a dialogue with the SSCP. To accomplish this, a subset of the SSCP functionality, called a **physical unit control point (PUCP),** resides in SNA nodes that do not contain an SSCP. A PUCP is responsible for connecting the node to and disconnecting the node from the SNA network.

Addressing

For one user to communicate with another, an address is required because messages are sent to a specific unit by using its address. Addressable components in SNA are called **network addressable units (NAUs).** An NAU can be an SSCP, an LU, or a PU. Network addresses are hierarchical in nature. You have already learned that an SNA network consists of domains. Domains consist of subareas. A subarea consists of a communications controller (such as a 3745) and all its NAUs or of a host/SSCP together with all of the locally attached NAUs. Figure 7-14 shows two subareas. Each subarea has a unique address. NAUs within one subarea are known by a local address. An SNA address consists of two parts, a subarea address and a unit address. The combination of subarea address and unit address uniquely identifies an NAU in the network. In SNA, addresses may be either 16 or 23 bits. The longer address is known as **extended addressing,** which allows for a larger number of NAUs in a network.

Figure 7-14

SNA Network with
Two Subareas

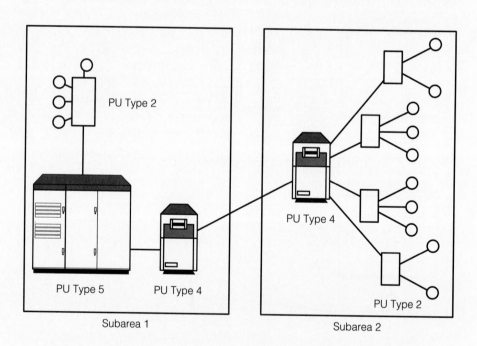

PU Type 2

PU Type 5   PU Type 4

PU Type 4

PU Type 2

Subarea 1   Subarea 2

In extended addressing mode, the first 8 bits represent the subarea and the last 15 bits represent the device within the subarea. The 16-bit address can be decomposed into a subarea and device address on a network-by-network basis, which allows two networks to decompose the address in different manners. One network could have an 8-bit address for both subareas and devices, whereas another could adopt a split of 7 bits for subarea and 9 bits for devices.

Communication Between Users

If Users A and B are in the same domain, communication between them is established as follows. The logical unit representing User A sends a message to the SSCP requesting a session with User B. On behalf of User A, the SSCP contacts the User B LU to request a session and also to provide information about User A, including User A's access profile and type. User B either accepts or rejects the session request. If the session is rejected, User A is so notified. If User B accepts the invitation to enter into a session with A, a communications path must be established. Communication between users in different domains is established in a way similar to that for a single domain, except that the SSCPs in both domains are involved: The request goes from an LU to its SSCP to the SSCP in the other domain and then to its LU.

Path establishment was easy in early SNA implementations because only one path existed between LUs. Presently, two routing methods are supported: end-to-end routing and virtual routing. In **end-to-end routing,** for which at least one of the nodes must be a Type 5 physical unit or terminal, the path is determined and maintained through the entire session (unless the path is broken). In **virtual routing,** no permanently established path exists; instead, each node consults its routing table to determine to which node the message should be forwarded. The path control half-session layer is responsible for path allocation. Each available path is given a weighting that assists in route determination. A route might be selected based on best use according to such factors as security, speed, and propagation delay (as for satellite links). Up to five different paths between any two LUs can be described.

Additional SNA Elements and Capabilities

Network Control Program. The **Network Control Program (NCP),** which resides in a communication controller such as the 3745, controls communications lines and the devices attached to them. It works with the Virtual Terminal Access Method (VTAM) that resides in the host. VTAM serves as the interface between application programs and the network.

Advanced Communications Facility. The **Advanced Communications Facility (ACF)** was introduced in 1979. It provides such features as interdomain communication, improved error and testing capabilities, and dynamic device configuration.

Network Performance Analyzer. The **Network Performance Analyzer (NPA)** provides performance information for the system, including information on lines, buffers, errors, queue lengths, and data transmission rates.

Network Problem Determination Aid. The **Network Problem Determination Aid (NPDA)** collects, maintains, and reports information on error conditions within the network. It also allows for testing of the system concurrent with production operations.

Netview, Netview/PC, and Netview/6000.   In 1986 IBM announced two network management packages for use in SNA systems. **Netview** runs on IBM hosts, and **Netview/PC,** on microcomputers. With Netview, IBM has consolidated several previous network management facilities (including NPDA) and enhanced them to provide more comprehensive management capabilities. **Netview/6000,** introduced in 1992, is designed to provide network management functions for open systems, specifically non-SNA networks. The functions found in Netview are covered in Chapter 9, which addresses network management.

SNA Distribution Services.   SNA Distribution Services (SNADS) allow users to exchange documents using the SNA network. Document interchange differs from the typical SNA session. In a typical SNA session the sender and receiver are synchronized regarding information exchange. By *synchronized* we mean that the users communicate (through their LUs) and agree to carry on a conversation. In contrast, with document exchanges the users may not be synchronized. A sender may dispatch a document without first coordinating the transmission with the recipient. The recipient can then request access to the document at his or her convenience. SNADS provides the ability to distribute documents in such a manner. This is particularly helpful for office automation applications such as network mail and document distribution.

Advanced Peer-to-Peer Networking (APPN).   Advanced peer-to-peer networking (APPN) allows independent LUs to enter into sessions without the cooperation of the SSCP. APPN reduces the dependence on a host node and allows applications to specify session characteristics such as the type of path and security required. Non-IBM vendors have implemented APPN interfaces on their systems. This capability together with LU 6.2 provides an easy way for programs to independently enter into a session and a way for applications that run on non-IBM computers to communicate via the services of SNA.

Other SNA Capabilities.   SNA is being upgraded continually to meet the changing demands of communications. It has evolved from an IBM-only network architecture to include internetworking with other networks. Accommodations made in this regard include:

- Support for the TCP/IP suite
- Accommodations for LAN interfaces
- Alterations that reduce the hierarchical nature of the network and provide support for peer-to-peer communications via APPN
- Support for distributed databases
- Internetworking

INTERNATIONAL NETWORKS

Data communications networks are not confined to national boundaries, and today many companies are international in scope. International computer networks help many of these companies manage their data and provide communication among employees. International networks are used by banks for money transfer and financial planning applications. With international networks, manufacturing companies can schedule production of parts in multiple locations for assembly at a central location. All international companies can use international networks and electronic mail for immediate communication. Electronic mail also helps eliminate the problems of time-zone differences. For example, working hours may not overlap between offices in England and Australia, but electronic mail provides quick communication during an employee's normal working hours. Designing and implementing international networks is more difficult than building a national network. The problems that may be encountered include politics, regulations, hardware, and language.

Politics

On occasion the problems to be resolved with international networks are political rather than technical. One company reported that it was given permission to install a microwave link in a particular country. That country's government, however, suggested that the company double the capacity of the network. Upon completion, the microwave system was nationalized by the government, and the company that built it was "given" half the carrying capacity of the network.

Regulations

Networks require communication links. In many countries the communications networks are controlled by an agency we shall call the postal, telephone, and telegraph (PTT) authority. The PTT often is a government agency or government-regulated agency with exclusive rights to provide communication facilities. The regulations under which the PTTs operate generally were designed for their original mission of postal, telephone, and telegraph communications. These regulations sometimes impede the establishment of international data communications.

Sometimes regulations are established to protect or subsidize certain interests. In some countries, restrictions exist regarding which equipment can be connected to a network. A few countries require that hardware used in a network be manufactured in whole or in part within the country. Pricing regulations in some countries are structured so data communications services help subsidize individual telephone services. Regulations frequently prohibit competition in providing communication facilities. Thus, it is often difficult to set up a network using services provided by a single communications carrier. Many PTTs recognize that regulations need to be changed to meet the needs of international networks; therefore, some countries have begun to deregulate their communications industry. Deregulation typically means opening competition regarding equipment that can be attached to the network and the cost and provision of communications facilities.

International networks sometimes also conflict with other national interests. Some countries impose an import duty on software. Sometimes the duty is on the value of the carrying medium, such as a magnetic tape; other countries tax the value of the imported software. International networks provide the ability to import software over the network, making the collection of tariffs more difficult. Some countries view international networks as potential threats to national security. Data regarding national resources, the economy, and people can be more easily collected and transmitted to another country through international networks. Several nations are attempting to legislate solutions to these concerns.

Hardware

When discussing regulations we mentioned that in some countries restrictions exist regarding the source or type of equipment that can be attached to the communications facilities of a PTT. Several countries require that all or part of the equipment used within the country be locally manufactured. Some do not require the equipment to be manufactured in-country but still restrict the equipment that can be used to that manufactured by a select group of companies. Most countries require that equipment attached to communications networks meet minimum technical specifications. Specifications also differ among countries. A communications controller that is certified for operation in the United States may not meet the tighter specifications for grounding that exist in Australia.

Another technical difference that must be accommodated is variations in power supplies among countries. When ordering equipment for a specific node, we must be sure that the equipment's power supply needs are consistent with the power available in that location. Many times, new hardware also must be certified by a host country before the hardware can be attached to the communications network. For example, a company that introduces a facsimile controller that connects to the common carrier's network must first undergo testing and evaluation by the host country. It is not unusual for certification to take several months and require that equipment and circuit schematics be provided for the evaluation process. Thus, introduction of new equipment into a network can incur substantial delays.

Language

Another problem needing resolution in international networks is language-related. Network managers at different locations must be able to communicate to resolve differences. Several different countries and hence several different languages may be involved in solving one problem. This makes it necessary to have not only technical expertise but also linguistic expertise in the network management organization. Data generated in one location in the in-country language also may need to be translated when used in another country. Such translation may be manual or through language-translation programs. Accompanying the need to translate from one language to another is the need to have hardware and software capable of displaying local character sets, such as Kanji in China and Japan, Hongul in Korea, and Farsi in Arab countries. Accommodations also must be made when the number of characters in a national character set exceeds the capacity of a particular code. For example, 7-bit ASCII codes can accommodate 128 distinct characters, but the number of Kanji characters exceeds 30,000.

Other Issues

An international network typically involves the coordination of several communications providers. One of the easier methods of creating an international network is to use the services of existing X.25 networks. The ease derives from the fact that most public X.25 network providers have established interconnections and the network implementer need not be concerned about PTT interfaces. If a company decides to procure exclusive links such as leased lines, creating the network may be more difficult. Determining the correct interfaces and problem resolution must be assumed by the company. Problem resolution can be somewhat difficult in an international network. Consider a link from Australia to France. The end-to-end connection may use links from Australia to the United States, to England, and then to France. Thus, four PTTs, several protocols, a variety of vendor equipment, and several time zones may be involved. If a problem arises in transmitting data between the French and Australian nodes, the multiplicity of involved vendors can cause delays in resolution. On more than one occasion a problem has been allowed to continue while two PTTs debated which body was responsible for the problem.

Costing an international network can present several difficulties. First, collecting tariff information can be time-consuming. When multiple nodes exist within a country, we typically must deal with local tariffs and international tariffs. In some cases, there may be multiple circuit providers, a variety of available rates, and variations between local and long-distance rates. In addition to tariffs for the use of lines, in some countries we also must determine the costs of taxes applied to the movement of data over a country's borders and taxes on imported software.

The International Telecommunications Union (ITU), the Consultative Committee on International Telegraph and Telephony (CCITT), and other international communications organizations realize the existing limitations and problems in implementing international connections and are addressing the issues. Standards such as OSI, X.25, and X.400 electronic-mail interface ease the burden of establishing international networks. Deregulation of the communications industries in some countries has allowed the introduction of new equipment and competition among providers of communications links. Issues such as the rights of communication facilities provided from a foreign country, such as a Canadian PTT operating circuits in the United States, are being discussed. All these efforts should make establishing international networks easier; however, the problems inherent in international networks will always be greater than those for domestic networks. Another international body, the General Agreement on Trade and Tariffs (GATT), an organization of 97 nations, has proposed a treaty that will ease the problems of international networks. Among the treaty provisions are stipulations regarding the use and cost of private lines.

SUMMARY

Data communications software works closely with the applications, database, and operating system software to provide the functions required of today's systems. Two major components of networking software are access methods and transaction control processes (TCPs). In some cases, access method software provides the linkage between application programs and terminal devices. Access methods always provide an interface with different terminal devices, providing terminal and application independence. TCPs also provide a link between applications software and terminal equipment. A TCP will also use the access method software to interface with terminal devices. The functions provided by TCPs in interfacing applications and devices go beyond those provided by the typical access method. These added capabilities include data edits, message switching, data formatting, and transaction definition and recovery.

Wide area networks are usually built around a particular vendor's network software. Although most major computer vendors offer network capabilities, the leader in proprietary network software is IBM's SNA. SNA provides an architecture for building networks, and many vendors support some type of connection to SNA networks. One way vendors can communicate with an SNA network is via the LU 6.2 protocol. Microcomputers are increasingly found as wide area network components. Their versatility makes them a cost-effective network tool.

SNA continues to evolve and mature as a network product. Internally, new network functions such as those provided by LU 6.2 and SNADS are being included in the architecture. Gateways to other networking products continue to be implemented, together with SNA interfaces between IBM SNA components and other manufacturers' equipment. Some vendors have gone so far as to implement PU Type 4 and PU Type 5 capabilities within their systems. SNA may be the most significant influence in WAN implementations today.

KEY TERMS

access connection 206
access method   193

Advanced Communications Facility
(ACF)   219

REVIEW QUESTIONS

1. Describe how a terminal access method is used to connect a terminal and application.

2. Describe the functions of a data communications access method.

3. Describe how a transaction flows through an online system.

4. Describe the functions of a TCP.

5. Compare and contrast the functions of a TCP and a data communications access method.

6. Why are audit (log) trails important?

7. Compare multithreading and single threading.

8. Why is multithreading of a TCP an attractive feature?

9. Describe the configuration of the Internet.

10. Explain the two Internet address formats.

11. What services are provided by the Internet?

12. What are the four types of physical units in SNA? What is the role of each in the network?

13. What is a half-session layer in SNA? What is its purpose?

14. Explain how a session is established in SNA.

15. List the six functional layers in SNA.

16. Discuss the influence of SNA on other computer vendors.

17. How does SNA relate to the OSI reference model?

18. Describe three potential problem areas in setting up an international network.

8

NETWORK INTERCONNECTIONS

CHAPTER OBJECTIVES

After studying this chapter you should be able to:

- List the ways networks can be interconnected
- Describe the principal methods for making network connections: repeaters, bridges, routers, and gateways
- List the capabilities of the transmission control protocol/Internet protocol (TCP/IP) suite
- Describe the network interconnection functions of TCP/IP
- List capabilities of network interconnection utilities
- Describe the workings and advantages of a packet-switching network

*T*he computing resources of organizations are diverse. They range from a single microcomputer to multiple local and wide area networks that connect hundreds of different types of computers: microcomputers, minicomputers, mainframes, and supercomputers. Today, a large organization may have several microcomputer LANs, a WAN, and perhaps connections to public computer networks. When one organization has a variety of computers and networks, those computers ordinarily must be interconnected to provide better use of hardware and software and to allow users to communicate more easily. A LAN may need to be connected to another LAN, to a single, large host computer, to a WAN, to remote workstations or terminals, or to public networks, and it may be necessary to connect two or more different WANs. In this chapter we cover the principal ways these connections are made.

WHY MULTIPLE NETWORKS?

By definition, a LAN serves a limited geographic area, and most LAN specifications place a limit on the length of the medium used. Companies that have LANs in geographically separated locations, or LANs that cover distances longer than the maximum allowed must implement multiple LANs and frequently have a need for inter-LAN exchanges. Users on one LAN may want to exchange electronic mail messages with users on the other LAN, or a user on one LAN may want to use resources located on another LAN.

Distance or geographic separation is not the only reason for having several LANs. Departmental computing is another rationale for having a multiple LAN environment. A company that is interested in department-level computing might implement a LAN for each department or for groups of departments. For example, a computer software manufacturer may go to great lengths to protect the integrity of their new products. Often details of new developments are not shared with those employees who are not directly involved with a new product. Having separate LANs allows the company to separate functions and provides additional security of information. Among the software company's departments, there might be a LAN shared by software development and documentation, one for software support, one for accounting, one for personnel, and one for marketing. This separation will reduce the likelihood that software being developed will inadvertently or intentionally be made available to customers through the support or marketing LAN. Likewise, personnel information can be more easily protected if it is on a separate LAN.

A third reason for LAN connections is to consolidate independent LANs that were formed in an ad hoc manner. Superficially this reason is similar to connecting departmental LANs. The difference is that department-oriented LANs are a planned separation, whereas workgroup-oriented LANs were implemented as needed by individual departments or workgroups. This situation is common in many colleges and universities, where the departments or colleges of computer science, business, engineering, and nursing may have implemented LANs independently. Another reason for forming several small LANs rather than one large one is limitations on medium capacity. LANs supporting graphics and multimedia applications need to send high volumes of full-motion video and sound data in short amounts of time. Only a small number of multimedia workstations can be supported on media operating at 10 or 16 Mbps.

A fourth reason for having multiple LANs is the number of users per LAN. A LAN with hundreds of users might provide poorer performance than the same LAN with tens of users. A LAN administrator attempts to maintain the responsiveness of a LAN even when more users are added. Responsiveness can be maintained by adding more resources to an existing LAN—more memory, more disks, or another server—or by splitting the LAN into two or more smaller LANs. When splitting a LAN, the administrator strives for a proper balance of users and resources; however, a perfect balance is not always attainable due to distance, physical location, or differences in workgroup sizes. Because inter-LAN communications involves more overhead than intra-LAN communications, an administrator must consider grouping of users and resources so the number of inter-LAN messages is reduced. Members of a department or workgroup often communicate with each other more than with members of other departments or workgroups. Thus, splitting a LAN because many users are being serviced frequently results in a configuration split along departmental or workgroup lines.

Companies also may have several WANs. One reason for having multiple WANs arises from corporate mergers and acquisitions. When two companies combine, each may have a WAN already in place. These WANs sometimes use different vendors' network architectures. After the merger, it is usually desirable to interconnect those networks; however, preexisting incompatibilities may make it necessary to retain separate WANs. Sometimes independent networks are started in regional areas and later need to be connected to form national and international networks. Finally, a company may want to connect its network to external networks such as the Internet. Different WANs also can arise from the need to support different work tasks. A bank might use one vendor's hardware and network architecture to set up a network of automatic teller machines and a different network to support its back office, platform, and administrative applications. Similarly, a manufacturing company may use one type of hardware and network to support research and development operations and another for sales and administrative purposes.

There may be other good reasons for having several different networks in an organization. Regardless of these reasons, at some point, there is often a need to have these separate networks connected into one enterprise network. As a generic model for connecting separate networks, we use LANs as an example of both LAN-to-LAN and WAN-to-WAN connections. This is appropriate because the first two types of connections, repeaters and bridges, are most common in LANs. Routers are common to both network types.

THE OSI REFERENCE MODEL REVISITED

Throughout this text we have discussed the OSI reference model. Because network interconnections are established at the physical, data link, and network layers of the OSI reference model, and may involve functions at the transport layer as well, you may want to review the sections covering the functions of these four layers.

What do we mean when we say the connection interface is made at the physical, data link, or network layer? An interface that operates at the physical layer must be sensitive to signals on the medium; one that operates at the data link layer must be aware of data link protocol formats; and one that operates at the network layer must use a common network layer protocol and be able to route messages to the next node along the path to its destination. The interconnection at a specific layer must be knowledgeable of the implementation details of that layer. We begin by looking at physical layer interconnections.

Repeaters

You are undoubtedly aware that the sound of someone talking fades with distance and at some point becomes unintelligible. Similarly, as data communication signals are transmitted through a medium, the signals weaken, a circumstance called **attenuation.** A signal eventually will become unintelligible unless it can be amplified or regenerated. To guard against this in the telephone system, repeaters are placed at regular intervals along a telephone line to amplify or regenerate the signal. Amplification simply strengthens the signal, and for analog transmission it also will amplify any errors that have crept into the transmission. This is illustrated in Figure 8-1(a). A digital signal can be regenerated and restored to its original strength and values. Because a digital signal has only two states, a 0 or a 1, a regenerator can examine an incoming signal, decide which of the two states the signal represents, and restore the signal to its original value and strength as illustrated in Figure 8-1(b).

Figure 8-1

Signal Amplification and Regeneration

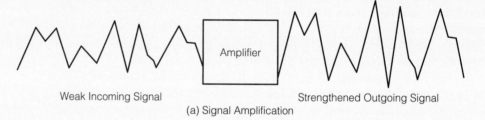

Weak Incoming Signal   Strengthened Outgoing Signal

(a) Signal Amplification

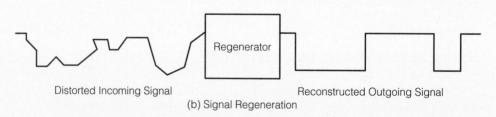

Distorted Incoming Signal   Reconstructed Outgoing Signal

(b) Signal Regeneration

A hardware device that amplifies or regenerates a signal at the physical layer is called a **repeater.** Figure 8-2 illustrates the relationship between a repeater and the OSI model. The function of a repeater is similar to that of some nonelectronic data transmission techniques. You may be familiar with communications techniques such as semaphore flags. Semaphores are line-of-sight transmissions. If the message must be transmitted over relatively long distances, **relay stations** are necessary. For example, if Station A in Figure 8-3 needs to transmit a message to Station D, the signaler at Station B will read the signal sent from Station A and resend the message to Station C, where the message will be repeated and sent to Station D. At each relay station the signal is essentially amplified. If an error in transcribing or transmitting the message is made at any point, the error will be propagated to subsequent stations.

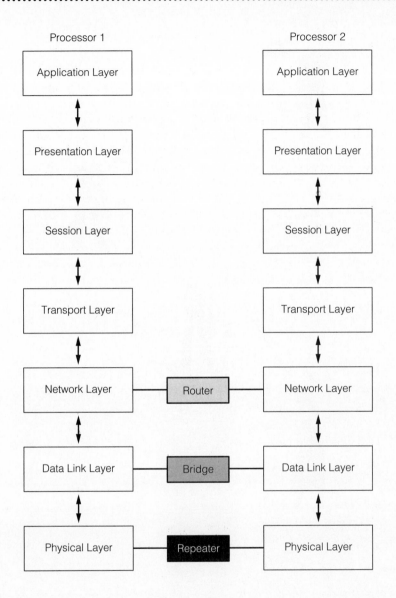

Figure 8-2

A Repeater, Bridge,
and Router and the
OSI Reference Model

Every LAN has a distance restriction. The length of the medium on a
LAN can be extended by repeaters. Because it is a physical layer device, a
repeater must know and obey all the physical layer conventions regarding
signaling and connections. Unlike the repeaters used in the telephone system,
LAN standards limit the number of repeaters that can be used for a single
LAN and hence limit the maximum length of the LAN medium. One of the
IEEE 802.3 standards, 10Base5, specifies a maximum medium segment
length of 500 meters. To span longer distances, a repeater can be used to connect two segments. The standard allows for a maximum of four repeaters,
for a total distance of 2500 meters per LAN. Two repeaters connecting three
segments in an IEEE 802.3 network is illustrated in Figure 8-4.

Figure 8-3

Signal Relay Stations

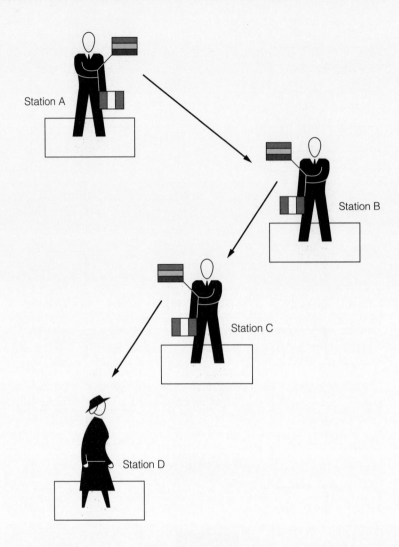

Station A

Station B

Station C

Station D

A repeater does not buffer messages and does not know about MAC protocols or data packets. A repeater also does not separate one segment of the network from another. If a station in segment 1 and a station in segment 3 of the network in Figure 8-4 try to transmit at the same time, a collision will occur.

Table 8-1 is a list of repeater capabilities and characteristics. Note that one capability of some repeaters is **media transfer.** Although it is not commonly needed, this capability allows an administrator to change media from twisted-pair wires on one LAN segment to coaxial cable on another segment at a repeater junction; the MAC protocol remains the same even though the medium changes. The LAN administrator also must keep in mind that a change in the medium can result in a change in the overall maximum length of the LAN.

Figure 8-4

Repeaters Connecting
Three LAN Segments

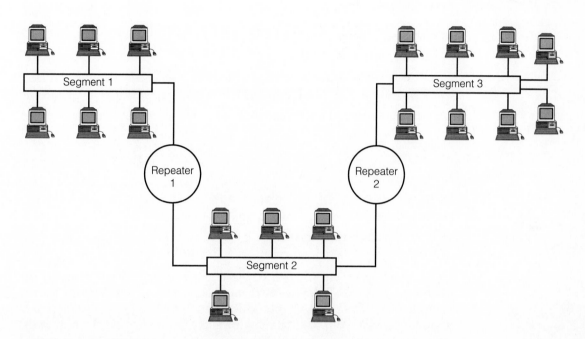

TABLE 8-1   Repeater Characteristics and Capabilities

Media transfer, such as coaxial cable to twisted-pair wires

Multiple ports allowing one repeater to connect three or more segments

Diagnostic and status indicators

Automatic partitioning and reconnection in the event of a segment failure

Manual partitioning

Backup power supply

Bridges

An interface that operates at the data link or media access control (MAC) layer is called a **bridge.** The relationship between a bridge and the OSI model is illustrated in Figure 8-2. Bridges are most commonly used in LANs to overcome limitations in distance or in number of workstations per LAN. A bridge is seldom necessary in WANs because they do not have distance limitations. WANs that limit the number of nodes per network usually use routers (see below) to interconnect two or more WANs. Some bridge functions are listed in Table 8-2.

TABLE 8-2   Basic Bridge Functions

Packet-Routing Function

1. Accept packet from LAN A.
2. Examine address of packet.
3. If packet address is a LAN A address, allow the packet to continue on LAN A.
4. If packet address is a LAN B address, transmit the packet onto the LAN B medium.
5. Do the equivalent for LAN B packets.

Additonal functions

Media conversion	Learning
Remote connection	Signal conversion
Speed conversion	Packet statistics
Token ring to Ethernet conversion	

Early bridges were used to connect two networks that both used the same MAC protocol. Today, we have products called bridges that also connect LANs having different MAC protocols. These newer bridges must be able to reformat packets from one data link protocol to another. Be aware that the use of the term *bridge* can vary. Sometimes a bridge is defined in the original sense—a device connecting two identical networks. Others use the broader definition of a device used to connect two networks at the data link layer. For example, you may encounter bridges that connect a token ring to an Ethernet LAN. Sometimes a device providing this capability will also be referred to as a **brouter.**

Packets sent between two nodes on the same LAN are not acted on by the bridge; only internetwork packets are forwarded by a bridge, as illustrated in Figure 8-5. Note that although the bridge is implemented at the data link layer, the data is transmitted from the data link layer down to the physical layer, over the medium to a physical layer, and back up to the data link layer.

A bridge must know about addresses on each network. Figure 8-6 shows a token-ring packet. Note that the packet contains both the source and destination addresses. This is also the case for Ethernet packets; however, an Ethernet packet format is different from a token-ring packet. Because the bridge knows the MAC protocol being used, the bridge can find the source and destination addresses in the packet and use those addresses for routing. (We use the term *routing* here to describe the process of the bridge deciding to which LAN the message must be transferred. In using this term we do not mean to imply that the bridge is performing the functions of a router.)

The only additional information the bridge must know is the direction in which the destination node is connected. This is determined in several ways. Older bridges indiscriminately transferred each message onto both LANs or required network managers to provide a network routing table. A **routing**

table contains node addresses and the LAN identifier for the LAN to which the node is connected. These older bridges are static regarding their ability to forward messages. If a node were added to one of the networks, the routing tables in all bridges had to be manually updated, and until that happened the new node would not receive inter-LAN messages. As shown in Figure 8-7, network interconnections using bridges can also be more complex than a single bridge connecting two networks. A network routing table for Bridge B1 in Figure 8-7 is shown in Table 8-3.

Figure 8-5

Bridge Packet Forwarding

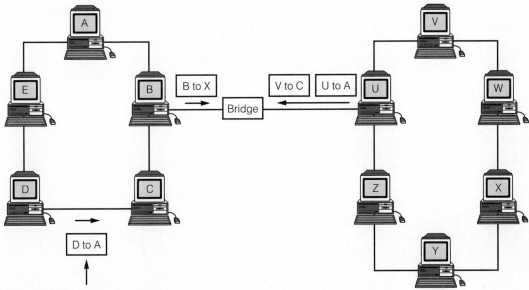

This message does not cross the bridge

Most bridges being sold today are referred to as **learning bridges** or **transparent bridges.** Learning bridges build their routing table from messages they receive. They do not need to be loaded with a predefined routing table. Essentially, the network administrator need only connect the bridge to both LANs, and the bridge is immediately operational. Two methods are commonly used for bridges to learn and build their routing table: spanning tree and source routing.

TABLE 8-3   Bridge B1's Network Rounting Table

Node	Port	Comments
N1	P1	
N2	P1	
N3	P2	
N4	P1	Bridge B2 routes
N5	P1	Bridge B2 routes

Start Delimeter	Access Control	Frame Control	Destination Address	Source Address	Information	Frame-Check Sequence	End Delimeter	Frame Status

Figure 8-6

A Token-Ring Packet

The Spanning Tree Algorithm.   In Figure 8-7, suppose Bridge B1 receives a packet from N1 destined for N2. Recall that each LAN packet contains the address of the sender, or source, and the recipient, or destination. The bridge examines its routing table for the destination address. In this case, the address is local because both the source and the destination addresses are on LAN A. Because the destination address is local, no further action is required; the bridge essentially does nothing. In a token-passing LAN, the bridge may need to forward the packet to the next node on the LAN. In a CSMA/CD LAN, the bridge will do nothing because packets are broadcast to all nodes.

Figure 8-7

Network Interconnections Using Bridges

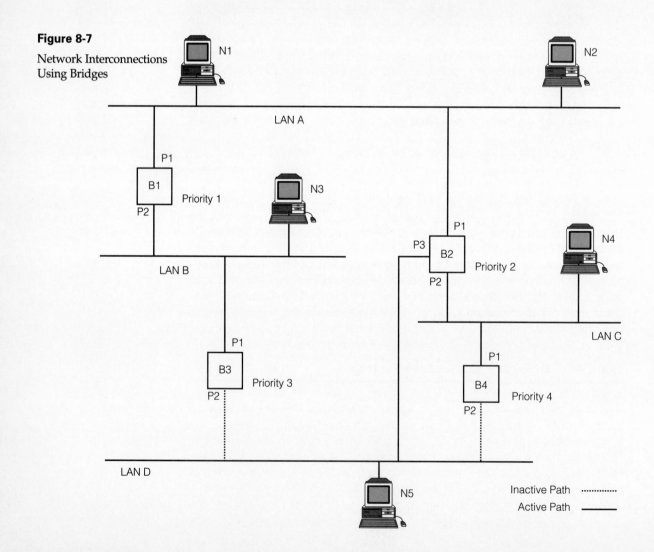

We illustrate the **spanning tree algorithm** here with a simple case. You may wish to refer back to Figure 8-7 during this discussion. Recall that each LAN packet contains the source address and the destination address. If Bridge B1 receives a packet on Port P1, the bridge assumes that the source address is a node local to LAN A. Because a bridge receives all network traffic on a LAN to which the bridge is connected (Bridge B1 gets all message traffic on LANs A and B), a bridge soon learns all of the "local" node addresses from the source addresses in these messages. If a source address is not found in the bridge's routing table, the address is added to the table.

Suppose Node N3 in Figure 8-7 sends a message to Node N2. If the destination address N2 is already in B1's routing table, the bridge forwards the packet accordingly. If the destination address is not already in the bridge's routing table, the bridge needs to locate the address. The bridge does this by sending the packet out on all ports other than the one on which it was received, which is called **flooding** (the packet will also be sent to all nodes on the LAN on which it was received). In this instance, the packet will be transmitted on Port P1. Flooding assures that a packet will arrive at its destination by sending the packet along all possible paths. The bridge will eventually receive either an acknowledgment that the packet was received or a message from the receiving station. The acknowledgment contains the address of the original recipient, N2 in this case. From this acknowledgment, the bridge will be able to determine the direction in which the node lies, and it adds this information to its routing table.

Source Routing.   The **source routing algorithm** relies on the sending station to designate the path for a packet. In Figure 8-7, suppose Node N5 wants to send a packet to Node N2. If N2 is in N5's routing table, the packet is sent along that route; otherwise, N5 must "discover" the best route to N2. N5 does this by sending a discovery packet on all routes available. In this case, the discovery packet will be sent on Port P2 of Bridge B4, Port P3 of Bridge B2, and Port P2 of Bridge B3. Each bridge will, in turn, transmit the packet on each port except the one on which the packet was received. Moreover, each bridge appends its information to the packet. Thus, Node N2 will receive several packets, each containing the identity of each bridge through which the packet traveled. All of these packets are returned to Node N5. N5 selects the path from all the alternatives returned. In our example, Node N5 will likely receive four discovery packets with paths B4–B2, B2, B3–B1, and B4–B2–B3–B1. Upon receiving the four responses from its discovery packets, Node N5 will choose one. B2 would probably be the best route, as there is only one bridge through which the message must pass. Realize, however, that path B3–B1 might be faster if B2's connections on ports P1 or P3 are slower than the connections for bridges B3 and B1.

After N5 discovers the path to Node N2, whenever Node N5 needs to transmit to Node N2, it appends the selected routing information to its packet. Each bridge along the way investigates this information to determine by which route to send the packet.

The advantage of the source-routing algorithm is that bridges are not responsible for maintaining large routing tables for extensive networks. Each node is responsible for maintaining routing information only for those nodes with which it communicates. The disadvantages are the overhead of sending numerous packets during discovery and the extra routing data that must be appended to each message.

Other Bridge Capabilities.   In the preceding discussion, we did not consider the interconnected LANs' location and media. Bridges are available that will accommodate media differences. Suppose LAN A in Figure 8-7 uses coaxial cable and LAN B uses twisted-pair wires as the medium. You could therefore select a bridge that has BNC connectors for coaxial cable on one port and RJ-45 connectors for twisted-pair wires on the other port.

There are also several interconnection options for connecting geographically distributed LANs. The most common of these are listed in Table 8-4. The speed of the connection between remote LANs usually is much slower than the speed within either LAN. This speed difference can cause the bridge to become saturated with messages if there are many internet packets. Bridges have memory that allows some messages to be buffered, which helps reconcile the differences in transmission speed. If too many messages arrive in a short period, the buffer will become full, and newly arriving packets will be lost. Note that this condition can occur when two local LANs are connected. A bridge also must do some processing to determine where a packet must be routed. Except for very slow LANs, the processing time may exceed the arrival rate. Thus, bridges connecting LANs with high packet arrival rates can also become saturated. Each bridge has a packet forwarding limit. It is important to select a bridge that has a packet forwarding capacity equal to or greater than the peak internet packet exchange rate.

TABLE 8-4   Remote Bridge Connection Alternatives

RS-232 serial lines

Synchronous transmission at 56 Kbps or 64 Kbps

T-1 Line, 1.5 Mbps

Factional T-1, 64 Kbps, and multiples thereof

X.25 packet-switching network

Integrated services digital network (ISDN)

High-speed switches

Routers

The network layer of the OSI reference model is responsible for packet routing and the collection of accounting information. Networks use a variety of routing algorithms. CSMA/CD and token-passing LANs send messages to each node using broadcast routing. WANs are more selective in their routing because broadcast routing in a WAN causes too much overhead and delay. You may want to refer back to Chapter 6 for a review of WAN routing algorithms. Several routing paths may be available in some networks, as illustrated in Figure 8-8. The network layer is responsible for routing an incoming message for another node onto an appropriate outbound path. Thus, a message for Node X that arrives at Node B in Figure 8-8 will arrive at the physical layer and be moved up through the data link layer to the network layer. If the packet is not intended for an application on Node B, the network layer determines the outbound path for the message and sends it down to the data link layer, which formats the packet with the proper data link control data (perhaps a data link protocol different from that of the arriving message). The data link layer then passes the packet down to the physical layer for transmission to the next node along the path to the final destination.

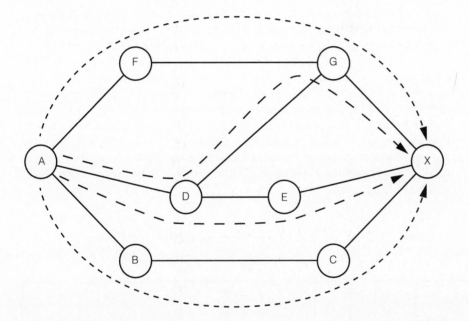

Figure 8-8

Several Routing Paths in a Network

An interconnection interface that operates at the network layer is called a **router.** Figure 8-2 shows the relationship between a router and the OSI layers. A router is not sensitive to the details of the data link and physical layers. Thus, a router can be used to connect different types of networks, such as a token-ring LAN to an IEEE 802.3 LAN or a LAN to a WAN. A router looks at the destination address of a message, determines a route the message should follow to reach that address, and provides the addressing required by the network and data link layers for delivery. This function is provided by the **transmission control protocol/Internet protocol (TCP/IP)** in the Internet, whereas Novell networks typically use a protocol called **sequenced packet exchange/internetwork packet exchange (SPX/IPX)** to transfer packets between nodes. The TCP and SPX portions of these protocols operate at the transport layer, and the IP and IPX portions operate at the network layer. Some networks use a different type of protocol, such as the **Xerox Network**

System (XNS). Because of protocol format differences, an SPX/IPX router will not be able to forward TCP/IP packets, and a router that knows only the XNS protocol cannot forward SPX/IPX packets. For two nodes to exchange data using a router, they must share a common network layer protocol.

When a message arrives at a network node, it gets passed up through the OSI reference model layers. At the data link layer, the data link's protocol headers and trailers added by the node on the other side of the link are removed by the receiving node. The error-detection algorithm is invoked to check for transmission errors. If the message is error-free, it is passed up to the network layer. If the message is destined for an application in the receiving node, it is passed up to the higher layers; otherwise, it must be transmitted on to the next node on the path to the destination node. The network layer protocol is instrumental in carrying out these tasks.

In making its determination regarding keeping or forwarding a message, the network layer must know where to find the destination address in the message. The network layer protocol provides this important information. Examine the network headers illustrated in Figure 8-9. Figure 8-9(a) illustrates the message headers attached by the IP section of the TCP/IP suite and Figure 8-9(b) illustrates the IPX headers. Note that the addresses are in different locations and of different lengths in the two figures. Consequently, if an IP frame is received by the IPX protocol, it will be unable to find the destination address and will be unable to handle the message correctly. For this reason, when routing, all sending and receiving network layers must be using the same protocol. Using TCP/IP as a model, let us look more closely at how routing operates.

Figure 8-9

IP and IPX Header
Formats

Version	IP Header Length	Type of Service	Packet Length	Identification	Flags	Fragment Offset	Time to Live	Protocol	Header Checksum	Source Address	Destination Address

(a) IP Header

Checksum	Length	Transport Control	Packet Type	Destination Network	Destination Node	Destination Socket	Source Network	Source Node	Source Socket

(b) IPX Header

TCP/IP

TCP/IP was developed by the Advanced Research Projects Agency (ARPA) of the U.S. Department of Defense (DOD). Originated as an internetwork protocol, it has evolved over time into a suite of protocols addressing a variety of network communications needs, one of which is that of a router. Note that TCP/IP is not just a microcomputer protocol. On the contrary, it was developed on large systems and was later transported to microcomputers. Because TCP/IP runs on a wide variety of platforms, it is an ideal choice for a routing protocol. Other functions provided by the TCP/IP suite include file transfer, electronic mail, and logins to remote nodes.

Figure 8-10 illustrates how networks might be connected using TCP/IP. Routing nodes are denoted by R and nonrouting nodes by WS. Note that internetwork connections are made through specific network nodes. Thus, Node R1 on Network A has a physical connection to Node R2 on Network B, and Node R3 on Network A has a physical connection to Node R4 on Network C. You should also realize that the networks we are discussing can be either a LAN or a WAN, and routing nodes that communicate with each other must share a common data link protocol and a physical link. Although we speak of routers operating at the network level, for messages to transmit from one node to another they must pass through the data link and physical layers of each computer. The key is that the information needed to determine how to forward the message is understood by the network layer's logic. In Figure 8-10, assume that Network A is a CSMA/CD LAN, Network B is a token-ring LAN, and Network C is a WAN. Nodes R1 and R2 must share a common data link protocol over Link L1, and Nodes R3 and R4 must share a common data link protocol and medium over Link L2. The data link protocols at L1 and L2 may be different.

As the abbreviation implies, TCP/IP consists of two distinct protocols, the transmission control protocol (TCP) and the internet protocol (IP). The TCP operates at the transport layer and the IP operates at the network layer. Before tracing the flow of a message transfer using TCP/IP, let us first look at the functions of each protocol.

TCP/IP Routing in a Network

The IP provides two basic services: breaking the message up into transmission packets, and addressing. Figure 8-10 shows several network interconnections, and each connection may use a different data link protocol. Many data link protocols have a maximum size for transmission packets. For example, an Ethernet LAN packet contains at most 1500 characters. Some networks have a maximum packet size of 128 characters. An IP must be aware of these data link differences. The IP is also responsible for packet routing. On occasion this requires that the IP break a message into smaller packets of the appropriate size. To do this, the IP must determine the address of the next node on the path to the message's destination.

There are several functions an IP does not perform. The IP is not responsible for guaranteeing end-to-end message delivery. The TCP is held accountable for message delivery. If a packet is lost during transmission, the TCP, not the IP, is responsible for recognizing a message that has been lost and for resending the message. Also, the IP does not guarantee that individual packets will arrive in the correct order, a function that also is provided by the TCP. Thus,

Figure 8-10

TCP/IP Routing in
a Network

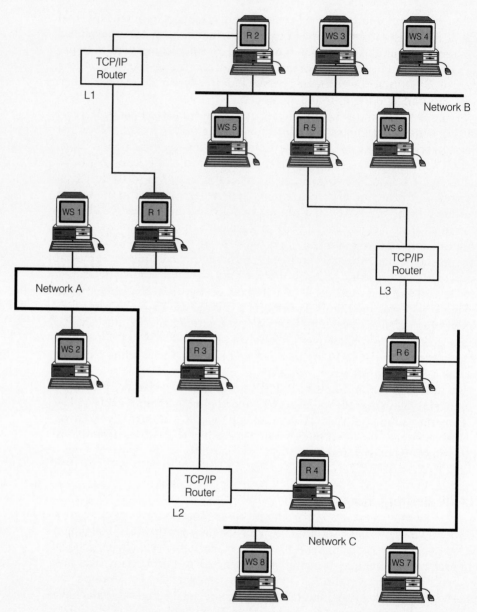

the primary functions of the TCP are to provide message integrity, to provide
acknowledgment that a complete message has been received by a destination
node, and to regulate the flow of messages between source and destination
nodes. The TCP also may divide the message into smaller transmission segments. These segments usually will correspond to an IP transmission packet.

We now consider how the TCP and IP cooperate in sending a message from
one node to another. This example also serves as a model for the functions
of a generic router. For this example we assume that Node WS1 on Network
A needs to send a message to Node WS5 on Network B in Figure 8-10.
TCP/IP uses the following procedure to carry out this transmission.

1. To start the process, the TCP in Node WS1 receives a message from an application. The TCP attaches a header to the message and passes it down to the IP in Node WS1. The message header contains the destination address and error-detection fields such as a cyclic redundancy check (CRC) and a message sequence number. These are used to ensure that the message is received without errors and to ensure that messages are received in the proper sequence or can be reordered into the proper sequence.

2. Node WS1's IP determines whether the destination is an internetwork address. If the address is on the local network, such as Node WS2, then the IP passes the message to the local network routing facility, which transports the message to the proper node. If the destination is a node on another network, the IP finds the best path to the destination and forwards the message to the next IP node along that path. In this case, the IP in Node WS1 will send the message to Node R1.

3. The IP at Node R1 receives the message, examines the address, and determines the address of the next node, R2 in this example. The IP may break the message up into packets of the appropriate size. The IP adds a header to each packet and passes it down to the data link layer. The data link layer appends its transmission information and transmits the packets over the link between R1 and R2.

4. The data link layer at R2 receives a packet, strips off the data link layer control data, and passes the message to R2's IP. If the destination is local to that IP's network, as it is in this instance, the IP delivers the message to the local network routing facility for delivery. If the destination is on another network, the IP determines the next node along the path and sends the message to it. If the node address were WS7, the packet would be routed to Node R5 and then to Node R6. Ultimately the message arrives at the destination node.

5. When the message arrives at the final destination node, it is passed up to the TCP, which then decodes the header attached by the sender's TCP. The receiving TCP checks for errors, such as message sequence errors or CRC errors. If no errors are detected, the TCP determines the destination program and sends the message to it.

On the path from source to destination, the message may pass through several IP nodes and traverse links with several different data link protocols. The router, TCP/IP in this example, is responsible for generating the destination address and intermediate addresses along the way, and for ensuring the correct delivery of the message.

TCP/IP is continually being extended to meet new communications needs. One extension, **Xpress transfer protocol (XTP),** enhances TCP/IP performance by reducing the amount of processing and allowing some functions to be worked on in parallel. One example of parallelism is the ability to transmit data while the CRC is being computed.

From the preceding discussion you should realize that a LAN node that must communicate with a node on another network must run both the TCP and the IP software. Most of today's LAN operating system vendors have

TCP/IP software available in DOS, OS/2, and UNIX versions. You will also find this software and associated utilities available from independent software vendors. A variety of TCP/IP utilities can be found in the public domain and are thus available at no cost or at a minimal cost.

Bridge/Router Flows Through Layers

At this point, shift to the CBT module entitled "Bridge/Router Flows Through Layers" to get additional information on how bridges and routers operate.

ISO Routing Standards

The International Standards Organization (ISO) has also developed standards for functions similar to those provided by TCP/IP. The counterpart to IP is the **connectionless network protocol (CLNP).** In addition to forwarding messages, CLNP can provide message services such as message priorities, route selection parameters, and security parameters. The ISO has defined five classes of transport protocols that are abbreviated as TP0, TP1, TP2, TP3, and TP4. The classes are based on the error characteristics of the network. The lower classes assume better network error performance and hence provide less end-to-end support. TP4 makes no assumptions about the error characteristics of the network and provides the highest level of error detection and recovery. Combining the transport protocols with CLNP yields a service similar to that of TCP/IP. The ISO services are abbreviated **TPn/CLNP,** where n represents a number between 0 and 4.

Gateways

Network connections that operate at the network layer or above are generically called **gateways.** A gateway is similar to a language interpreter. If I speak only English and you speak only French, we are unable to communicate. However, if we find someone fluent in both languages, he or she can provide the translation that allows us to exchange information. Similarly, a gateway is used to connect dissimilar networks or systems by providing conversion from one network protocol to another. A gateway might be used to connect a LAN to a WAN as illustrated in Figure 8-11. In making this interconnection, the gateway must accept packets from the LAN, extract the data from the packets, and format the data in a packet according to the WAN protocol, or vice versa.

A gateway is basically a protocol converter. A gateway reconciles the differences between the networks it connects. With a repeater, a bridge, or a

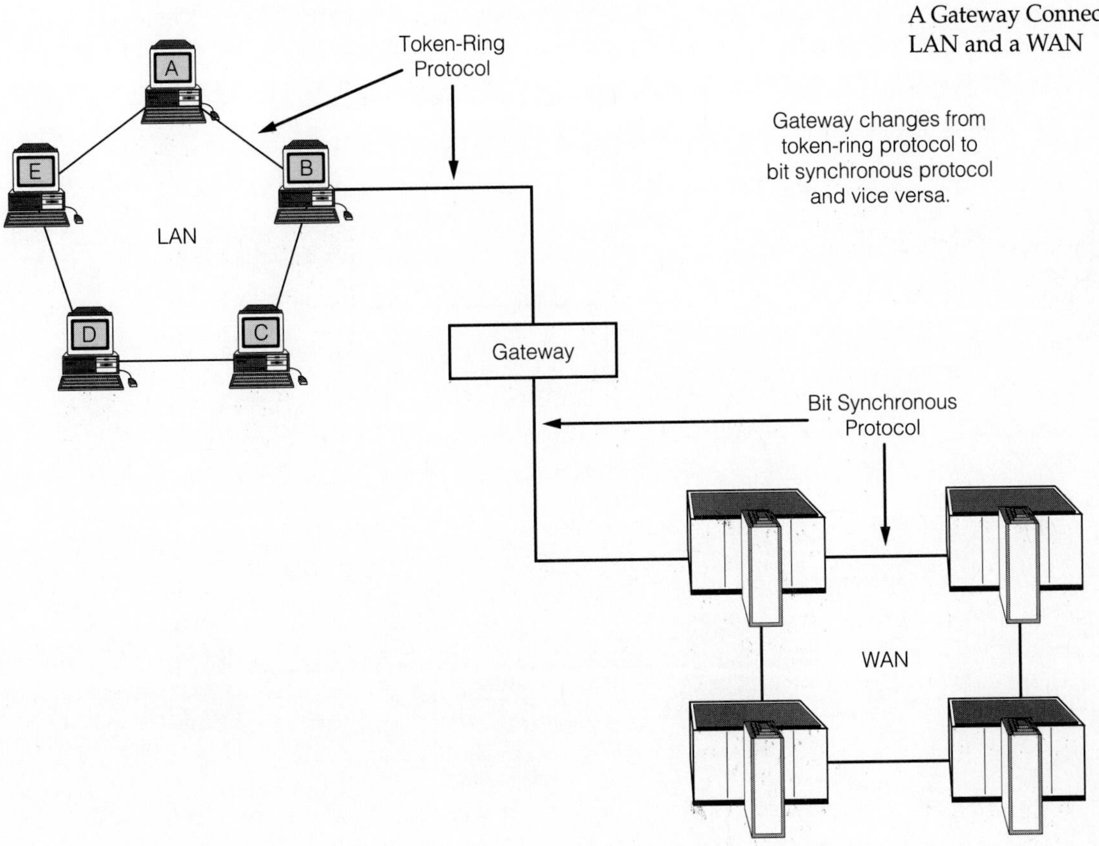

Figure 8-11

A Gateway Connecting a
LAN and a WAN

Token-Ring
Protocol

Gateway changes from
token-ring protocol to
bit synchronous protocol
and vice versa.

LAN

Gateway

Bit Synchronous
Protocol

WAN

router, the communicating nodes share a common protocol at the physical, the data link, or the network layer, respectively. If it is necessary to connect two nodes that do not share a common protocol, a gateway or protocol converter can be used to make the connection. Naturally, the gateway must be able to understand the protocol of the two nodes being connected and also must be able to translate from one protocol to the other.

The components of a gateway are the network interfaces and the logic that carries out the conversion necessary when moving messages between networks. The conversion must change the header and trailer of the packet to make the packet consistent with the protocol of the network or data link to which the message is being transferred. This may include accommodating differences in speed, packet sizes, and packet formats. For example, if both a LAN and a WAN interface to a packet-switching network (X.25 network), the X.25 network can serve as a gateway that allows stations on the LAN and the WAN to communicate. In this case there are two gateways: one from the LAN to the X.25 network and one from the X.25 network to the WAN. This is illustrated in Figure 8-12.

Figure 8-12

LAN-WAN Interconnection
Using an X.25 Network

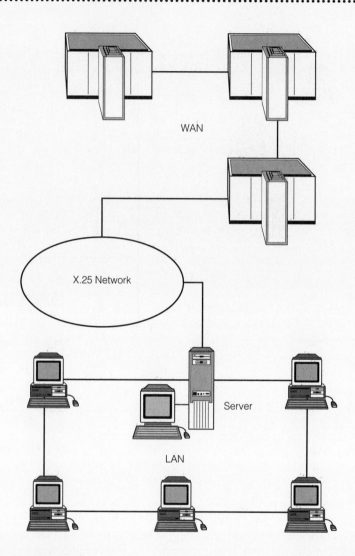

X.25 NETWORKS

The concept of a packet-switching network was first introduced in 1964 by
Paul Baran of the Rand Corporation as a process of segmenting a message
into specific-size packets, routing the packets to their destination, and
reassembling the packets to re-create the message. In 1966, Donald Davies of
the National Physics Laboratory in Great Britain published details of a store-
and-forward packet-distribution network. In 1967, plans were formulated
for what is believed to be the first packet-distribution network, ARPANET,
which became operational in 1969 with four nodes. The ARPANET has since
expanded to more than 125 nodes and generally evolved into the NSFNet.
NSFNet and several other regional networks are integrated into one supernetwork, the Internet.

A packet-switching network is sometimes referred to as an X.25 network,
a packet-distribution network (PDN), a value-added network (VAN), or a

public data network. We primarily use the term X.25 network. Packet distribution and packet switching both refer to how data is transmitted: as one or more packets with a fixed length. The X.25 designation stems from CCITT's recommendation X.25, which defines the interface between data terminal equipment (DTE) and data circuit-terminating equipment (DCE) for terminals operating in the packet mode on public data networks. The term *public data network,* which derives from the X.25 recommendation, is somewhat of a misnomer because packet-switching networks also have been implemented in the private sector. When the network is public, users subscribe to the network services much like they subscribe to telephone services. The term *value-added network* is used because the network proprietor adds not only a communications link but also message routing, packet control, store-and-forward capability, network management, compatibility among devices, and error recovery. These are all services associated with the OSI physical, data link, and network layers.

Packet-distribution networks specify a selection of different packet sizes, with sizes of 128, 256, 512, and 1024 bytes being most common. All packets transmitted must conform to one of the available packet lengths; individual users subscribe to a service providing one of the available packet sizes. Limiting the number of variations in packet size makes managing message buffers easier and evens out message traffic patterns.

X.25 Networks and the OSI Layers

Only three OSI layers have been described for X.25 networks, because an X.25 network is responsible only for message delivery. The three layers of the OSI reference model responsible for message delivery are the physical, data link, and network layers. From the X.25 network user's perspective all seven OSI layers exist; the application, presentation, session, and transport layer functions are implemented in the user's segment of the network.

Current X.25 Network Implementations

The use of X.25 networks has increased significantly since the first X.25 network was established, and most computerized countries currently have access to at least one. In addition to the NSFNet, public networks in the United States include those offered by AT&T, CompuServe, GE Information Services, Infonet Services, MCI Communications, and Sprint Corporation, to name a few. Implementations outside the United States include Datapac in Canada, Transpac in France, EuroNet in Europe (essentially an extension of Transpac), Britain's Packet Switching Service (PSS), Germany's DATEX-P, and Japan's Nippon Telephone and Telegraph (NTT) DDX-2 system. Interconnections exist among these networks, providing international networking capabilities at a reasonable cost. Several CCITT recommendations, covering different aspects of X.25 network access and use, are listed in Figure 8-13 where applicable.

Figure 8-13

A PDN General
Configuration

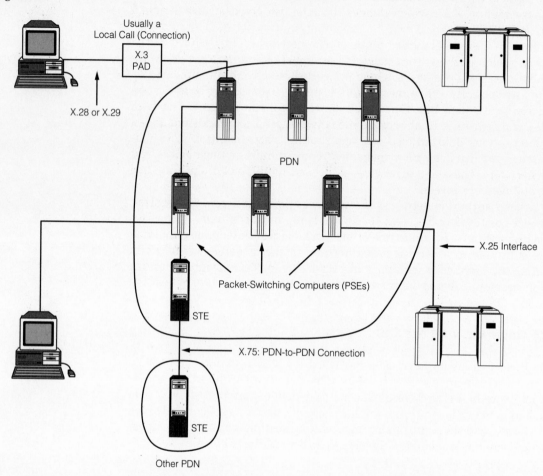

Connection Options

An X.25 network provides up to three types of connection options: switched virtual circuit, permanent virtual circuit, and datagram service. A **virtual circuit** is a communications path that is established between the sending and receiving nodes.

Switched Virtual Circuit.   A **switched virtual circuit (SVC)** is similar to a switched communications link in that both are established when needed by a session and dissolved when the session ends. When an SVC session is established between two users, an end-to-end circuit is allocated for the duration of the session. This is accomplished via a call-setup request that is initiated by the user. On receiving a call-setup request, the X.25 network establishes a transmission link for the session. The switched virtual circuit is dissolved at the end of the session, a process referred to as **call clearing**.

Permanent Virtual Circuit. A **permanent virtual circuit (PVC)** is usually selected when two nodes require almost continuous connection. A PVC is similar to a leased communications link, as described in Chapter 2. With a PVC, the circuit is permanently allocated between two nodes and hence no call-setup is required.

Datagram Service. The third type of connection option is **datagram services.** A **datagram** is a message that fits completely into the data field of one packet. Because a temporary path is established for each datagram, two datagrams from the same source can have two different circuits established. This type of circuit allocation is called connectionless because a dedicated connection is not established. Datagram service has the potential of fast service for short, unrelated messages.

Although they have lower overhead because they do not require a virtual circuit, certain features of datagrams make them undesirable for many applications. First, the arrival order of datagrams is not guaranteed, as each datagram sent by a particular node may take a different route. Second, and more important, arrival itself is not guaranteed, because the X.25 network establishes datagram arrival queue depths, and a datagram is discarded if the queue is full when the datagram arrives. This problem is compounded by the fact that recovery of lost datagrams is the responsibility of the user, not of the X.25 network, making datagrams best suited to messages of relatively low importance and messages where speed is more critical than the possibility of lost data (such as in process control environments and certain military situations). Datagram service, though included in the X.25 standard, has seldom been implemented in existing systems.

Example of an X.25 Network

To see how an X.25 network functions, we follow a message as it proceeds from the starting terminal to its destination address, using a switched virtual circuit connection.

Establishing the Virtual Circuit. The user connects to the X.25 network by dialing the nearest X.25 network access port (a local telephone call in most large cities). After a login procedure, the address of the other node is supplied. The X.25 network then goes through the process of establishing the virtual circuit. The call sequence is as follows:

1. A call-request packet is sent from the sending node to the receiver. The call request is delivered to the receiver as an incoming-call packet. The receiver may accept or reject the call.

2. If the receiver wishes to accept the connection, it transmits a call-accepted packet that is presented to the sender as a call-connected message. This establishes the connection, and data exchange may begin.

3. To terminate the connection, either node can transmit a clear request to the other. The recipient of the clear request acknowledges the disconnect with a clear-confirmation control packet.

Packet Assembly/Disassembly (PAD).   The first step in sending the data is to assemble the packets, a function performed by a **packet assembly/disassembly (PAD) module.** The PAD function is not considered a part of the X.25 network; rather, it is the responsibility of the data terminal equipment. However, because many terminals used in X.25 networks lack the intelligence to perform this function, most X.25 networks still provide this capability. PAD functions are specified in the CCITT X.3 standard. The PAD acts on one end to transform a message into one or more packets of the required length and then reassembles the message at the other end. The PAD is also responsible for generating and monitoring control signals such as call setup and clearing.

Once the message has been transformed into packets, the packets are passed to the X.25 network in accordance with the X.25 interface. The X.25 network then moves the data through the network for delivery to the destination. The standards do not discuss the internal workings within the X.25 network, such as routing and congestion control. The receiving PAD takes the information from the data portion of the packet and reassembles the message.

X.25 Network Equipment

Two types of machines have been defined for use within a X.25 network: **packet-switching equipment (PSE),** which accepts and forwards messages, and **signaling terminal equipment (STE),** which is used to interface two different X.25 networks according to CCITT standard X.75. The standards for a packet-switching network specify interfaces and functions of the PSEs and STEs, but not the nature of the equipment itself. Figure 8-14 illustrates the connections between users' equipment and the PSE.

Advantages and Disadvantages of an X.25 Network

X.25 networks have several advantages. First, the user is charged for the amount of data transmitted rather than for connect time. Applications that send low volumes of data over a relatively long period will find the charges for a X.25 network lower than those for either leased lines or switched lines. The X.25 network also gives access to many different locations without the cost of switched connections, which usually involve a charge for the initial connection plus a per minute use fee. Access to the X.25 network is most often via a local telephone call, which also reduces costs. Maintenance of the network and error recovery are the responsibilities of the X.25 network.

There are also disadvantages to using a X.25 network. Because the X.25 network is usually shared, users must compete with each other for circuits. Thus, it is possible for message traffic from other users to impede the delivery of a message. In the extreme case, a switched virtual circuit to the intended destination may even be unobtainable. This is also true for a switched connection from a common carrier. If the number of data packets to be transferred is great, the cost of using a X.25 network can exceed that of using leased facilities. Because the X.25 network is controlled by its proprietor, the individual user is unable to make changes that might benefit an individual application, such as longer messages or larger packets, longer message acknowledgment intervals, and higher transmission speeds, all of which are set by the X.25 network administrators.

Figure 8-14

Connections in an X.25 Network

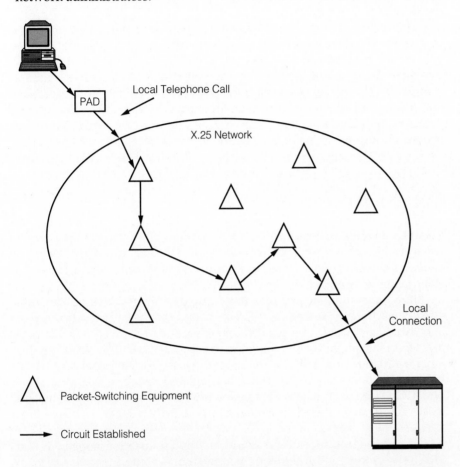

Another disadvantage of X.25 networks is a general inability to transmit data at the high speeds required by many of today's networks. A newer technology called **frame relay** is being used to supplant X.25 for high-speed networks.

X.25 Frame Relay

To see how frame relay works and to gain more insight into the use of X.25 networks, step through the CBT module entitled "X.25 Frame Relay".

Which Interface Is Right for You?

We have defined three network interconnection capabilities: repeaters, bridges, and routers. How do you choose the right one? In general, you should choose the connection at the lowest OSI level possible. Thus, a repeater is usually preferable to a bridge, and a bridge is usually preferable to a router. As you move up the OSI layers, your connection must be more intelligent, do more work, and has a lower packet exchange rate. These are not the only deciding factors, however.

A bridge can replace a repeater, and a router can replace a repeater or a bridge; however, the opposite is not always true. A repeater cannot always substitute for a bridge and a bridge cannot always substitute for a router. If you have the option of using a repeater, you might instead choose to use a bridge. This decision makes sense if the bridge can handle the message traffic and if you already have the bridge components. A bridge also allows some LAN isolation capability that a repeater does not provide. Thus, you might choose a bridge over a repeater to provide an extra level of network security.

LAN-TO-HOST CONNECTIONS

The preceding discussion explored ways of connecting networks, specifically, ways in which a LAN can be connected to another LAN or to a WAN. For many companies another LAN connection need is that of connecting a LAN to a stand-alone computer.

Many companies entered the microcomputer age with a large computer already installed. As these companies increased their use of microcomputers and then installed one or more LANs, the large computer continued to play an important role in those companies' computing needs. For example, the large computer, often called a host, might be used for payroll or large database applications. Even companies that replaced or are replacing the host with LAN technology go through a period when both computing environments exist. Companies that use hosts and LANs usually need to exchange data between the two environments. This can be done via media exchange: Data on the host can be copied onto a disk or tape and transferred to the LAN and vice versa. Often, a **LAN-to-host connection** is a more efficient way to accomplish data exchange. Figure 8-15 illustrates a host computer connected to a LAN. Before discussing the ways the LAN-host connection can be made, we look at several ways a LAN user can interact with a host.

In Figure 8-15, a user at Node N1 might need to view, update, or evaluate data stored in the host's database. This user can do the work on the host or she can do the work on her LAN workstation. A user at Node N2 might need to send an electronic mail message to a user at Terminal T1. A user at Node N3 might need to run an application that exists only on the host. The application may be available only on the host for a variety of reasons: It has not yet been implemented on the LAN, it needs special hardware available only on the host (such as a typesetting machine), or it requires computing power beyond that available on the LAN.

The three preceding examples cover most of the general connection needs of LAN users. These needs can be summarized as follows:

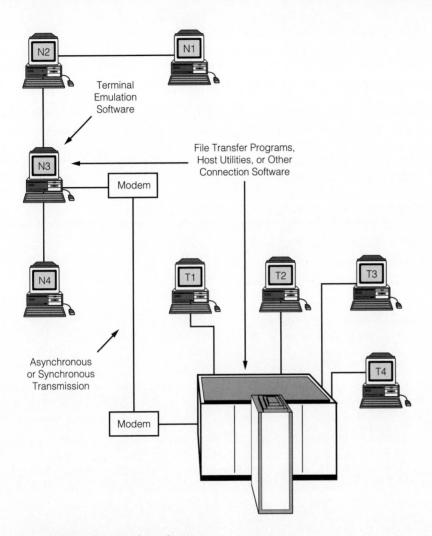

Figure 8-15

LAN-to-Host Connection

- Using host data and applications
- Transferring data from host to LAN or LAN to host
- Using host hardware or software resources
- Communicating with host users

A host user will likely have the same basic needs for LAN resources. You have already read about two ways a LAN-host connection can be made, routers and gateways. We now consider other ways these connections can be made.

The Host as a LAN Node

Some hosts have the ability to connect to the LAN as a node. This is the most effective way of establishing the connection. The host can thus operate as a server, providing all the above needs and at high data transfer rates.

Asynchronous Connections

In Chapter 6 we discussed the asynchronous data link protocol. Virtually every computer has the ability to send and receive asynchronously. You are probably familiar with the term *serial port* concerning a microcomputer. The serial port is an asynchronous communications port. Because most computers support this protocol, it is sometimes used to link a microcomputer to a host. Usually a microcomputer attached to a host asynchronously operates in one of two modes, file transfer or terminal emulation. Terminal emulation software capabilities are listed in Table 8-5.

TABLE 8-5   Terminal Emulation Software Capabilities

Scripts

Mouse support

File transfer: CompuServe, XModem, YModem, ZModem, Kermit

Terminal emulation: ANSI, DEC VT 220, IBM 3101, TTY

Electronic mail

Phone directory

Capture of data to a disk

Text editor

Password security

Dedicated Connection per Microcomputer.   Host computers can usually accommodate many asynchronous connections. Small minicomputers will usually support 32 or more, and large mainframes may accommodate hundreds. One way to connect a LAN node to a host is to provide a direct, **dedicated connection** between a port on the host and each microcomputer needing a host connection. This is illustrated in Figure 8-16. In the figure, Nodes N1, N2, N4, and N5 each have a dedicated connection to the host. Nodes N3 and N6 are not connected to the host.

A dedicated connection provides direct host access and the microcomputer does not use LAN resources for communicating with the host. The typical connection has the microcomputer appear to the host as though the microcomputer were a host terminal. In addition to the serial port, the microcomputer needs terminal emulation software to establish the connection and carry on a host session. Terminal emulation software is available from many sources and has the ability to emulate a wide variety of terminals. With dedicated connections, the LAN administrator and data processing department can easily control which LAN nodes have access to the host. Nodes without a direct connection will be unable to make a host connection.

A dedicated connection has several disadvantages.   First, as with all asynchronous connections, the speed of the link is slow. Asynchronous speeds can be faster than 100,000 bits per second (bps), but typically for microcomputer connections the speed is 28,800 bps or less. If many LAN

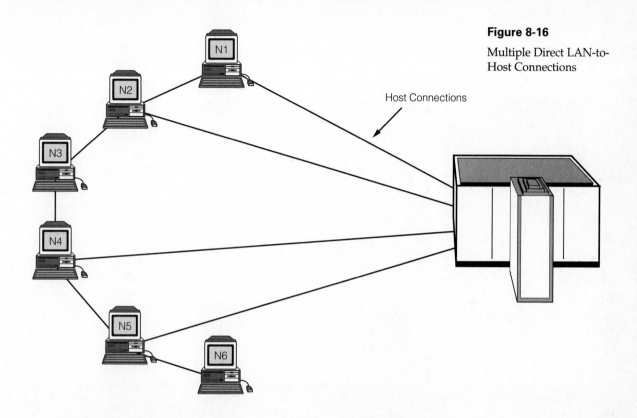

Figure 8-16

Multiple Direct LAN-to-Host Connections

Host Connections

nodes must communicate with the host, many host ports will be required. This not only reduces the number of ports available to the host's terminal users but also is somewhat costly. The cost for host ports can be significant and is burdensome for microcomputers that need only occasional access. Finally, when operating in terminal emulation mode, the microcomputer loses some of its processing capabilities. It can essentially do only what a terminal can do. Specifically, the microcomputer can send and receive data but (usually) cannot use this interface to have a local application, such as a database management system, directly access data on the host.

Multiplexing. A **multiplexer** is a hardware device that allows several devices to share one communications channel. Multiplexing typically is used to consolidate the message traffic between a computer and several remotely located terminals, as illustrated in Figure 8-17. This technique can also be used to allow several microcomputers to share a communications link to a host processor.

Shared Asynchronous Connections. In some applications, each LAN node needs occasional access to the host but the number of concurrent connections is far fewer than the number of LAN nodes. A dedicated line per node is excessive in such situations. A better solution is to share asynchronous connections. The most common way to share connections is via a **communications server** or front-end processor (FEP) as illustrated in Figure 8-18.

Figure 8-17

A Multiplexer Connection

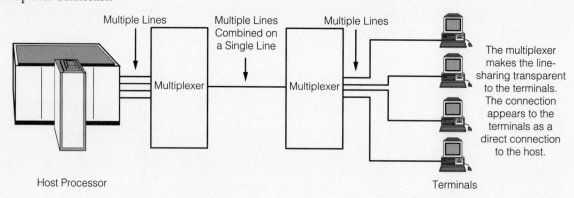

Figure 8-18

LAN-to-Host Connections
Using a Communications
Server

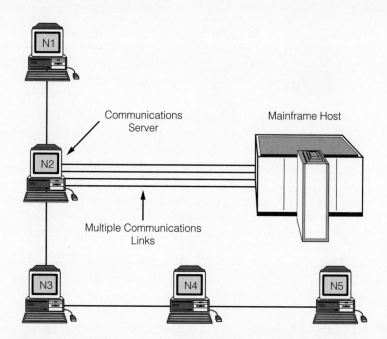

In Figure 8-18, the communications server has four connections to the host. A microcomputer needing host services will request a connection through the communications server. If all four ports are in use, the request will be denied. If a host port is free, the request will be honored and the microcomputer will be connected to a vacant host port. You might note that the communications server functions much like a telephone switch.

Communications servers also may provide connections for remote hosts. The usual way a connection is made to a remote host is via a modem connection. The line to the remote host may be dedicated or switched. A dedicated line is continuously available; a switched-line connection is established on an as-needed basis. The typical example of a switched line is a dial-up telephone line. The link between two devices is made via a telephone call, remains active during the length of the session, and is broken when the session is completed. Rather than providing each LAN node with a dedicated modem, the communications server can provide modem sharing. The technique for doing this is much like the sharing technique described in the previous paragraph.

Other Types of Host Connections

Asynchronous connections are common because they are easily implemented and are supported by most host systems. On the microcomputer side, all that is necessary is a serial port and terminal emulation or file transfer software. The only host-specific characteristic is the type of terminal being emulated or the file transfer software. Other types of vendor-specific connections exist.

Because of the dominant role played by IBM systems, many of these connections are based on IBM software and hardware technologies. These connections might also work on non-IBM equipment because many large-computer companies support one or more IBM communications protocols. Two of the most common IBM interfaces are described here.

IBM-3270 Emulation.   A mainstay of IBM's communications networks is the family of 3270 terminals. The family consists of a variety of terminals, printers, and cluster controllers. The communication protocol used for 3270 devices is a synchronous protocol, either binary synchronous (BISYNC) or synchronous data link control (SDLC), both of which were discussed in Chapter 6.

IBM-3270 emulation can be effected through a communications server or through individual LAN nodes. When emulation is implemented at individual LAN nodes, a synchronous communications controller must be installed in the microcomputer. The controller provides the necessary line interface. If a communications server is used, the server must have a synchronous communications port. Aside from the protocol interface, the connection works much like the asynchronous connection described earlier.

LU 6.2 Connection.   For many years IBM networks have been designed around IBM's Systems Network Architecture (SNA), which is discussed in Chapter 7. In SNA, users communicate through sessions and a variety of session types are defined. Logical units (LUs) represent users in establishing, using, and ending a session. One type of session allows programs to communicate with other programs. This type of session is called an LU 6.2 session. Support for LU 6.2 sessions is available for microcomputers and is being increasingly used to establish host connections. The advantage of an LU 6.2 interface is that a microcomputer application can communicate directly with a host application or with an application on another network node (as opposed to the microcomputer simply acting as though it were a terminal).

INTERCONNECTION UTILITIES

Having the ability to establish network connections is one part of communicating among networks. Another part is having utilities that help you exploit those connections. Many such utilities are available. Some are commercial products whereas others are available in the public domain for no or little cost. Some utilities you may find useful are briefly described below.

File Transfer Utilities.   **File transfer utilities** allow you to move files between network nodes. File transfer capabilities are an intrinsic part of many routers. Part of the TCP/IP protocol suite is a file transfer capability. **Kermit** is another file transfer utility that runs on a wide variety of computer platforms. It uses asynchronous communications links to transfer ASCII format files. Three common microcomputer file transfer utilities are **XMODEM** and **YMODEM**, and **ZMODEM.** Kermit, XMODEM, YMODEM, and ZMODEM are often included in terminal emulation programs.

Remote Login.   **Remote login facilities** allow users to logon to a remote system. A remote login essentially establishes a remote user as a local user on the remote node. Once a user has successfully logged on to the remote node, commands issued by that user are processed and acted on by the remote node rather than by the local node. When the user logs off from the remote node, his or her session is reestablished on the local node.

Access Servers.   **Access servers** allow remote microcomputers to access LAN resources remotely. Suppose you are working at your home microcomputer and must do some work at your office. Specifically, you may have remembered that you have a report due in the morning. If the software, files, and electronic mail essential to creating and distributing the report are available only on the LAN in your office, you have two options: You can drive to the office to complete the work or you can use the facilities of an access server. To access your LAN remotely, you need a serial port and a modem and a modem on the LAN end plus the communications software. This type of connection was described earlier.

Access servers provide more than just modem connections. If you tried to run a LAN application such as word processing remotely, the word processing program would have to be downloaded into your computer. If your line speed is 2400 bits per second (bps) and the size of the application is 360 Kbytes, it will take at least 25 minutes to download the program (2400 bps is about 240 characters per second). This level of performance is hardly acceptable. An access server is one solution to this problem. The access server runs applications at the LAN end of the connection and passes only the monitor display and keyboard data over the communications link. The remote processing can be accomplished by connections to remote access CPU boards (the user essentially has a dedicated remote CPU at the LAN) or by multiprocessing on a high-capacity microcomputer. The two approaches to access server technology are illustrated in Figure 8-19.

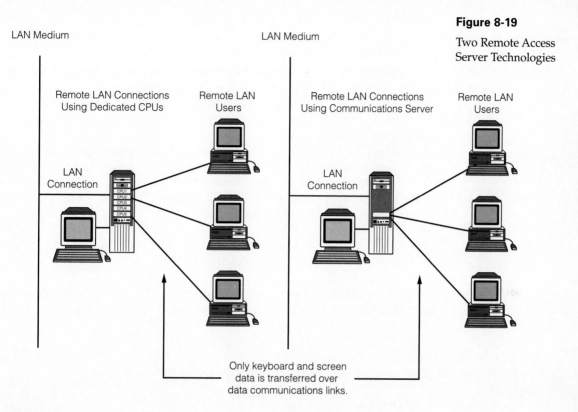

Figure 8-19

Two Remote Access
Server Technologies

LAN Medium

LAN Medium

Remote LAN Connections
Using Dedicated CPUs

Remote LAN
Users

Remote LAN Connections
Using Communications Server

Remote LAN
Users

LAN
Connection

LAN
Connection

Only keyboard and screen
data is transferred over
data communications links.

SUMMARY

Networks are not necessarily isolated islands of computing. Often there is a need to connect several LAN segments, connect homogeneous but separate LANs, connect heterogeneous LANs, connect LANs to WANs, connect one WAN to another WAN, or connect LANs to a single host. These connections can be made in many ways.

Repeaters are used to connect segments of a homogeneous LAN and thereby extend the length of the LAN medium. Repeaters operate at the physical level. They simply accept a signal from one segment, amplify or regenerate the signal, and forward the signal the next segment.

Bridges connect homogeneous but distinct LANs. A bridge operates at the data link (MAC) level. A bridge receives a packet, looks at its destination address, and, if the address is a node on a LAN other than the one on which the packet was received, the bridge transmits the packet onto another LAN. Most of today's bridges are learning bridges. Learning bridges use spanning tree or source routing algorithms to learn the location of network nodes. Learning bridges can adapt to changes in network paths.

Routers operate at the network layer and can connect homogeneous or heterogeneous networks. A router receives a message, determines the address of the destination, and chooses a route for the message to take. The message may travel through several intermediate networks to reach the destination.

Different data link protocols may be used in moving the message from the source to its recipient. Because they operate at the network layer, routers are independent of data link protocols.

A gateway is a name applied to network connections between heterogeneous networks. A gateway must perform translation functions such as packet formatting, speed conversion, error checking, and so on.

Sometimes LAN nodes must be connected to a host machine. A variety of connection types exist. Some hosts can connect directly to the LAN and operate as a LAN node. Asynchronous connections are common and easy to implement but are quite slow. Synchronous connections offer greater speed but usually require additional microcomputer hardware. Because of the wide variety of connection services available, you should be able to find ready-made solutions to most of your LAN connection needs.

KEY TERMS

access server   258

attenuation   230

bridge   233

brouter   234

call clearing   248

communications server   255

connectionless network protocol
   (CLNP)   244

datagram   249

datagram service   249

dedicated connection   254

file transfer utility   258

flooding   237

frame relay   251

gateway   244

Kermit   258

LAN-to-host connection   252

learning bridge (transparent bridge)   236

media transfer   232

multiplexer   255

packet assembly/disassembly (PAD)
   module   250

packet-switching equipment (PSE)   250

permanent virtual circuit (PVC)   249

relay station   230

remote login facility   258

repeater   230

router   239

routing table   235

sequenced packet exchange/internetwork
   packet exchange (SPX/IPX)   240

signaling terminal equipment (STE)   250

source routing algorithm   237

spanning tree algorithm   237

switched virtual circuit (SVC)   248

TPn/CLNP   244

transmission control protocol/Internet
   protocol (TCP/IP)   240

virtual circuit   248

Xerox Network System (XNS)   240

XMODEM   258

Xpress transfer protocol (XTP)   244

YMODEM   258

ZMODEM   258

REVIEW QUESTIONS

1. Give two reasons that a company might have two LANs in the same general location.

2. Identify the OSI level at which each of the following operates.

   a. bridge

   b. repeater

   c. router

3. Under what conditions can a repeater be used? What does a repeater do?

4. What does a bridge do? Under what conditions can a bridge be used?

5. What does a router do? Under what conditions can a router be used?

6. Compare the capabilities of repeaters, bridges, and routers.

7. Describe how TCP/IP sends a message from a node on one network to a node on another network.

8. Besides providing network interconnections, list three other functions you might find in TCP/IP.

9. What is a gateway? Why are only three layers defined for X.25 networks? Do the other OSI layers exist? Explain your answer.

10. Why is datagram service generally unsuited to business applications?

11. Are there any business applications for which datagram service is useful? If so, list them.

12. Compare and contrast a WAN and an X.25 network.

13. Describe three distinct LAN-to-host interfaces.

14. What are the advantages and disadvantages of asynchronous LAN-to-host interfaces?

15. Describe two common types of microcomputer interfaces to IBM systems.

16. What is the difference between a connectionless and connection-oriented circuit?

17. What provided the motivation to move from X.25 packet-switching to fast packet-switching?

18. Compare transmission error recovery in X.25 and frame relay networks.

19. Compare frame relay and asynchronous transfer mode technologies.

9
....

NETWORK MANAGEMENT

....

CHAPTER OBJECTIVES

After studying this chapter you should be able to:

- List the objectives of network management
- Describe ways of meeting network management objectives
- Describe the network management organization
- Distinguish between managing a WAN and managing a LAN
- Discuss the general workings of a network management system
- Compare the SNMP and CMIP network management standards
- Explain the capabilities of IBM's Netview network management system
- Explain the capabilities of Novell's Network Management System

Once a network is installed and operational, it must be managed. Proper management keeps the network components functioning in an optimal way. This chapter begins with a discussion of the objectives and functions of network management and how those objectives can be met. You will then read about both generic and specific network management systems and some of the issues surrounding managing a WAN and managing a LAN. We then provide an overview of two NMS protocols, and conclude with a brief look at two NMS implementations: IBM's Netview and Novell's Network Management System.

NETWORK MANAGEMENT OBJECTIVES

The three primary objectives of network management are to:

- Support system users
- Keep the network operating efficiently
- Provide cost-effective solutions to an organization's telecommunications requirements

Supporting System Users

Supporting system users means empowering them with the hardware and software tools to do their jobs effectively. Essentially it means keeping the network users satisfied. User satisfaction can also be enhanced by:

- Providing proper user training
- Forewarning users of periods when the network will be taken out of operation
- Fixing problems that limit user access to required network resources
- Keeping users informed of system changes and their consequences

Keeping the user community informed is one of the easiest and most over-looked ways to achieve user satisfaction. Users should be informed of scheduled down time, imminent down time, periods when other processing requirements are likely to adversely affect response times, certain changes in hardware or software, and changes in personnel with whom users will be interfacing. This information can be disseminated in several ways, the most direct being to reserve a portion of the terminal output area for system or network news bulletins. Another useful communication medium is newsletters, which can alert users to down times scheduled for preventive maintenance and recon-figurations, announce new capabilities, serve as a training aid, answer frequently asked questions, solicit comments and suggestions, and generally help people feel they are an integral part of the network team.

Measures of System Effectiveness

A system is effective if it provides good performance, is available when needed, and is reliable when being used. If all three factors are present, the system will be effective.

Good Performance.   **Good performance** means a predictable transaction response time. Response time depends on the nature of the transaction. Transactions differ in the amount of work to be accomplished and the number of characters to be transmitted. For every transaction in the system, a realistic response-time objective should be established. Predictable response times require that most transactions be completed within a small range around the established response time goal. For example, for an expected transaction response time of 10 seconds, it is realistic to expect 95 percent of all transactions of that type to be completed within 9–11 seconds and 100 percent of such transactions to be completed within 15 seconds. Erratic response times are generally perceived by users to be worse than slow but predictable responses. Of the two response-time components—processing time and communications time—the network manager ordinarily has little or no control over the application processing and database access components, but does have control over network configuration and line speed. The configuration aspects include the number of terminals on a given line, hardware employed (such as multiplexers, front-end processors, and concentrators), types of terminals used, number of intermediate nodes through which the message must travel (hops), networking software, and error characteristics. Each of these affects the performance of the system.

Availability.   **Availability** means that all necessary components are operable and accessible when a user requires them; for a terminal operator, these include the terminal, cables, connectors, modems, medium or media, controllers, processors, and software. **Accessibility** means the user can make use of the component when needed. In a LAN that has 10 available modems attached to a modem server and 100 users, all modems may be operable, but if all are in use when a user requests a modem connection, a modem is not available. Three factors influence availability: operational considerations, mean time between failures (MTBF), and mean time to repair (MTTR).

Operational considerations may require that portions of the system be taken out of service or that a needed resource like the modems in the preceding paragraph are already in use. Some areas of the online system may be available only during standard working hours. Thus, the payroll system may be unavailable at night, when payroll transactions are not anticipated. In some installations the online system is given priority during the day, whereas batch operations have priority on night shifts, when all or portions of the online system are shut down. Other operational requirements such as preventive maintenance and installation of new hardware or software can remove all or parts of the system from use. Generally, operational considerations can be planned so online users are able to work without being disrupted.

MTBF is the average period that a component will operate before failing. A printer with MTBF of 2000 hours that operates an average of 8 hours a day, 23 days a month, would be expected to fail once every $2000/(8 \times 23) = 10.86$ months. MTBF figures are provided by manufacturers to indicate the reliability of their products. The figures provided are sometimes unreliable and should not be assumed to be exact. Also, an MTBF figure does not predict the reliability of a single component. It is possible that a printer with a 2000-hour MTBF may fail within the first 100 hours of operation.

MTTR is the average amount of time required to place a failed component back into service. For certain components, repair time is relatively constant, such as replacing a failed modem with a spare. For a CPU, however, there may be considerable variations in repair time. CPU repairs often require the repair person to travel to the site and run a varying number of diagnostic routines and testing procedures. The simplified formula (a more exact and more complicated formula exists) for computing availability is:

$$A = \frac{MTBF}{MTBF + MTTR}$$

For example, suppose the printer with a 2000 MTBF has a MTTR of 3 hours. The availability using the simple formula is :

$$A = \frac{2000}{2000 + 3} = \frac{2000}{2003} = 0.9985$$

Logically this means that out of every 10,000 attempts to print on that printer, 15 will result in the printer being unavailable.

Availability with Multiple Components.   If several components—such as a microcomputer, LAN adapter, LAN medium, printer, and file server— must be linked to make the system available to the user, then system availability is given by the product of the availabilities of the component parts:

$$A_s = A_{pc} \times A_{La} \times A_m \times A_p \times A_{fs}$$

where A represents availability and the subscripts s, pc, La, m, p, and fs represent the system, personal computer, LAN adapter, medium, printer, and file server, respectively. If each component has an availability of 0.999, the user will see a system availability of

$$A_s = (0.999)^5 = 0.995$$

In this situation, statistically the user would find the system unavailable 5 times every 1000 attempts, or once every 200 attempts. The availability factor is important in determining how many spare components to stock and how much productive time might be lost when the system is unavailable.

Reliability.   **Reliability** is the probability that the system will continue to function over a given operating period. If a transaction requires 3 seconds for a response to be received, then the reliability of the system is the probability that the system will not fail during that 3 seconds. Reliability of the network includes error characteristics of the medium and stability of the hardware and software components. More specifically, network reliability is a function of the MTBF. In some cases the user will see circuit errors in the form of slow response times. Data received in error will cause retransmissions, slower response times, and congestion of the medium. If the errors are persistent, the retry threshold for the link might be exceeded and the link consequently removed from service. For some modems, a large number of errors will cause the modem to change to a lower speed to minimize the impact of the errors.

Failure of hardware and software components is usually seen by the user as down time on the system. With fault-tolerant systems the effect is either negligible or somewhat slower response times, depending on the system load. Even though the processor and all components of the system except one are functioning properly, the user, who is unable to continue working because of that one failed component, views the system as being down. The reliability function, which is the probability that the system will not fail during a given time (t), is given by:

$$R(t) = e^{-bt} \text{ where b is the inverse of MTBF}$$

Reliability with Multiple Components.   Like availability, system reliability is the product of the reliability of its components. If a system consists of a terminal, a medium, two modems, and a CPU, the reliability of the system from the user's perspective is

$$R_s = R_t \times R_m \times R_l \times R_m \times R_c$$

where s, t, m, l, m, and c represent the reliability of the system, terminal, modem, medium link, modem, and CPU, respectively.

Overall Effectiveness.   The overall **effectiveness** of a system is a measure of how well it serves users' needs. Mathematically, effectiveness is given by the following formula:

$$E = A \times R$$

where E is the effectiveness, A is the availability, and R is the reliability of the system. The formula shows that, for a given system effectiveness, when R is greater than A the amount of time available for repairing a fault increases, whereas if A is greater than R the repair time is reduced. Because R is entirely a function of the MTBF, an increase in R means more time can be devoted to repairing the system to attain the same overall effectiveness. This is illustrated in Figure 9-1.

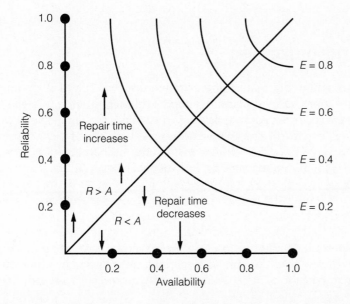

Figure 9-1

Reliability, Availability, and Effectiveness

Reliability of Backup Components. In many networks, alternate components are available should one component fail. Communication paths frequently have alternate links available, and fault-tolerant systems have available a backup CPU, disk drive, or other components. These backup components increase the MTBF of the system, which increases reliability, availability, and effectiveness. With backup components available, the reliability of the components operating in parallel is given by:

$$R_p = 1 - (1 - R_s)^2$$

where R represents reliability, p represents the components operating in parallel, and s represents a single component. If the reliability of a communications link is 0.995, the reliability of the link with a backup is

$$R = 1 - (1 - 0.995)^2 = 0.999975$$

Thus, you can see increased reliability provided by a backup component.

Cost-Effectiveness

The third objective of network management is to provide cost-effective solutions to the data communications needs of an organization. As shown in previous chapters, there are many solutions to communications problems. Network management is responsible for selecting solutions that are feasible and cost-efficient. If the network is unable to contribute positively to the financial position of a company, it probably should not be implemented. Cost-effectiveness can be enhanced through proper planning and using equipment that is scalable. Scalable means the capacity of the network can be increased or decreased in a modular fashion. **Scalable systems,** sometimes referred to as modular systems, avoid large capital investments when upgrades are required.

MEETING THE OBJECTIVES

The objectives of network management are met by a combination of competent staff, hard work, careful planning, good documentation, implementing standards and procedures, communicating with users, and being able to work with other people to resolve problems. Although every one of these elements may not be present in a successful network, the probability of success is directly proportional to how well these elements are realized.

Competent Staff

The most important element in meeting the objectives is creating a competent staff, who may even be able to overcome deficiencies in other areas. Specific staff qualifications depend on the hardware and software employed, but some generalizations can be made. The functions of network management can be grouped into the areas of design and configuration, system installation, testing, diagnosis, documentation, repair, and, on rare occasions, coding. The team must have detailed knowledge of both hardware and software; ideally, every member of the team would know both areas, but often one person is an expert on hardware, whereas another's specialty is software. The staff should be versatile and creative in resolving problems, because many solutions are ad hoc, temporary ones that require ingenuity. Finally, and perhaps most important, staff should be able to work well with both technical and nontechnical personnel. Being able to describe the technology to those not "in the know" and to elicit the necessary technical information from nontechnical users is critical to the team's success.

Design and Configuration

The staff should be skilled in use of the diagnostic and planning tools. In design and configuration, they should be knowledgeable of configuration alternatives and their strengths and weaknesses. They must be willing and able to keep up with changes in hardware and software of the existing system as well as capabilities continually offered by other vendors.

Diagnosis

Skill in diagnosing the cause of problems, often under considerable pressure, is essential. Whenever a problem in a production system is encountered that disables all or a portion of an online application, immediate resolution is needed. A failed system prevents employees from fully performing their job functions and decreases productivity. In some situations, direct revenue is also lost, such as in an airline reservation system.

Planning

Planning is another key to success. Because of the dynamic nature of networks, constant planning and replanning are necessary to ensure that objectives are met. Too often, network managers are so caught up in day-to-day activities that they ignore longer range planning. This type of behavior is both common and self-perpetuating. Without good planning, problems occur more frequently and require a greater amount of time to be solved. There is often truth to the adage, "If you fail to plan, you plan to fail." Corporate goals are set by upper-level management. Planning that defines the actions essential to accomplishing these goals should include short-term and long-term objectives. Short-term planning includes scheduling of personnel, hiring, training, budgeting, and network maintenance and enhancement activities. Long-term planning involves predicting and resolving expansion issues, integrating new technologies, and budgeting.

Documentation, Standards, and Procedures

Documentation, standards, and procedures are an outgrowth of good planning. Good documentation includes listings of the software, logic diagrams, internal and external specifications for the system, wiring and connection diagrams, hardware specifications, and users' manuals. Documentation is used in all phases of the management of the network. Standards and procedures together provide consistency in system management. Standards set minimal acceptable levels of performance and implementation. Procedural guidelines aid in operating and maintaining the system and are especially necessary in resolving problem situations.

In summary, meeting network management objectives requires a group of talented individuals who:

- Have the right tools in place
- Have a well-defined but flexible direction for the short term and the long term
- Are willing to work unusual hours in sometimes difficult or stressful environments
- Can work effectively with people at all levels of capability

The growth in network management has placed large demands on the supply of qualified people. As a result, network management personnel are currently among the most difficult to find and highest paid in the computer industry.

LAN VERSUS WAN AND ENTERPRISE NETWORK MANAGEMENT

In theory, you might expect LAN management to be essentially the same as WAN management. In practice that is not usually the case. WAN management typically involves:

- Geographically distributed nodes
- Some local autonomy in node management and control
- Diverse hardware platforms and network protocols
- A variety of media types and speeds
- Third-party media vendors

WANs typically grew out of data-processing departments and the management concerns are more technically oriented than those for LANs, which grew out of stand-alone microcomputer environments. If a site has interconnected LANs and WANs, responsibility for management of the interconnection interfaces often falls on the WAN management team. This means the WAN management team must be aware of large and small system concepts, whereas the LAN administrator is not usually required to have knowledge of large systems and WANs. Another term we might use in place of *WAN management* is *enterprise network management* because many companies that have a WAN also have one or more LANs, and these networks are interconnected in an enterprise network.

Consider the enterprise network portrayed in Figure 9-2. Each LAN will likely have an administrator who is responsible for keeping the LAN functioning. The enterprise network managers are responsible for:

- Keeping all WAN nodes operating properly
- Working with common carriers to obtain and maintain links between nodes
- Maintaining connections between subnetworks
- Coordinating efforts of subnet managers
- Managing LANs co-located with the WAN

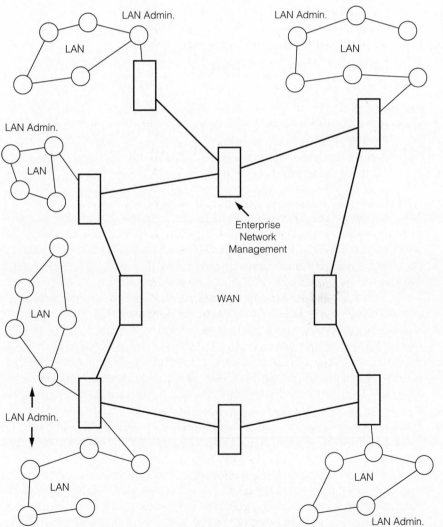

Figure 9-2

Network Management in an Enterprise Network

Having evolved from mainframe management environments, enterprise network management personnel are typically highly experienced data processing personnel who know the intricacies of data communications subsystems and large system operating systems. In contrast, a LAN administrator may be chosen from the ranks of skilled microcomputer users. Sometimes personnel chosen for this position have limited technical backgrounds as compared to their counterparts in WAN management. We have already described the profile of a network management team and the skills they need. Let us now look more closely at one of the entry levels of network management, LAN administration.

In a six-person office in which each person has a microcomputer workstation, how do you imagine the management and operations of the workstations are conducted? In most offices:

- Each person is responsible for backing up his or her data (if it is done at all).

- Each person is responsible for operating a micro.

- There is no office data processing manager (although there may be a local "expert" upon whom others rely for help).

- No provisions are made for security.

- If resource sharing exists, it is done via disk exchange or printer switches.

- If someone makes a mistake or if one system fails, it has little impact on the others.

- A certain amount of "trading" of software occurs because the office does not have one copy for each user.

- Everyone wants the best printer attached to their computer.

Now, suppose the office manager informs everyone that a LAN is about to be installed and that, after the dust settles, a more effective computing system will be available. The manager probably is correct with respect to the LAN providing a more effective computing platform. However, let us look at another implication of installing a LAN, LAN management.

In switching from a stand-alone microcomputer environment to a LAN, it is essential to have two or more people designated as LAN managers. If the LAN is large, several people may be actively involved as LAN managers; if the LAN is small, one person may be the principal manager and the second the alternate. (What constitutes a small, medium, or large LAN is difficult to define. For our purposes, small LANs are those with fewer than 50 workstations and only 1 server; a medium-size LAN will have from 50 to 150 nodes and 3 or fewer servers. Large LANs will be all other LANs. Be aware that some small LANs can be as complex to manage as a large one.) The alternate LAN manager assists the primary manager as necessary and fills in when the primary is absent.

During installation, LAN management is a full-time job. After the LAN is in operation, management tasks are less time-consuming. For a small LAN, management tasks may take less than one or two hours a day; for a large LAN, management may be a full-time position and may even require more than one full-time person. It is easy for a business to overlook the costs of LAN management.

LAN Management Tasks

Before the LAN is installed, LAN managers should be hired or existing personnel trained for that task. The amount of training varies according to the complexity of the system. At a minimum, managers should know the fundamentals of data communications and how to:

- Connect and disconnect workstations
- Diagnose and correct medium problems
- Add and delete users
- Create the users' environments
- Implement security
- Create, modify, and manage the printing environment
- Install and modify applications
- Take system backups
- Recover from system failures
- Monitor and evaluate performance
- Add resources, such as a new server
- Maintain LAN documentation and procedures
- Assist in setting up LAN interconnections
- Detect and remove viruses

Connecting and Disconnecting Workstations.   A LAN often is not static. New workstations need to be added and existing ones moved or removed, particularly during LAN installation and the initial stages of operation. The procedures for installing a new workstation vary from one implementation to another, but usually the following steps are required:

1. Install the LAN adapter in the workstation.
2. Establish a connection on the medium for the new workstation. This may require a new port on an MAU or wiring hub, a new BNC connection on a coaxial cable, or simply a tap into a cable.
3. Connect the workstation to the medium by establishing a connection between the LAN adapter and the medium.
4. Install network software in the workstation.
5. Boot the new workstation and test its ability to communicate over the network.

Once the new workstation is working, the network documentation ought to be updated to reflect the new address and wiring circumstances.

Diagnosing and Correcting Problems.   In some LANs, the most common problems are medium faults: wiring breaks, loose connectors, and unterminated cables. Being able to locate and correct these faults is critical to the success of the LAN. A host of other problems can occur as well. Some of these include:

- Improperly installed network software
- Improperly installed application software
- User errors
- Broken equipment
- Improper security settings

Solving these problems requires diagnostic skills and the right set of tools.

Adding and Deleting Users.   Each LAN user must identify himself or herself when logging onto the LAN. Each user is authorized to run certain applications and perform a set of actions on selected files. These privileges are described in the following chapter's section on security. The network manager must assign user IDs to individuals and delete or modify user IDs when a user leaves or changes job functions. Users are usually associated with a group, for example, one for personnel administration, one for payroll administration, and so on. Like users, groups have assigned privileges on the LAN. Again, it is the responsibility of the LAN manager to define the required groups and to assign individuals to one or more groups. Sometimes, the LAN manager will pass user and group administration functions to unit managers.

For each new user, the LAN administrator typically will create or assist in creating the user's environment. Some of the tasks that might be completed are:

- Create a home directory for the user
- Add the user to the network mail system
- Create a **user login script**—a set of actions to be taken when the user logs in, such as setting search paths and initial menus
- Set default security parameters
- Set limits on resource utilization, such as the maximum amount of server disk that the user can consume
- Set printer mappings

Creating the Users' Environments.   The LAN administrator must assist in creating the proper environment for each user. This includes providing access to the proper applications, setting up user menus as called for, setting up the proper printing environment, and providing access to the necessary servers. Much of this is accomplished via batch command files and user login scripts. The key to setting up these environments is to make LAN use transparent, so the user has access to the necessary LAN facilities without being made aware of the details of the LAN itself.

Implementing Security.   In making the transition from a stand-alone to a LAN environment, resources that were once private may become shared. A file that resided on a stand-alone system may be placed on a file server, a program that existed on one or two microcomputers may be placed on a file server, or a printer available to only one micro might be attached to a printer server. Being placed in a shared circumstance does not mean, however, that any user should to be able to read or modify the file, run the application, or use the printer. Instead, the LAN manager must create an access profile for each user, group, file, application, and hardware device. Some attributes thus defined are given in Table 9-1.

TABLE 9-1   Security Attributes

File capabilities

> Ability to examine a directory listing
>
> Ability to read or write a file
>
> Ability to delete, rename, or create a file
>
> Ability to execute an application
>
> Ability for several users to simultaneously use a file
>
> Ability to restrict a file to one user at a time
>
> Ability to define file ownership
>
> Ability to pass privileges on to another user

User and Group Capabilities

Allow file access according to the capabilities just described by user and group

Require a password

Require passwords to have a minimum number of characters

Require passwords to be changed at certain intervals

Allow logins only during specified times

Allow a user to login only from selected workstations

Inclusion of users in a group

Specify account expiration date

Restrict amount of disk space used

Detect multiple login attempts and deactivate workstation or account

> Monitoring capabilities
>
> Identify users logged on to system
>
> View information about users
>
> View information about jobs
>
> View a user's activity on servers
>
> View what is displayed on a workstation
>
> Take control of a workstation's keyboard

There may be more or fewer capabilities depending on the particular implementation. Additional utilities frequently can be purchased to enhance the capabilities provided with the LAN software. For example, most LANs do not provide remote control software that gives the LAN administrator the ability to view what is displayed on a workstation's monitor or to take control of the keyboard. Several third-party utilities exist that can do this, and the presence of such a utility can significantly help the LAN administrator diagnose a user's problem.

Creating, Modifying, and Managing the Printing Environment.   There can be two types of printers on a LAN: dedicated or private, and shared. **Dedicated printers** are attached to workstations and can be used only by a person at that workstation. **Shared printers** are those controlled by a server and available to designated users. The latter type of printer is discussed in this section.

The general layout for a LAN printing system, a **spooler,** is illustrated in Figure 9-3. An application might go through the following steps to print a document on a shared printer:

Figure 9-3

Spooler Configuration

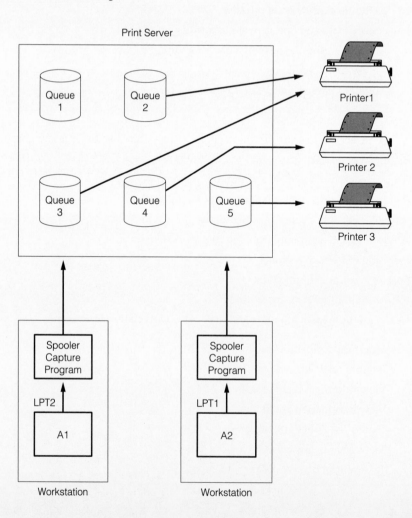

1. The application opens a printer port, such as LPT1 in a DOS system, and begins writing to that device.

2. The LAN printer software intercepts the print stream and routes it over the network to the server.

3. The server print collector accepts the print stream and stores it in a file.

4. Steps 2–3 continue until the application closes the connection to the printer port or until a time-out limit of no print output is reached. In either case, the workstation software sends an end-of-job designater to the print server.

5. The server closes that print job and schedules the job to be printed.

6. The print process looks at the scheduled jobs, selects the one with the highest priority, and prints it on the printer.

7. On completion of printing a job, the printer process selects the next available job and prints it, and so on.

From each user's perspective, the needed printer is always available and dedicated to that user. It is the spooler that provides this virtual printer capability. The spooler can also provide other functions, such as:

- Printing multiple copies
- Printing a document on several printers
- Holding a document on disk after printing or instead of printing
- Printing selected portions of a document
- Printing banners before each print job

At the more detailed level, there are many factors to consider and parameters to set when installing and controlling a printing subsystem. The factors are too many to cover in detail here, and the ways in which they are established vary from one LAN to another. In essence, the LAN administrator carries out the following tasks:

- Mapping printer ports on workstations to a print queue
- Mapping print queues to one or more printers
- Associating a printer with one or more print queues
- Changing the configuration described in the three preceding steps
- Assigning a printer priority scheme, such as printing small jobs before large jobs
- Monitoring the print jobs on disk
- Removing print jobs from disk
- Starting or stopping print jobs or printers
- Adding or deleting printers

Being able to obtain printed output is one of the basic needs of a LAN system. With all the configuration options typically available, the LAN administrator can provide an environment that meets or exceeds the needs of the LAN users; on the other hand, a poorly designed configuration can hinder printing effectiveness and consequently the effectiveness of the LAN itself.

Installing and Modifying Applications. When installing a new application, the LAN manager must plan how the application will be used, which users will need it, and on which server(s) the application will reside. Applications not designed for shared use must be installed in a way that prohibits concurrent usage. Applications that can be used concurrently need to be installed in a manner that maximizes their capabilities for each user. Most important, the LAN administrator must understand and comply with the application vendor's software license agreements. License agreements vary considerably. Some software programs are licensed for only one workstation; some are licensed for a specific number of concurrent users, such as four concurrent users; some are licensed to allow access for all users on a specific server; and some are licensed to allow access for all users on all servers. Obviously, understanding the license agreements is important for both application selection and installation.

Each application user ideally will be able to match his or her hardware with the application's features. Accordingly, a user with a color monitor ought to be able to tailor the application and have it display that user's preferred foreground and background colors. A user with a monochrome monitor will have a different user profile that runs correctly on his or her workstation. Other features that might be accounted for include the type of graphics adapter, display size, amount of memory available, and so on. Once the application is operational, the LAN administrator is responsible for installing application upgrades. A major application release sometimes will provide significant changes in how the system works and the user interface to the system. The LAN manager must plan for the transition from the old system to the new one. In such cases, it is usually prudent to have both application versions available to make the transition to the new application easier.

Taking System Backups. Recall that in the stand-alone microcomputer environment, each user is responsible for backing up his or her data files. On a LAN, this responsibility is assumed by the LAN administrator. The administrator must design a backup policy that will allow data files and programs to be recovered. Various backup devices are available. The main options are given in Table 9-2. Associated with the backup devices is backup software. Most LAN systems provide this software. Some companies choose to purchase separate backup software that provides a more robust set of capabilities than the LAN version. Table 9-3 lists common backup capabilities.

TABLE 9-2   **Backup Device Alternatives**

Diskette	Hard Disk	Magnetic Tape (several different technologies)
Optical Drive	Digital Audiotape	Digital Videocassette

TABLE 9-3   Common Backup Options

Time backups where the backup is scheduled to start at a specific time	Only backup files that have been modified since the last backup	Ability to specify a list of files or directories to backup
Ability to specify a list of files to exclude from the backup	Ability to backup files for a specific user	Ability to back up hidden and system files
Ability to change the directories of the files being backed up	Ability to preserve or change file ownership and attributes during backup and restore	Data compression to reduce the number of bits stored on the back-up medium
Allow wildcard naming conventions	Ability to back up open files	Ability to back up local drives on a workstation
Data verification during backup	Ability to resume back-up after interruption	Ability to create and review backup audit and error logs

Recovering from System Failures.   The main purpose of taking backups is to recover from failures. The LAN administrator must prepare procedures that will be implemented if the LAN fails. Because some failures do not affect files, the recovery procedures must encompass more than file recovery. For example, a workstation may fail in the middle of an application. The LAN administrator ought to have a procedure for recovering the application and lost work.

Monitoring and Evaluating Performance.   LAN usage is likely to change over time. Users might be added, some workstations deleted, and applications added or deleted. The LAN administrator must monitor the LAN usage and plan necessary changes. If usage increases, a new server may be needed, or, if multiple servers exist, the usage may need to be better balanced among them. Things the LAN administrator may monitor include:

- Printing environment
- Disk usage
- Number of active users
- Application usage
- Transmission faults
- Server-busy statistics

Based on the performance statistics, the LAN administrator will plan corrective action as necessary.

Adding Resources.   The LAN administrator must plan the acquisition and integration of any new LAN resources into the system. If a file server is added, the LAN administrator must decide which files are to be placed on the new server and which users the file server will primarily serve. After integrating the new server, the administrator will monitor the LAN activities to ensure that service is satisfactory and that all components are used effectively.

Maintaining LAN Documentation and Procedures.   Much of the success of data processing administration stems from having good, current documentation and procedures. The LAN administrator is responsible for creating and updating this documentation.

Assisting in Setting Up LAN Interconnections.   In Chapter 8 you read about the ways one network can be connected to another network. The LAN administrator is involved in setting up the proper hardware and software interfaces on the LAN side of the connection. If two LANs are being connected, the administrator may be responsible for all of the interconnection details.

Detecting and Removing Viruses.   One concern of network administrators at all levels is the proliferation of computer viruses and similar disruptive programs or code modules. Today's network administrators must have up-to-date virus detection and removal software and procedures. There are several sources of software for virus detection, and many of them can stay memory resident and provide continuous scanning. All network administrators need to include computer viruses in their planning and procedures.

WAN Management Tasks

The responsibilities of WAN managers differ somewhat from those of a LAN manager. A LAN administrator is an integral part of the network management team; however, in this section the term *WAN management team* refers to the group of network managers whose responsibilities include WAN management. Some LAN management tasks typically not carried out by a WAN manager are:

- Creating user environments, a task typically carried out by programming personnel
- Creating, modifying, and managing the printing environment, a task typically carried out by operations personnel
- Installing and modifying applications, a task typically carried out by programming and operations personnel
- Taking backups, a task typically carried out by operations personnel

A representative list of WAN management tasks is given below:

- Connect and disconnect workstations
- Diagnose and correct medium problems
- Add and delete users
- Implement security

- Recover from system failures
- Monitor and evaluate performance
- Add resources, such as a new server or communications line
- Maintain LAN documentation and procedures
- Assist in setting up LAN interconnections
- Detect and remove viruses
- Interface with a common carrier
- Estimate equipment and media costs
- Configure network components to meet transmission and cost requirements
- Interface with corporate and vendor personnel in devising network solutions
- Resolve problems regarding international telecommunications
- Develop and maintain network software
- Coordinate and consolidate network management

Items in this list up to and including detecting and removing viruses are tasks common to LANs and WANs and have been discussed above. Let us look at those management tasks that are unique to WANs.

Interfacing with a Common Carrier. As technology advances, we may see increasing instances of LANs being implemented using a medium provided by a common carrier. Currently, the use of common carrier media in LANs is uncommon whereas in WANs it is commonplace. In the United States, a company can choose from among several common carriers. Each common carrier will have characteristics that sets it apart from its competitors. Differences among common carriers may include rates, types of media and services, locations serviced, and quality of service and support. The WAN management team must be familiar with the advantages and disadvantages of each common carrier and choose the most cost-effective alternatives.

Network problems can be caused by a company's equipment, by a common carrier's equipment, or by the interface between the two. When problems occur that cannot be isolated to the company's equipment, the network management team must work with the common carrier in diagnosing and correcting the problem.

Estimating Equipment and Media Costs. A LAN administrator will also carry out this task; however, the number of options and range of prices are much greater in a WAN. In configuring portions of a WAN, the management team must evaluate several common carriers, perhaps several services per common carrier, and data communications equipment from a variety of vendors. Often the number of possible solutions will be large. If a company considers three common carriers, two services per carrier, and five different data communications providers each of which has three pieces of equipment to consider, the number of combinations of vendors, services, and equipment is 90. Choosing the best one requires considerable analysis and expertise.

Configuring Network Components.   Like estimating equipment and media costs, configuring network components is a process of evaluating a large number of alternatives. A LAN's standard and topology limits the ways in which network components can be added. In a WAN there are usually fewer restrictions, the configuration task is much more complex, and the cost of solutions is often greater than for LAN configuration solutions. For example, adding a node to a LAN usually means finding the closest wiring hub or cable and attaching the node to it. Adding a node to a WAN often requires obtaining one or more communications lines from a common carrier, deciding which existing nodes the new node is to be linked to, procuring the hardware and software for the new node, preparing the site for installation of the new node, and training personnel to manage the new equipment.

Resolving Problems Regarding International Telecommunications. In Chapter 7 you read about issues regarding international networks. LAN administrators need not be concerned with international issues. Managers of international WANs must address the issues raised in Chapter 7. These issues are:

- Politics
- Regulations
- Hardware
- Language
- Tariffs

The WAN management team must consider these issues in estimating network costs, use, and configuration.

Developing and Maintaining Network Software.   A LAN administrator is responsible for setting up a user's application environment but seldom gets involved in fixing or writing network software. The WAN management team may need to customize some characteristics of the network or install corrections to faulty network programs. If a company has a unique device that needs to be attached to the network, the WAN management team may need to write the network interface code or modify an existing interface. When errors are detected in network software, the software vendor may distribute patches to the code. The WAN management team will be responsible for inserting the patches and testing the system to ensure it works properly.

Coordinating and Consolidating Network Management.   A   LAN administrator is usually responsible for one or more LANs in a specific location. The WAN management team is responsible for the coordination and consolidation of all aspects of network management to include the operations and interconnections of subnets. The knowledge and responsibilities of the WAN management team are far beyond those of the LAN manager. Problems that cannot be solved by local operations or LAN management personnel become the responsibility of the WAN management team. WAN managers must remain aware of problems in all segments of the network to avoid duplicating diagnosis and correction of problems that have already been encountered and resolved.

System Management Issues

To learn more about the systems management issues described above and to explore other system management issues like auditing, accounting, software distribution, and version control, you should now switch to the CBT module entitled "System Management Issues".

NETWORK MANAGEMENT SYSTEM SOFTWARE

A network should be under continuous scrutiny to ensure that the objectives of customer satisfaction and cost-effectiveness are met. Too often, network problems surface through user complaints. This is usually not the way a network manager wants to learn about problems. A far better way is to have potential problems detected and reported by a network management system, so problems may be corrected before users become aware of them.

A **network management system (NMS)** is a combination of hardware and software used by network supervisors to monitor and administer the network. The NMS must be able to determine the status of network components such as modems, lines, workstations, servers, terminals, multiplexers, and so on. If a device's status indicates that malfunctions are occurring, the NMS will either take automatic corrective action or alert a network supervisor of the condition. The network supervisor may then use network control functions of the NMS to take corrective action. An NMS also gathers network statistics, such as line utilization information, together with capabilities for evaluating those statistics. The information produced assists network supervisors in capacity planning.

In the past, most network software vendors neglected the area of network management. With few exceptions, the network software and hardware were built and installed with little support for managing them. Although management of small networks is not difficult, the composition of networks has changed as more businesses made the move to online systems. Two of these changes have had a significant impact on the ability to manage networks. First, the number and complexity of network nodes have increased. Early networks may have consisted of one central processor with communications controllers and terminal devices. The host assumed a supervisory role and provided a centralized point of control and management. Often the communications links were point-to-point leased or switched lines. In contrast, many of today's enterprise networks have multiple processing nodes and hundreds or thousands of connected devices. The network may consist of LANs, X.25 networks, leased lines, satellite and microwave links, switched lines, and PBX systems. Numerous interfaces between different types of equipment and networks are relatively common.

Second, many of today's enterprise networks are a hybrid of workstations, servers, large systems, terminals, controllers, modems, and other components from different vendors. Managing a homogeneous network in which all the components are provided by one vendor is difficult. In the past, effectively managing a large network with components from multiple vendors approached the impossible. This problem fortunately is being recognized by network managers and vendors alike, and NMSs are being sold from both network vendors and independent software companies. Let us first consider the requirements of a generic NMS and then discuss the specific capabilities provided by IBM's Netview, Netview/PC, and Netview/6000 and Novell's Network Management System. These products were chosen for two reasons: their applicability to a large body of users and functionality. The reader should be aware that other products exist, some of which provide more comprehensive management features.

A Generic Network Management System

To understand an NMS, consider a hypothetical network of a large, international manufacturing firm. This company has processing nodes in many locations throughout the world. A small portion of this network from one manufacturing location is shown in Figure 9-4. The backbone network is an SNA network (see Chapter 7), and there are two domains. The major components of the system come from seven different vendors. The host processors in both domains are from Company A. The communications controllers were purchased from Company B, but run IBM NCP (Network Control Program) software. The Engineering and Development Department has an IEEE 802.3-compatible LAN to support its design efforts. The workstations are special purpose and were provided by two companies, C and D. A router to the SNA network is provided using Company D's equipment. The interface to the SNA network is via LU 6.2. The office automation system uses equipment from Vendor E and interfaces to the SNA system in the same way as the engineering router. The PBX system obtained from Vendor F is also tied into the network. Modems and multiplexers were all obtained from Vendor G. What will the network management team need to know to keep this network running efficiently? A summary of this information appears in Table 9-4.

In a large network, if all the data being gathered is sent to the network managers, both the network and the network managers would have a difficult time keeping up with it. Simply receiving the data is not enough; it must be received in a usable format. The NMS is responsible for ensuring that the correct data is received and that it is in a usable format. The network segment illustrated in Figure 9-5 shows a network component, a portion of the NMS, and the connection to the control center. The NMS will continually obtain status and operational data from the component(s) it is monitoring. Ordinarily the data will be routine, and either ignored or logged for later evaluation.

TABLE 9-4 Network Management Information

A. Host processors
  1. Status
  2. CPU busy rates
  3. Internal queues, such as on TCP
  4. Transaction turnaround time in the CPU
  5. Buffer utilization
  6. Peak activity times
  7. Performance during peak activity
B. Communications controllers
  1. Status
  2. Processor busy rates
  3. Buffer utilization
  4. Queues
  5. Peak activity time
  6. Performance during peak activity
C. Lines
  1. Status
  2. Number of failures
  3. Number of retries
  4. Aggregate data rate
  5. Peak activity time
  6. Performance during peak activity
  7. Active devices on the line
  8. Line quality
  9. Changes in line quality
D. Modems
  1. Status
  2. Errors
E. Terminals
  1. Status
  2. Number of failures
  3. Failure types
  4. Number of transactions
  5. Type of transactions
  6. Transaction response time
F. Processing nodes
  1. Status
  2. Number of transactions
  3. Response time
  4. Type of transactions

Specifically, if the component being monitored is a communications line, some of the information the NMS will receive could be the number of errors encountered since the last status report, current status, line quality, number of retries on the line, and number of characters transmitted or received. When some out-of-tolerance event occurs, it must be brought to the attention of the network managers, which is called an **alert** or **alarm.** If a problem has occurred, the NMS should also assist the managers in solving the problem by indicating the potential causes and perhaps even solutions.

Figure 9-4

Integrated Network

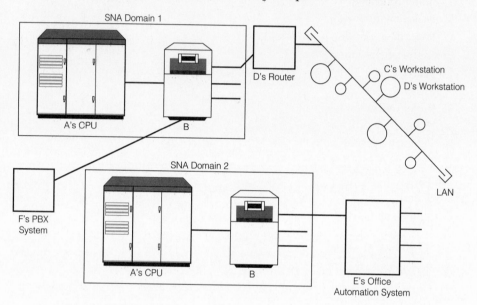

If the values received are within tolerance, and if data collection is enabled, the data will be logged. Later it may be evaluated for trend analysis and capacity planning. If the data is not within accepted tolerance levels, this must be brought to the attention of the network managers. An alert is necessary for a data communications line if the line is down, the error rates have exceeded some threshold, the number of retries is excessive, or the line is congested. A change in service level also may be cause for an alert for a component that is being closely monitored. For example, if a line has been operating between 20-percent and 25-percent capacity and suddenly experiences 50-percent load capacity, an alert may signal this change.

When an alert condition has been detected, it must be forwarded to the network management center. Steps that may be taken in this process include:

1. Identification of probable causes of the alert condition.

2. Formatting the message for the NMS presentation services. Component addresses, status, and probable causes must be identified. In Figure 9-5 this function is performed by the software component identified as a **filter,** which is used to screen and format data sent to the management center. A filter can perform many functions, one of which is to control the flow of data to the center. Flow control avoids flooding the control center with repetitious status messages.

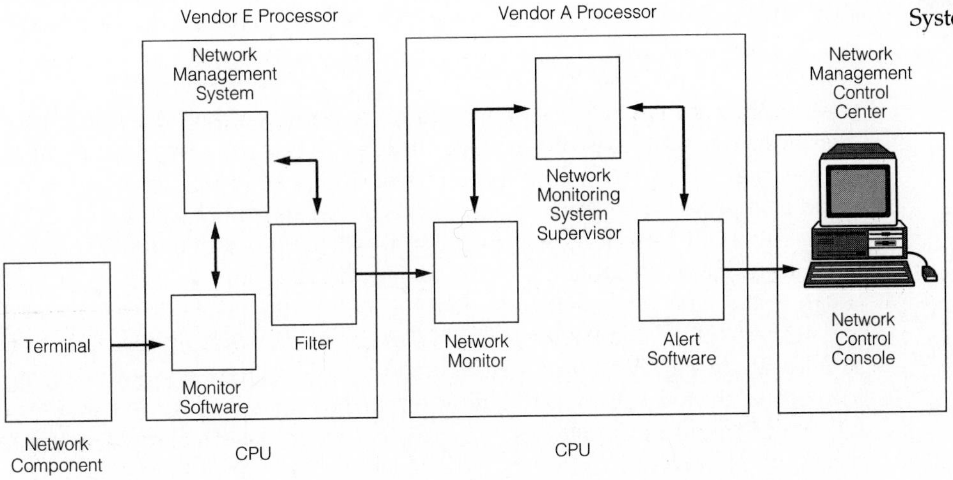

Figure 9-5

Network Management
System

3. Transmission of the data to the control center for display.

4. Passing the message through a formatter at the control center, which determines where and how the message is to be displayed. Many NMS presentation services utilize color monitors to present the data. Warnings may be displayed in yellow, outages in red, and major catastrophes in blinking red with an audio signal. The message will also usually be logged to an alert history file.

5. The network management team acting on the alert as necessary and documenting the event and its solution.

As mentioned earlier, obtaining the proper information to manage a network is difficult enough in a homogeneous network environment. In a mixed-vendor configuration, additional complexities must be resolved. In Figure 9-5 the network management control center is attached to one of the host processors and uses software provided by that vendor, Vendor A. Vendor A's network management tools are designed to monitor only its own equipment and to present messages in a specific format. In the configuration shown, terminals attached to Vendor E's processors may be involved in a session with a host logical unit. This terminal also may not be supported by the host system.

The problems that must be resolved in this type of environment include obtaining status information from each vendor's equipment, formatting the alerts in a manner consistent with the host's requirements, and routing alerts and their associated data to the host node for display. Once the alert has been raised, the system managers must react to it. For example, if a device is malfunctioning and disrupting the network, the device needs to be deactivated until the problem is fixed. The NMS will provide an interface that allows the network managers to deactivate the device and later bring it back online.

If several vendors are represented, each vendor is likely to have different peripheral control utilities and different command languages. In Vendor A's environment the command to bring a failed terminal—such as the terminal known to the system as TERMINAL-X—back online may be RESTORE TER-MINAL-X, whereas in Vendor E's system the same command may be DEVICE TERMINAL-X UP. Thus, once the alert has been received, correction in a mixed-vendor network may not be simple. One cannot expect network managers to know the command languages required to remedy faults on several different vendor systems. Even on one system there may be several interfaces for fault correction. One interface may be used for physical devices and another for logical devices and connections. If a terminal has failed and needs to be restored, it may be necessary to activate the terminal on the line via a peripheral utility program and, using a different utility, notify application programs that the terminal is again available.

To reduce the complexities of dealing with multiple-vendor equipment, and sometimes even a variety of interfaces from one vendor, the NMS may provide a **command mapping function.** This allows the network managers to work with one command language that has a consistent interface. The command mapping function will select the proper interface program(s) to receive the message and translate the command into a format acceptable to these programs.

NETWORK MANAGEMENT PROTOCOLS

Network interconnection raises an additional network management problem. The problem is how to monitor nodes on one subnetwork from a node on a different subnetwork, such as monitoring a node on a token ring from a network management console attached to an IBM SNA network. To facilitate the exchange of management data among network nodes, a network management standard or protocol is essential. If such standards exist, network designers can build their networks with the ability to exchange management and control data. Two such standards have evolved: the **simple network management protocol (SNMP)** and the **common management information protocol (CMIP).** CMIP is also sometimes referred to as the **communications management information protocol.**

Network Management Overview

To gain an understanding of these two protocols, switch to the CBT module entitled "Network Management Overview".

IBM'S NETWORK MANAGEMENT SYSTEM

Netview and **Netview/PC** were introduced by IBM in 1986, and another version, **Netview/6000,** was introduced in 1992. The original Netview consolidated and extended several network management packages that had been used to monitor and control SNA networks. Netview is thus oriented to managing the host SNA environment. Netview/PC contains logic for monitoring IBM's token-ring network, PBX systems, and other vendors' equipment. Netview/6000 runs on IBM's UNIX-based systems and provides support for multivendor networks with no centralized host system.

Netview

Netview runs on an IBM host system and is the NMS for monitoring and controlling an SNA network. The functions it provides include control services and diagnostic control capabilities, such as hardware monitoring, session monitoring, and status monitoring. Hardware monitoring collects status information from physical devices, and session monitoring provides information on SNA sessions. Status monitoring provides display information regarding system components and assists in restarting system elements following a failure. The control function provides the ability to activate and deactivate devices. In addition to the management and control functions, Netview provides two other basic facilities: help and a user interface. The help function provides users with online assistance as well as an operator tutorial. The user interface allows scripts, called Clists, to be prepared by users to monitor devices and/or to automate startup and shutdown sequences.

Netview/PC

Netview/PC, as the name indicates, runs on a microcomputer. Netview/PC is an important component in IBM's open communications architecture (OCA). IBM recognizes that networks tend to have a mixture of vendor equipment. OCA opens an IBM network from a management perspective by providing other vendors with interface specifications. Through these, other vendors can have their equipment integrated more completely into the network. Within Netview/PC this integration is effected through an application program interface (API).

The API allows users to write applications that can interface to non-IBM devices. The API applications can be written to have device-specific interfaces as well as a Netview interface; this allows the application to establish the management connection between the device and IBM's network management tools. Within Netview/PC, IBM provides this interface to its token-ring LAN and to computerized PBX systems. Status information collected by the microcomputer running Netview/PC may be stored on the microcomputer's local disk and/or forwarded to Netview, which runs on the host system. If alerts are received, they either may be handled at the microcomputer or may be forwarded to the host for operator intervention and resolution. The interface between the host and the microcomputer is either via an SNA 3270 terminal or as an LU 6.2 session type.

Netview/6000

Netview/6000 represents IBM's NMS for decentralized networks and networks using the SNMP. Netview/6000 requires fewer system resources than Netview and can run on smaller platforms. Netview/6000 has the ability to monitor up to 30,000 different objects and will support SNA capabilities such as LU 6.2, the virtual terminal access method (VTAM), and advanced peer-to-peer networking (APPN). Netview/6000 also provides support for managing LANs and devices such as bridges, wiring hubs, and routers.

Netview Architecture

The **Netview architecture** identifies three types of control points: focal points, entry points, and service points. A **focal point** is a central point for network management and monitoring functions. Focal points provide host-oriented functions including functions related to billing, line optimization, and performance analysis. **Entry points** relate to IBM or IBM-compatible network elements. Entry point functions include remote management and control modules, which allow the element to be controlled remotely from the control center and to communicate with Netview. **Service points** are gateways into the Netview system from non-SNA devices. Service points are characterized by Netview/PC and the devices it monitors and controls.

To summarize, through Netview and Netview/PC IBM has created a system that allows centralized control of a distributed system that consists of IBM, IBM-compatible, and non-IBM equipment. Netview provides the ability to monitor and control the SNA network, and Netview/PC provides the same function for other network components. With Netview/6000, the management and control functions have been extended to include decentralized networks and multivendor networks.

NOVELL'S NETWORK MANAGEMENT SYSTEM

The acronym **NMS** is used to represent both a generic term for a network management system and Novell Corporation's specific system, also called **NetWare Management System.** Novell's NMS contains a collection of tools oriented toward managing LANs using Novell's network operating system. The main functions managed by NMS are network faults, performance, configuration, security, and accounting.

NMS consists of several components including NetExplorer and NetWare Management Agents. NetExplorer essentially provides a database that represents all LAN components, such as details about servers, workstations, LAN adapters, wiring hubs, bridges, and routers. The database is a resource for other NMS components. In addition to collecting network configuration data, NetExplorer can graphically display the complete or partial network configurations.

NetExplorer Manager and the **NetWare Management Agents (NMAs)** components work together to provide statistics and alerts to the NMS console. The NMS polls NMA for statistics similar to the way in which SNMP collects data from device agents. The NSM can organize and report on data collected. A dedicated or nondedicated workstation is used as the LAN administrator's interface to the NMS. Other features found in Novell's NMS include:

- Application program interfaces to give third-party vendors access to NMS functions
- Modules for monitoring packets, protocols, and media
- Modules to track wiring hub performance
- Automatic server fault detection and alert notification
- An interface to IBM's Netview
- Graphical and text reporting
- Setting of thresholds for devices

SUMMARY

As the use of data communications expands, so will the role and importance of network management. The keys to effective network management are personnel who are competent and knowledgeable and who can work well with a broad spectrum of users; planning; and the effective use of network management tools. Network management is involved in the design, testing, and operations of a system. A certain amount of implementation or development is also required in some installations.

Network management is both a function and an application. The application portion should be designed and implemented like any other business application. The primary functions for computerized implementation are problem-reporting systems, tools, network management software that reacts automatically to problems in the network, and diagnostic systems. With careful management, the network can be a valuable asset to a company; with poor or no management, even the best designed application system can fail. If the network is incorrectly designed, is not modified to meet changing demands, or is frequently inoperable, and if problems are not readily resolved, users will lose confidence in the system, and the network's effectiveness will be diminished.

Managing a network can be a complex task requiring a wide range of information and tools. NMSs and utilities assist the administrator in managing the network and correcting network problems. An NMS collects statistics on network components, provides alerts when proper operation is threatened, and generates standard reports to allow the network manager to monitor performance and take corrective actions before problems develop. Two network management protocols, *simple network management protocol (SNMP)* and *common management information protocol (CMIP),* have been defined to assist vendors in creating software and hardware that can be monitored. The SNMP is part of the TCP/IP suite and is widely used in a variety of hardware and software platforms. The CMIP is an International Standards Organization recommendation for collection and reporting of management information. Although more comprehensive than the SNMP, CMIP is not yet widely implemented.

A number of vendors provide NMSs. IBM's Netview has three variations, Netview, Netview/PC, and Netview/6000. Each is designed to support different network configurations. Netview is designed to support SNA networks, Netview/PC provides interfaces to non-IBM devices in an SNA network, and Netview/6000 is designed for noncentralized networks using a variety of vendor platforms. Novell Corporation's NMS is called NetWare Management System (NMS) and provides management capabilities for LANs running under Novell's NetWare LAN operating system. NMS services are also provided by a variety of other vendors.

KEY TERMS

REVIEW QUESTIONS

1. What are the two main objectives of network management?

2. Why is user satisfaction an important network management objective?

3. Describe the functions performed by the network management team.

4. How do problems get reported and resolved? What documents are generated as a result of the problem-reporting system? Who receives copies of these documents?

5. How are statistics used in network management?

6. Describe the documentation created and maintained by the network management team.

7. List ten LAN management tasks.

8. What must a LAN manager do when installing a new workstation?

9. How are statistics used in network management?

10. What functions are performed by network management systems?

11. Describe how IBM's Netview and Netview/PC interact with each other.

12. Compare and contrast Netview and Netview/6000.

13. Describe the capabilities of Novell's NetWare Management System.

14. Compare the simple network management protocol (SNMP) and the common management information protocol (CMIP).

15. Why are SNMP and CMIP important?

10
....

SECURITY, NETWORK APPLICATIONS, AND DISTRIBUTED SYSTEMS

....

CHAPTER OBJECTIVES

After studying this chapter you should be able to:

- Compare the three major classes of security: physical, data access, and encryption
- Discuss the types and capabilities of groupware
- Describe a distributed system
- Trace the evolution of distributed systems
- Explain the concepts of client/server computing
- Describe the functions of a remote file system
- List the advantages and disadvantages of distributed systems
- Describe the requirements of distributed systems

*I*n this chapter we begin with a discussion of security. Security helps protect network resources by limiting access by unauthorized users and preventing authorized users from making mistakes and making unauthorized data accesses. Networking, particularly LANs, has given rise to a new class of applications called groupware. In this chapter you will read about several varieties of groupware applications and how they support the interaction of individuals in a workgroup.

In providing users access to network applications and utilities, the network administrator must ensure that the software is used in accordance with provisions stipulated by the software vendor. Failure to adhere to these provisions may result in legal action and associated penalties. One direction of network technology has been creating the ability to effectively distribute processing resources such as hardware, software, and data, as well as the use, management, and control of these resources. We conclude by discussing the characteristics of distributed systems.

SECURITY

Security does not prevent unauthorized access to a system; it only makes such access more difficult. The additional difficulty in accessing the system should delay the intruder long enough either to make unauthorized access cost-prohibitive or to give the system manager time to detect and apprehend the perpetrator, or both. In the first case, the rewards of unauthorized access would be less than the cost of breaking into the system. In the second, the attempted penetration would be detected and further attempts suppressed. From the system owner's perspective, the cost of security should be no more than the potential loss from unauthorized system access.

There are levels of security from which we can choose. No security means that any user can access and use anything on the system. On a personnel system with no security, a user could give himself or herself a raise or a good performance rating. On the other hand, total security means no one can access or use anything on the system. Obviously, selecting the proper security level for each user is important. Imposing tighter security makes the system more difficult to use and increases the system overhead. Security should protect data from intentional or accidental loss or disclosure, without adversely affecting employees' ability to perform their jobs.

Vendor-Provided Security

Security needs are as various as the number of users. Each organization has its own security objectives, and it is therefore difficult to provide one security system that meets everyone's needs. Vendors of hardware or systems software tend to provide only basic security features. This security is generally found only in vendor-provided user interfaces, such as command interpreters and operator- or programmer-level interfaces. When provided, such facilities are generally limited to system and file access. **System access** is usually user identification and authentication via a user identifier and a corresponding password. At the data level, additional protection includes security for access to files, such as like the ability to control read, write, or file-delete capabilities. Furthermore, the operating system may provide safeguards, such as prohibiting one process from interfering with the data of another process and viewing the data of an active or recently terminated process. This section addresses security concerns more directly affecting the data communications network, and does not include operating system security.

Physical Security

Physical security means using techniques such as door locks, safes, and security guards to deny physical access to areas containing sensitive information. Because physical security is independent of hardware or software, it can be planned long before the installation of a network and hardware. If access is prevented to physical components of the system such as file servers, wiring closets, and user offices, the likelihood of unauthorized access is significantly decreased. However, physical security will not prevent an authorized user from accidentally or intentionally misusing the system. This is significant because studies have shown that the biggest security risk companies face is not unknown hackers but the accidental or intentional destruction or misuse of data by employees.

Because of the notoriety given to hackers, for some people security is associated with issues such as user IDs and passwords to protect against unauthorized remote access. However, security was a requirement for some applications before remote access was common and in some current systems that do not provide remote access. Enforcement of security in these systems is easier than it is in most of today's networks. A batch processing system is an example of a system that might not allow remote access. Consider the security implications of such a system. All the computerized data and devices that can access that data can be contained within a single computer room. Paperwork used for generating batch inputs and printed outputs are the only forms of data that need to leave the computer facility. Security for this system can be primarily satisfied by regulating physical access to the computer room.

Because gaining access to computerized data in a pure batch facility requires gaining access to the computer room, security locks on computer room doors and proper staff training regarding computer room access provide a security level adequate for many installations. While the computer staff is on duty, they control computer facility access; during off-shift hours, security guards can take over. The hard-copy documents that are removed from the computer room can be controlled through corporate policies for dissemination and protection of paperwork.

Another common physical security measure is a surveillance system. Security personnel can use this system to screen entry to the premises. The premises may be the property on which the facility is located, individual buildings, rooms within a building, or combinations of these. Additional security can be provided for sensitive areas with closed-circuit television monitors, motion sensors, alarms, and other such intrusion-detection devices. Many installations can justify features such as closed-circuit television and motion sensors because they provide for equipment protection as well as data protection. Use of these devices may result in reduced insurance rates and partially offset their cost. Other physical security measures that may be used include the following:

- Equipment should be located in secure areas with controlled personnel access when possible. For example, LAN servers should be located in a room with controlled access.

- Nonsecure transmission media, such as broadcast radio, should be avoided where possible because such transmissions are easier to intercept. Use a conducted medium rather than a radiated one for such transmissions.

- If broadcast radio must be used, all transmitted data should be encrypted (encrypting only sensitive data identifies it as such to a potential penetrator and makes his or her work easier).

- Switched lines should be avoided, if possible. Recall that switched lines are those that can be accessed through the telephone company's switching equipment. If you have a switched line, any person with a computer and a modem has the ability to access your system. When they are used, switched lines should be physically disconnected during the hours they are not required, thus limiting the potential for unauthorized use.

- Computers being used for highly sensitive applications should be disconnected from networks whenever possible, placing an additional barrier to access from other network nodes. For example, some U.S. military computers are connected to a national network, except those that are used for processing highly classified data.

In most current processing environments, protecting an entire network by physical security is not sufficient to protect data. Access to data is available via terminals or workstations distributed throughout the organization. Many online systems also have the ability to access the system remotely via switched circuits. Because physical security is not enough, other security levels—encryption and access security—must be added.

Encryption

Encryption which is defined as encoding or scrambling data to make it unintelligible to those without the **encryption key,** should be used with all media carrying sensitive data. A variety of **encryption algorithms** exist. The particular encryption algorithm chosen should be capable of deterring unwarranted use by making it too costly or time-consuming to decipher the message.

Data Encryption Standard

One of the most common yet controversial encryption algorithms is the **Data Encryption Standard (DES)** adopted by the National Bureau of Standards. DES is an algorithm that uses an encryption key to transform data, called **plain text,** into an encoded form called encrypted text or **cipher text;** likewise, someone who knows the encryption key can retransform the encrypted data to its original plain text. Making the transformation from encrypted text to plain text without the encryption key is a laborious and time-consuming process.

The DES controversy surrounds the effectiveness of the standard. In 1976 it was estimated that it would take the most powerful computers available between 91 and 2000 years to break the DES code. Opponents of the algorithm countered that the code could be broken within 12 hours at a cost of approximately $5000. The primary criticism of the DES is that only 56 bits are used for the encryption key. Critics believe this allows for too few different possible data permutations because systematic attempts to decrypt the message would allow message decryption within a reasonable time. With the increasing speed and lower cost of computer hardware, most critics and proponents agreed that the algorithm had an effective life of approximately ten years, meaning it should now be at the end of its effectiveness.

Encryption introduces overhead to a network and has the potential of slowing communication. This is particularly true if the encryption is done with software. Therefore, most DES algorithms make use of integrated circuits designed for encrypting and decrypting data. The chips may be integrated onto processor or controller boards or used in stand-alone external boxes. The encryption devices can be placed between individual nodes or at the origin and destination of the message. Figure 10-1 illustrates several configuration options.

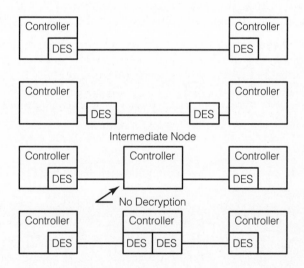

Figure 10-1

Encryption Configurations

Encryption algorithms other than DES are being used. One of the more promising, referred to as **trapdoor encryption** or the **public key method,** utilizes large prime numbers and two keys, one key made public and the other kept secret by the message recipient. The public key encrypts the data; the private key decrypts the cipher text. A new encryption chip called the **Clipper chip** is being proposed by the U.S. government for encrypting data on networks and telephone lines. If this chip is installed in telephone and computer equipment, the U.S. government also wants to reserve the right to tap communications lines and decode messages that may pertain to criminal investigations. Most practitioners agree that secure communications is a good idea but have concerns over abuses that might arise if the government has the ability to decrypt all messages.

Key administration is an important function in an effective encryption program. Administration includes:

- Key creation
- Key distribution
- Key storage/safeguarding/restoration
- Setting standards for frequency of changing keys

Standards organizations have recognized the critical nature of key management and have adopted several standards to guide key administrators. Among these are **ANSI X9.17,** which addresses key management for financial institutions, and **U.S. Federal Standard 1027,** for security requirements of equipment using the DES standard. An organization that is serious about security and encryption should have one or more persons designated as security administrators whose function is to implement security and detect attempts to breach security. Security measures that might be implemented are given in Table 10-1.

TABLE 10-1 Sample Security Measures

All users must have a password.

Passwords must be at least six characters long.

Passwords must be changed at least monthly.

Passwords will be changed immediately if there is suspicion that a password has been compromised.

Passwords will not contain users' initials, month abbreviations, or other obvious character strings.

Passwords must contain non-numeric and non-alphabetic characters like #, [, etc.

Passwords must not be written down.

Passwords must be created randomly so they do not contain sequence numbers or other instances of succession.

Unsuccessful attemps to logon to the system will be recorded. Data recorded will include the time, terminal from which the attempt is made, and the user ID for which the login is attempted.

All unsucessful login attempts will be investigated.

All sensitive data will be encrypted.

Encryption keys will be changed regularly.

Two people will be responsible for encryption key administration.

No single individual can change the encryption key.

Switched (dial-up) lines will be disconnected when not in use.

Manual answer and user verification must be used for all switched connections or call-back units will be used.

User Identification and Authentication

Encryption is only one aspect of security. In most systems the first level of security is user identification and authentication. **User identification** runs the gamut from simply providing a user name to biological measures such as retina scans, voice prints, palm prints, or fingerprint identification, which are usually employed only in high-security systems such as those of the intelligence and military communities. In business applications, identification is generally supplied by user name or electronic badge. After identification comes **authentication,** which requires the user to provide additional information unique to that particular user, such as a password.

Passwords

A **password** is the most common form of authentication. It is maintained in a file of information about system users, which typically includes user ID, password, defaulted security attributes for any files created, and possibly an access profile. Because this file contains the information needed to access any portion of the system, it should be carefully secured and encrypted. Passwords should be changed frequently, either centrally by the network administrators or in a decentralized manner by the users. If centrally managed, passwords are sure to be changed regularly and assigned on a random basis.

The major flaw of centralized management is the timing of distribution to users: Dissemination of new passwords must be timely and well coordinated. The logistics in a large, distributed network are considerable. The distribution process also is likely to be the weakest element in the security system: Because passwords are usually distributed in written form via mail or courier, ample opportunity exists for unauthorized users to obtain them. **Personal identification numbers (PINs)** are passwords associated with automatic teller machine (ATM) cards. The card distributor usually mails the card to the user and mails the PIN in a separate envelope. This reduces the risk of an unauthorized person obtaining both the card and the password, but it is not a very secure method. Consequently, some banks now allow users to select their own PIN, which avoids the need to send the password through the mail.

Decentralized password changes rely on users to change their passwords regularly, either by themselves or through their managers. Individual users can change their passwords without leaving any written record of the password, and they can usually make changes as often as they like. The password file can be centrally examined periodically, and if users have not changed their passwords within a specified time they can be so notified or their access privileges can be revoked. Some systems contain provisions for **password aging.** In this case, the security administrator can specify that users must change passwords regularly, such as monthly, and users who have not changed their passwords in the allotted time are warned during their login.

The security administrator may allow the user several **"grace" logins,** which is the ability to login without changing the password after the password has expired. If the user still fails to make a password change under the established rules, his or her account is deactivated. The user will then need to see the security administrator to have the account reactivated. The biggest problem with user-assigned passwords is that they are typically nonrandom, because users like to select a password that is easy to remember, such as their initials or birth date or names of family members. Unfortunately, this type of password is also more easily guessed by a potential intruder. Some dos and don'ts regarding password selection are included in Table 10-1.

Ultrasensitive Applications

Identification and authentication are usually insufficient for sensitive applications, as we must also identify what functions a given user may or may not perform. The two most common ways of controlling user access are by adding layers of identification and authentication, or by employing user or application profiles.

Layered IDs.   Layers of identification and authentication help to screen access to sensitive transactions. Once users have been logged onto the system via the initial identification procedures, they can be asked to provide additional identification and authentication information every time they attempt to access a new application or a sensitive transaction within an application. In a banking application, an operator might be required to provide another password or authorization code to transfer funds from one account to another. The operator will use one user ID and password to gain access to the system. This level of access will allow the operator to check account balances and make changes to data other than account balances. If the operator needs to run a transaction that will change an account balance, he or she must first provide another password. If the transaction exceeds a certain dollar limit, an additional password may be required. The advantage of layered IDs is that each application or transaction can have its own level of security, so applications that are not sensitive can be made available to everyone and those that are very sensitive can be protected with one or more levels of security. The disadvantage of layered IDs is that the user must remember several different authentication codes, thus increasing the probability of the codes being written down and thereby made accessible to others.

User Profiles.   A **user profile** contains all the information needed to define the applications and transactions a user is authorized to execute, such as a user in a personnel application who is authorized to add employees, delete employee records, and modify all employee data fields except salary. The profiles maintained in a user file can be very detailed, covering each application or transaction, or relatively simple, including only a brief profile. With a brief profile, a user might be assigned an access level to the system for each of four functions: read, write, execute, and purge. Specifically, suppose a user has been given Level 8 read access, Level 6 write access, Level 8 execute access, and Level 2 purge access. Each file and transaction are also given an access profile. A user is granted access to the file or transaction only if his or her access number is equal to or greater than that of the file or transaction. Thus, if the payroll file has access attributes of 8, 8, 10, and 10 for read, write, execute, and purge, respectively, the user just described will only be able to read the information in the file. This is because the user's read access meets or exceeds the file's security profile. A write access of 8 is insufficient to allow the user to write to the file.

Time and Location Restrictions.   **Time** and **location restrictions** play an important part in system security. In a stock trading application, for instance, buying and selling stock on the exchange is limited to a specific period, so any attempt to trade stock outside of that period will be rejected. In a personnel application, it would be prudent to restrict those transactions that affect employee salary or status to normal working hours. This kind of security can be further enhanced by making sensitive portions of the application system unavailable during nonworking hours.

Transactions also can be restricted by location. A money transfer transaction would be denied to a bank teller terminal if such transactions had to be initiated by a bank officer. Also, money transfer transactions could always be denied if the terminal is attached to a switched or dial-up communication line. In a manufacturing plant, any user at a shop-floor terminal would be unable to start an accounts receivable or payable transaction, because those transactions are limited to terminals in the accounting department. This can be implemented either by attaching applications to specific terminals or by terminal identification coupled with its location and a transaction profile. A terminal profile could list the location of the terminal and the transactions valid from that terminal. Time and location restrictions with user controls provide a hierarchy of security precautions.

Switched Ports with Dial-In Access

Perhaps the most vulnerable security point of any system is a switched port that allows dial-in access. The dangers of this should be evident: It enables any person with a telephone and a terminal to access the system. For that reason, extra security precautions should be taken. The switched line should be operational only during the periods when transactions are allowed. In an order entry application, this would likely be between 8:00 A.M. and 8:00 P.M.; in a university environment this might be 24 hours a day. During the period when transactions are disallowed, the line should be disabled. For increased security, a **call-back unit** can be attached to switched lines. A call-back unit is a security device that can be used to ensure that only calls from authorized locations are received.

When switched lines are used, user identification and authentication procedures and restricting transactions are very important to maintain system security. The telephone numbers of the switched lines should be safeguarded as carefully as possible. A manual answer arrangement can be used in high-security installations, thus allowing person-to-person authentication as well as the usual application-based authorization. Another method used to stall unauthorized users of switched lines is to hide the carrier tone until an authentication procedure has been provided, a solution that is most practical when telephones are manually answered. This method is meant to foil hackers who try to gain access to systems by randomly dialing business telephone numbers until a computer installation is reached.

Recognizing Unauthorized Access Attempts

All the security techniques we discussed are simply delaying tactics, and thus their implementation alone may not provide adequate security. A tight security system should recognize that an **unauthorized access attempt** may be occurring and should provide methods to suppress such attempts. In the movie *War Games*, a computer was used to generate passwords until a correct one was found. Even relatively unsecured systems would discourage this type of activity. A very simple way to counter such attempts is to temporarily deactivate the terminal or user account, meaning that the system would not accept input from that terminal or login attempts for that user for a specified period. Such an algorithm might work as follows: After three unsuccessful access attempts, no input from that terminal would be accepted for 5 minutes. Assuming a 6-character password of only letters and numbers, which gives more than 2 billion possible passwords, if 1 billion of these were tried, with a 5-minute delay between each try, more than 9500 years would be needed to gain access. Alternatively, the security system might deactivate the account, disallowing its use to both authorized and unauthorized users. This method is included in a security feature called **intruder detection** in Novell's NetWare operating systems.

A second algorithm employed in some systems simulates a successful logon. After a certain number of unsuccessful logon attempts, the user receives a successful logon message. Rather than actually being granted access to the system, however, the user is provided with a fake session. While this session is being conducted, security personnel can determine the terminal from which access is being made and the types of transactions the user is attempting to run. This type of simulated session can also help keep the penetrator busy while security personnel are dispatched to the location for investigation. Again, switched connections make such an activity more difficult, especially with respect to apprehension.

Automatic Logoff

People are often the weakest security link. All too frequently, operators write their passwords on or near the workstation or they leave the work area with their workstation still logged on, allowing anyone to perform transactions on their behalf. This not only jeopardizes the security of the system but also can place the employee's job in jeopardy. The system can assist operators through **automatic logoff,** whereby any user who has not entered a transaction within a certain amount of time, such as 2 minutes, is logged off. Operators who leave their terminals for more than 2 minutes will have to go through the identification and authentication procedures upon returning. Alternatively, the user can be required to go through an authentication procedure for every transaction. Unfortunately, this adversely affects operator performance. The first alternative is relatively simple to implement on most systems, and in most cases operator efficiency will be unimpeded.

Transaction Logs

Transaction logs are an important adjunct to security. Every logon attempt should be logged, including date and time, user identification, unsuccessful authentication attempts (with passwords used), terminal identification and location, and all transactions initiated from the terminal by that particular user. If several unsuccessful logon attempts are made, the information could also be written on the console of the operator or security personnel so other actions—such as investigation—can be initiated. Transaction logs are also beneficial to electronic data-processing (EDP) auditors and diagnostic personnel.

Computer Viruses, Worms, and Trojan Horses

The need for a new type of security surfaced in the 1980s with the introduction of computer viruses, worms, and Trojan horses. Most security countermeasures until that time were oriented toward individuals actively attempting to breach security for personal gain, revenge, or personal gratification. During this type of security violation, the perpetrator of the breach or the perpetrator's system was actively connected to the network. In contrast, computer viruses, worms, and Trojan horses operate independently of the person who implanted them.

Various **computer viruses** have been discovered, and although their implementation differs, there is usually a common objective: to bring down a system or disrupt users. A virus is typically a fragment of code that attaches itself to a legitimate program or file. The virus has the ability to duplicate itself to other programs and files. Once attached, the virus may attack a variety of resources. Some have destroyed or altered disk files, some simply display annoying messages, and others have caused system failures.

Detection and correction of viruses or viral equivalents can be time-consuming and expensive. Special **antiviral software** often is purchased to eliminate and detect viruses. Viruses can be introduced intentionally or accidentally. An unintentional infection can occur when an employee uses an infected disk, unaware that the disk carries a virus. Within a short time the entire network might be infected. Detection may be made more difficult because some viruses remain dormant for a period of time, propagating themselves before becoming active. New virus strains called **stealth viruses** or **polymorphic viruses** also change their appearance by encrypting themselves, which makes them quite difficult to identify.

Antidote programs exist for most known viruses, and using these antiviral programs can help keep a system healthy. Additional measures also should be taken to prevent infections, including procedures to prevent employees from using personal disks in workstations, checking new software on a virus-free system separate from a production system before installing the software for general use, and closely monitoring the source of all new files. Using diskless workstations is another excellent way to limit exposure.

A **worm** is a self-replicating, self-propagating program. Original worm programs were benign. They were designed to replicate themselves on network nodes that were relatively idle and carry out useful work. However, the most famous worm program was a rogue known as the Internet worm. The **Internet worm** surfaced in 1988 on the Internet. It replicated itself primarily on computers using the UNIX operating system. Once established on such a computer, the worm began replicating itself on other network nodes. Eventually, some of the network nodes became saturated with copies of the worm program, reducing the amount of useful work the nodes could perform and in some instances causing the computers to fail. Although the worm was not released intentionally, the consequences were far-reaching. The Internet worm illustrated the disruption that can be caused by such programs.

A **Trojan horse** program contains code intended to disrupt a system. Trojan horse programs are code segments hidden inside a useful program. Trojan horse programs have been created by disgruntled programmers. In one such instance, a programmer inserted code that would periodically activate and erase accounting and personnel records. A Trojan horse program differs from viruses and worms in that it does not attempt to replicate itself. Although the implementation of viruses, worms, and Trojan horses differs, their consequences are often the same: system disruption. A comprehensive security system must guard against each.

WORKGROUP SOFTWARE

Most LAN implementations have the potential for effectively using **workgroup software,** often referred to as **groupware.** In this section, you will learn what a workgroup is and some of the application tools used to increase the group's productivity. Before you can fully appreciate the functions of workgroup software, you must understand what we mean by a workgroup and the functions needed by the group. First, a **workgroup** consists of two or more workers. In doing their jobs, these workers must share information, communicate with each other, and coordinate their activities. Specific work tasks that are group activities include meetings, office correspondence, and group decision-making. Groupware is designed to make arranging and carrying out these tasks easier and less time-consuming.

The functions performed by groupware are not new. For years they have been done manually or with limited degrees of computer support. Networked systems in general and LANs in particular provide the communication link that was previously missing in computerizing many of these tasks. The groupware applications that have been created thus far fall into the following broad categories:

- Electronic mail
- Conferencing
- Work-flow automation
- Decision support
- Document coauthoring and document management

Electronic Mail Systems

One of the earliest workgroup applications was electronic mail (e-mail). An e-mail system has many of the capabilities of a conventional postal system such as collecting and distributing correspondence. An e-mail system also should be able to accept correspondence of various sizes and types and route the correspondence to its recipients in a timely manner. We have, however, come to expect many more capabilities from an e-mail system. Before we discuss these, we first consider how an e-mail system might operate on a LAN, by tracing a piece of correspondence through a hypothetical system. For specifics, suppose a LAN user, Maria, must send a mail message announcing a meeting to five other department heads: Alice, Mike, Tom, Shelly, and Chen.

Creating the Message. Before a message can be sent, it must be created. In general, there are two ways to create a message: through the facilities of the mail system or through an external word processing, desktop publishing, or other text/graphics system. If an external message creation facility is used, Maria can start that application, create the message, and save it on disk. Following that, she starts the mail application and imports the message into the mail system. Alternatively, most of today's e-mail systems allow users to designate their message creation software. Thus, the message can be composed from within the mail system itself (i.e., the word processor is invoked from the mail system and essentially becomes a mail job).

Sending the Message. Once the message has been created, it can be scheduled for delivery. The mail administrator, the person responsible for installation and management of the e-mail application, will have identified all eligible e-mail users and their associated mail addresses. In sending her message, Maria gives either the name of each user or the name of a predefined distribution list containing those names, or perhaps a combination of these two alternatives. A **distribution list** contains the names of individual users or the names of other distribution lists, and thus provides a simple mechanism to send messages to workgroups. Maria may have defined a distribution list called DEPT-HEADS that includes the names of the other five department heads. The e-mail system takes care of breaking the distribution list into its individual components so each name on the list receives the message.

When the delivery system gets the message and a list of the recipients, it can route the message to the proper destinations. For each recipient, the mail message is delivered into a disk file called the user's "mailbox." The message is available to each recipient almost immediately.

Reading the Message.   A message is available for reading once it has been delivered. Suppose Chen has just logged onto the LAN. If mail is waiting, he receives a message that he has mail. If a mail message arrives while he is working at his workstation, he receives a mail-waiting message. To read his mail, Chen starts the mail application and receives a list of his mail headlines. After viewing the available messages, usually identified with the sender's identification and a subject line, Chen has several available options including, but not limited to, the following:

1. He can ignore Maria's message altogether.
2. He can leave the message in his mailbox for later viewing.
3. He can delete the message without reading it.
4. He can read the message and delete it.
5. He can read the message and file it in an electronic folder.
6. He can read the message and forward it to other mail users.
7. He can read the message and send his response to the originator, Maria.

Responding to the Message.   If Chen decides to read and respond to Maria's message, he can enter his comments on the message and choose the message response option. He also may send his comments to other recipients and to a third party. After responding, Chen may delete the message, print it, or file it in an electronic folder.

Other E-Mail Features

Other capabilities you may find in an e-mail system are described in this section.

Expiration Dates and Certified Mail.   If the message is not read within a designated time limit, it can be automatically deleted from the user's mailbox. A sender can also send "certified mail." When a recipient reads the message, the sender receives a notice that the message has been read. A notice is also sent if the message expires without being read.

Mail Classes and Mail Agents.   There may be several classes of mail, such as first, second, and third classes. First class can be used for individual correspondence and second class for business news such as company stock quotes and product announcements. Third class can be used for junk mail such as garage sales, want ads, and social-group announcements. A **mail agent** is a software module that can automatically act on behalf of a user. For example, if a user goes on vacation, a vacation agent can forward the user's mail to another user or file the mail in an electronic folder. The vacation agent might also send each correspondent a message stating that the user is on vacation and nominate an alternative recipient.

Broadcast Messages and Message Attachment.   A broadcast message is one sent to all users (or all but a few users) on the network. Broadcast capability is convenient for sending messages of general interest to all network users. Sometimes this correspondence is an assemblage of several discrete components. For example, a mail message may consist of text created by a word processor, graphic images created by a graphics or spreadsheet application, fax images, and digitized voice. The mail service may maintain an electronic bulletin board. Users can be notified that there are general-interest messages posted to the bulletin board. This keeps user mailboxes from being filled with messages while giving users an opportunity to both read and post general-interest messages.

Miscellaneous Capabilities.   Mail systems seem to be constantly expanding in capabilities as software vendors strive to surpass their competition or just remain competitive. Capabilities offered include:

- Spelling checker
- Notification of mail arrival
- Search messages for keywords
- Message priorities
- Voice overlay
- Carbon copies
- Security and message encryption
- Notification of failure to deliver a message
- Ability to create user profiles
- Interactive mail

Electronic Conferencing Applications

Electronic conferencing applications range from simply arranging meetings to conducting the meetings themselves. Arranging a meeting or conference requires that the participants be notified and that a mutually agreeable meeting date and time be set. Conferencing applications provide assistance with one or more of these tasks. If each attendee has an electronic calendar, groupware can book the meeting at the best time. Given an interval during which the meeting must take place, the groupware application consults the calendars of the attendees. It notes the date and time that all attendees are available and schedules the meeting on their electronic calendars. If scheduling conflicts arise, the application can help resolve them. Some schedulers even double-book participants and allow them to choose which appointment to keep. Others report the conflicts and suggest alternative meeting times with no or reduced conflicts, allowing the person calling the meeting to find the best possible time. Once a meeting is scheduled, the electronic calendar software can issue an RSVP notice to the participants. Like personal calendars, groupware calendars can issue reminders of forthcoming events. The reminder might be a mail message or an audio tone. Some groupware allows users to declare meetings to be recurring, such as weekly, monthly, biweekly, and so on. The scheduler then automatically books these meetings for the attendees.

If the meeting is held with participants in different locations, teleconferencing groupware can also assist with communications among the attendees. Some teleconferencing applications allow images displayed on one computer monitor to be displayed on remote monitors. Individuals at all locations can modify the screen image and have the changes immediately reflected on the screens of the other participants. Thus, conference attendees can both view and modify computer-generated data and graphs. Viewing and modifying data coupled with audio transmission and freeze-frame or full-motion video allows geographically distributed conferences to be held, saving both travel costs and personnel time. Another conference or meeting communications aid is the creation and distribution of electronic minutes.

Work-Flow Automation

Attendees at a meeting may accept action items they must complete, or a **work-group manager** may assign tasks to workgroup members. One responsibility of a workgroup manager is monitoring the progress of such tasks. Progress monitoring is not a new concept. For many years, managers have used **Program Evaluation and Review Technique (PERT) charts** or similar methods to track a project's progress and determine its critical path. The **critical path** of a project is the sequence of events that takes the longest to complete. Often, a project can be divided into several tasks. Some tasks can be done in parallel, whereas other tasks cannot start until one or more tasks have been completed. For example, in building a house, the roof cannot be put on until the building is framed. Plumbing and electrical wiring can possibly be done concurrently. The project cannot be completed until the path with the longest duration is completed. Thus, project managers pay close attention to the project's critical path(s) to avoid delays. Although some project management work has been computerized for many years, much of the monitoring work was done by people. Groupware has extended the abilities of earlier systems by automating the tracking function.

Figure 10-2 is a PERT chart for selecting a LAN vendor. The critical path for the selection process is indicated by the heavier line. It is the critical path because it has the longest elapsed time between the start and the end points. Groupware helps in monitoring the critical path and keeps the group working together. Through the groupware application, group members can also keep aware of the status of other tasks that may affect their work.

With **work-flow automation** groupware, a manager can assign tasks to individuals or groups (through the group leader). The individual can either accept the task, negotiate a change, or refuse the task. Once a task is accepted, a completion date is set. The worker uses the groupware application to record his or her progress and to signal the completion of the task. The manager can then either agree that the task is complete and close it out or reach the decision that the task has not been satisfactorily completed and refuse to accept the work. In the latter case, the worker is notified and must rework the task until the result is acceptable. The groupware work-flow application tracks all tasks and evaluates progress. The group manager can query the system and obtain reports of each task's status. If several tasks are in progress at once and other tasks are awaiting the outcome of those tasks, the groupware monitors the progress of the critical paths and helps the manager keep the project on schedule.

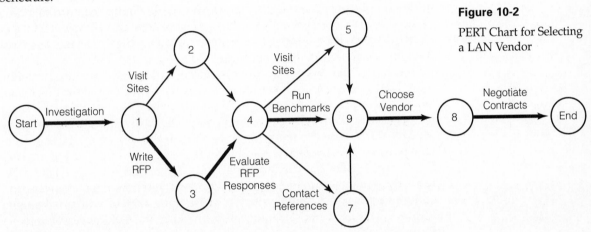

Figure 10-2

PERT Chart for Selecting a LAN Vendor

Other functions that may be simplified with work-flow automation software include:

- Establishing and monitoring to-do lists
- Task delegation
- Holding completed tasks until released by a manager
- Task deletion
- Preventing a worker from modifying an accepted task
- Setting or resetting task start and stop times
- Adding, deleting, or changing the people responsible for tasks
- Providing task and group reports

Document Coauthoring and Document Management

Word processing, text editors, and document exchange software were among the early computer applications. Most of these systems, however, were designed to allow only one person to manipulate a document at one time. If you have ever worked on a team to write a program, a report, or a manual, you are probably aware of the limitations inherent in these systems. If you and one of your team members wanted to work on the document at the same time, you found either that it could not be done or that concurrent document updates created contention problems. In a workgroup, it is often desirable and sometimes necessary to have several workers actively working on one document simultaneously. Document coauthoring and management applications provide this capability.

A full-function **document coauthoring system** allows two or more workers to work on one document concurrently. Concurrent processing presents some complex problems regarding posting changes to the same pages. Some current coauthoring systems do not provide this ability; however, they do provide the management and control abilities that allow a document to be shared without risk of contention problems. Some document managers help control the flow of documents through the production cycle. Group users are identified as the principal document author, coauthors, or editors. The document manager assists in the production of the document by controlling the flow of the document from one designated user to another.

Document management software can control access to the document by a checkout mechanism. Workers can check out all or portions of the document. Once a portion is checked out, update access to that portion of the document by other users is typically restricted because the worker checking it out may change it. If a worker changes the document, the document management software monitors the changes and records the identity of the person making the change. When the document is ready for review, the application can route the document to the proper reviewers and editors. The reviewers and editors then can make notations and suggestions, with or without changing the document itself, and the application will keep track of the person making those remarks.

Other document management features include document organization, archiving, location, and full file searches. Imagine the number of documents generated per year by a large law office. Some law offices generate more than 50,000 documents per year including wills, contracts, legal briefs, and trial notes. Keeping track of this volume almost necessitates the use of a system that allows documents to be stored, archived to backup media, and retrieved when needed. For such large systems, standard directory and file naming conventions are often severely limited. A document management system allows users to store a single document under a variety of different subjects. The document can then be found by attorney, client, subject, date created, last date accessed, project, department, author, and a variety of other descriptive categories and keywords. Some systems allow users to specify combinations of these attributes as well. Full file searches systematically search files stored on disk or archival directories, looking for user-defined text strings.

Group Decision-Support Software

Group decision-support software on LANs facilitates the communication of ideas among the members of a group. Each participant has a workstation from which to make comments and suggestions; these comments are then exchanged among the users in an anonymous way. This allows the lowest member in the organizational hierarchy to feel free to criticize suggestions made by the highest member. The key to making this work is protecting the source of ideas and comments. Included in the software are tools to gather and manipulate data from a variety of sources, such as a database, a spreadsheet, and graphic images. Companies that have used decision-support technology have found that better decisions are reached in a shorter period of time.

It is important to emphasize that groupware is not intended to replace person-to-person interactions. Our future should not be one in which we get assignments via computers, are computer graded, and are fired or promoted via the computer. Instead, groupware complements person-to-person interactions. Groupware provides a tool for assigning and monitoring the group's tasks with the objective of making the group more productive.

Time-Staged Delivery Systems

Time-staged delivery systems have some characteristics of a mail system. Time-staged delivery software allows users to identify a transmission package, designate one or more recipients of the package, initiate the delivery of the package, and specify a delivery priority. If we relate time-staged delivery and electronic mail to regular mail service, electronic mail is like express mail service whereas time-staged delivery is equivalent to parcel post or surface mail. Electronic mail is usually oriented toward short messages of several pages or less. Time-staged delivery systems may be used for short messages, for transaction routing, or to transmit entire files.

With time-staged delivery, the user specifies a required delivery time. The system then schedules the message transmission to meet the requested goal. Suppose a user needs to send a lengthy report from New York City to each of five manufacturing plants, and that the message must be available at each plant by 9:00 A.M. local time. The report to London needs to arrive several hours before the one destined for California, so it will have a higher priority in transmission than the California-bound package. The delivery system also can use the delivery time to defer transmission until a more convenient time. Rather than sending data in real time, when the system may be quite busy, it can delay transmission until a less busy time, such as early morning hours. In distributed processing environments, the ability to designate transmission packages and delivery times can be an important capability. An example of a time-staged delivery system is IBM's SNA delivery system (SNADS).

DISTRIBUTED SYSTEMS

There are various kinds of **distributed systems.** In Chapters 3 through 8 you read about LANs and WANs, and although it was not explicitly stated, many of those networks' resources are distributed. For example, a LAN's processing load is split among servers and workstations, both acting in concert to help workers attain their objectives. In this use of the system, processing is distributed. Data also can be distributed over two or more nodes, such as on file servers, SQL servers, and workstations. However, although data is distributed, there is not always a distributed data management capability. In these instances, the distributed data is treated as "islands of data" without the benefit of the comprehensive, coordinated management of a distributed database management system. The same may be said for WANs.

The ultimate goal of distributed processing and databases is to essentially make the network the computer. In early computing systems, all data and processing were confined to one computer. In early networks, we were able to distribute the computing load among several computers by essentially replicating what was done on individual computers. If a network had three nodes, processing was taking place simultaneously on all three computers, but most of the processing entailed a single program on one system accessing and processing data on the same system. The network was used primarily to transport completed reports, for data input on terminals attached to a remote computer, and so on. Ideally, we would like to have the aggregate resources of a network applied as appropriate to cooperatively work on problems. In this context, a single transaction might use processing resources of several computers, access and update data in a database distributed over multiple disk drives on multiple computer nodes, and perhaps output data in several geographically distributed places. Such distributed collaboration of hardware and software naturally will be transparent to users of the system. Before we introduce the technology of distributed processing, we first more precisely define the various aspects of distributed systems.

First, there is a distinction between distributed processing and distributed databases. From the preceding paragraph, you may have an intuitive idea about these distinctions. **Distributed processing** refers to the geographic distribution of hardware, software, processing, data, and control. The data communications system is the glue that holds the distributed system together and makes it workable. Geographic distribution does not mean great distances. As stated earlier, a LAN is a distributed processing system and, by definition, serves a limited area. A company also can have a distributed system contained in a single computer room. The key factor in having a distributed processing system is networking two or more independent computing systems where there is an interdependence among the nodes thus connected. The dependence can be for processing power, data, application software, or use of peripherals.

Often distributed systems also are characterized by distribution of control. If the nodes are placed in different locations, there is local responsibility for each node. A manufacturing organization may have processing nodes in the headquarters offices, regional offices, and warehouses. In each location an operations staff will be responsible for running the systems. There may also be a local support and development organization responsible for developing, installing, and maintaining applications and databases.

One objective of distributed processing is to move data and processing functions closer to the users who need those services and thereby to improve the system's responsiveness and reliability. A second objective is to make remote access transparent to the system user, so the user has little or nothing special to do when accessing the other nodes of the system. How these objectives are met is explained below. First, however, we review how distributed systems evolved.

EVOLUTION OF DISTRIBUTED SYSTEMS

At the dawn of the computer age, computers were big and expensive, and operating systems were either nonexistent or incapable of supporting multiple job streams. As a result, for the organizations that could afford it, computer systems were acquired for every department needing computational power. In a manufacturing organization, one computer would be dedicated to inventory, one to accounting, and one to manufacturing control. These were decentralized processing systems, but they were considerably different from the current concept of distributed systems in one important respect: the sharing of resources.

Duplicated Databases and Inconsistent Data

Processors in those early systems usually were not connected via communications links. As a result each maintained its own database, often with duplicated data. Both the warehouse database and the accounting department database contained the same customer information, the former for shipping and the latter for invoicing. When a customer moved, the address change was not likely to be reflected in both databases at once, and in some instances not before a considerable amount of time had elapsed. Such redundant storage of data, with the attendant update problems, created data inconsistencies.

Data inconsistencies often are manifested by conflicts in reports. Managers are generally intolerant of such conflicting reports. Perhaps more important, shipments or invoices could be sent to the incorrect address and perhaps be lost. Because each department was essentially the proprietor of its own system, there was little sharing of computer resources. This meant that one system might be completely inundated with work while another was relatively idle. Figure 10-3 shows one possible early **decentralized processing system.**

Centralization

The early decentralized systems were far from ideal. In addition to data inconsistencies, there were extra costs for hardware, operations, maintenance, and programming. As systems grew larger and operating systems more comprehensive, there was a movement to large, **centralized systems,** as illustrated in Figure 10-4. Large, centralized systems had the benefits of a single operations center, control, and—according to some—economies of scale, as a single large system was likely to cost less than several smaller, decentralized systems. In many organizations having centralized systems, a single programming department was established for all application development and maintenance. To reduce data redundancy and promote data sharing among users, centralized databases also were established.

Figure 10-3

Early Distributed
Processing System

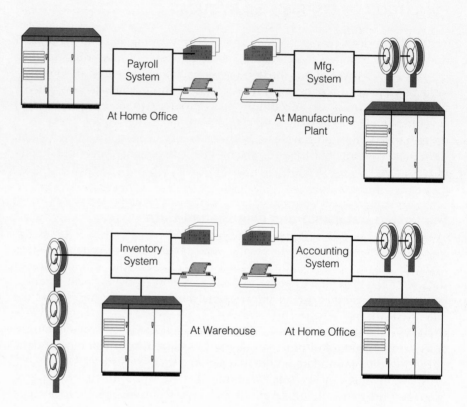

Figure 10-4

A Centralized System

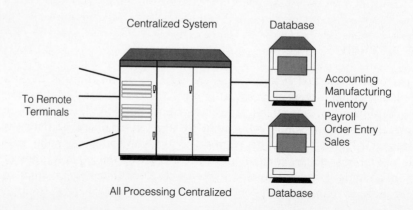

Disadvantages of Centralization

It was later found that large, centralized systems also have inherent problems. First, if the large central system fails, the entire system fails, and if a component fails, all or part of the application system also may be unavailable. In the decentralized approach, failure of one node results in part of the overall system being lost, but many processing functions can be continued. In this respect, decentralized systems are more reliable than the single centralized system.

Many end users—the accounting department, warehouse, and so forth—found their needs inadequately met by a centralized system. Because the system was shared, users often found it unresponsive, particularly regarding when jobs would be run and getting resources for new development. With a departmental system in a distributed or decentralized environment, a user contends only with other users in the department, so it was relatively easy to establish priorities. Setting interdepartmental priorities, however, sometimes was not easy. The same held true for programming. In the centralized environment, a programming team may have been assigned to develop an application or a new report for a department. Because developers were not under the direct control of the department, it was sometimes difficult for the department to change priorities and directions.

Expansion and growth of the large, centralized system posed another problem for some companies, that of controlling system growth. Too often growth was not in small, manageable increments but in giant steps, such as conversion to a larger processor with a different operating system. This conversion meant down time while the new system was being installed. Sometimes programs had to be revised and new program bugs were encountered. The change was usually disruptive to all users. In contrast, with distributed system upgrades, growth was generally in smaller, more manageable increments. In addition, if a new processor became necessary, only those using that node were affected, not the entire user community.

Networked Systems

Networking provides some of the benefits of both centralized and distributed environments: more localized processing and control with shared data, processing power, and equipment. We again use a LAN as an example; these comments generally apply to wide area networks as well. In a LAN, end users have workstations capable of performing various application functions such as word processing, working with spreadsheets, and so on. Each workstation also is able to call on the processing power and database capabilities of a larger system—a server or host processor—to accomplish more complex and time-consuming processing tasks.

Some of the data required frequently by a user at a workstation may be resident on the workstation's local disk drives. This may include documents in process and budget data for spreadsheets. Data that either is used infrequently or needs to be shared among several users can be maintained at a server. Despite this data being maintained by another node, the workstation can access that data as though it was stored locally. Workstations are also able to share other network resources such as printers and magnetic tape drives. The key to a distributed system is making resource distribution transparent to the users. When the resources being distributed are data, sophisticated network software is necessary. The software responsible for doing this is called a distributed file system (DFS).

DISTRIBUTED FILE SYSTEMS

In **distributed file systems (DFSs),** users must have the ability to locate and use remote files as though those files were locally resident. The objectives of a DFS are given in Table 10-2 and described below.

TABLE 10-2 Distributed File System Objectives

Provide transparent access to distributed files

Provide operating system independence

Provide file system independence

Provide architecture independence

Provide contention resolution

Provide security

Provide file directory information

Provide location independence

Transparent Access.   **Transparent access** means that a user at one node must be able to access distributed files as though they were located on the user's local node. This means a user should be able to use the file system commands of the local system to access remote files—even if the remote file is located on a node with a different operating and file system.

Operating System Independence.   In building a distributed system, a designer should be able to configure heterogeneous systems. This may mean that different operating systems and file systems are involved. Not only should designers be able to build a system composed of different hardware and software, but also they must make these differences transparent to users.

File System Independence.   With file system independence, different file systems, such as DOS, UNIX, and VMS, may be used in one network. Just as important, the differences among the file systems should be transparent to users. For example, the local file system commands should be functional when accessing a file on a remote node that uses a different file system.

Architecture Independence.   The DFS should allow any network configuration—star, bus, ring, interconnected, and so on. Neither the architecture nor the network software should limit the ability to distribute files.

Contention Resolution.   The DFS ought to provide a mechanism that prevents data corruption due to contention. Such corruption can result when two or more users try to access and update the same file or record.

Security.   A DFS must provide the requisite level of security. Files should be able to be secured for local access only or for remote access. When remote access to a file is allowed, the DFS must be able to grant or deny requests based upon the requester's ID. Inherent in this requirement are the abilities (1) to provide user identities for users on a node that does not support user IDs, such as a single-user microcomputer, and (2) to reconcile network differences among user IDs.

File Directory Information.   The DFS is responsible for transparently satisfying user requests. This means it must maintain a directory of remote files and their locations. When a user requests access to a file, the directory is consulted to find the node(s) that houses the file.

Location Independence.   Location independence means a file can be located at any node in the network. A file also must be able to be moved from one node to another without disrupting applications or end-user access to that file.

Several DFS implementations exist.   The one most often used for networks with equipment from a variety of vendors is the Network File System (NFS), developed by Sun Microsystems. It is implemented not only on Sun systems but also on a variety of UNIX-, VMS-, and DOS-based systems. Sun Microsystems has placed the NFS protocol specifications in the public domain to allow other vendors to implement it. The objective of publishing the protocol was to spread its use and establish NFS as a standard.

CLIENT/SERVER COMPUTING

Networks are changing the way we view computing and how we design application systems. Data processing has evolved from batch-oriented systems on stand-alone computers, to online transaction processing with terminals and a host computer, to distributed application processing using several computers in a network. One of the distributed software architectures on networks is called client/server computing.

Client/server (C/S) computing divides the work an application performs among several computers. In C/S computing one application called the **client** requests processing services from another application called the **server.**

In LAN systems, the client and the server processes typically run on different computers. Some of the more common server functions are database services, in which a database server processes database requests, and mail services that route and store mail messages. A client process may use the services of several different server applications in carrying out its work.

The concept of C/S computing is a technology developed neither for LANs nor even for networking; however, networks in general and LANs specifically have created an environment supportive of C/S technology. Perhaps looking at the precursors of today's C/S environment will make it easier to understand the LAN implementations. Figure 10-5 shows a large computer to which many terminals are connected. Terminal users each have a set of applications and transactions they are allowed to run, and different users may have different sets of capabilities. A person's job needs determine which applications and transactions may be used. Figure 10-5 shows three classes of software components in the host processor: a transaction control process (TCP), applications, and a database management system.

Let us consider the needs of Kim, a specific terminal user. Kim works in the personnel department. Some of the functions she can do are adding employees, updating employee records, and deleting the records of employees who left the company more than three years ago. The add-employee transaction requires the services of three different applications, one each for employee, insurance, and payroll updates. When Kim requests that a certain transaction, such as adding an employee, be run, her request is received by the TCP. The TCP is responsible for routing the transaction to the appropriate applications. In this case, three applications will need to work on the transaction, a capability we can call **cooperative computing.** In this scenario, the TCP requests each application to perform a service. In some systems, the TCP is called a requester and the applications are called servers. In today's terminology the TCP could be called a client. The client makes requests that are carried out in whole or in part by other processes called servers. In this example, the applications in turn make requests of the database management system and the operating system for services they perform. Thus, a server can also become a client.

In WANs, some companies have extended the notion of this type of C/S technology by allowing the server processes to be on nodes different from the one on which the client is running. This provides a distributed processing environment in which the hardware, software, and data resources of several computers combine to solve a problem. In essence, with C/S computing the network becomes the computer. We can also talk about server classes. A **server class** is represented by one or more applications, all of which can carry out certain tasks. With server classes, a client does not need the services of a particular server process because any process in the class can perform the requested service.

Figure 10-6 shows a C/S LAN configuration. This figure offers two instances of C/S computing: a database or SQL server and an electronic mail (e-mail) server. (*SQL* is an abbreviation for Structured Query Language, a standard database language.) Earlier we described how a database server works. An e-mail server operates like a post office for its clients. An e-mail server will perform functions such as supplying mail addresses given a user's name, distributing mail, and providing mail agent functions. There are several types of mail agents, one of which is a vacation agent. An e-mail vacation agent can provide services such as collecting incoming mail in an electronic folder or rerouting mail to another designated user while the original recipient is away.

A Processor

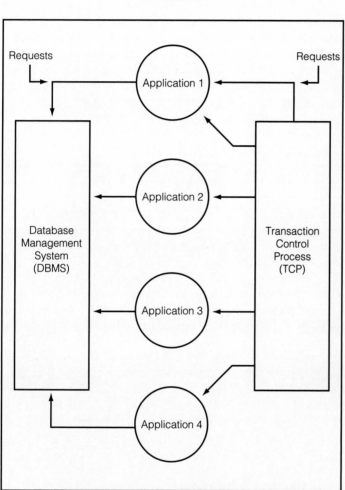

Figure 10-5

Client/Server Computing in a Mainframe Computer

TCP has a role as a client with applications as servers.
Applications have roles as clients with DBMS as a server.

In LAN C/S technology, clients typically run in workstations and request services from microcomputer, minicomputer, or mainframe nodes that operate exclusively as servers. Alternatively, C/S computing can be implemented in a peer-to-peer LAN. In a peer-to-peer C/S environment, server and client processes can be running in the same node. In Figure 10-7, both Client A and Server 1 are running in Node 1.

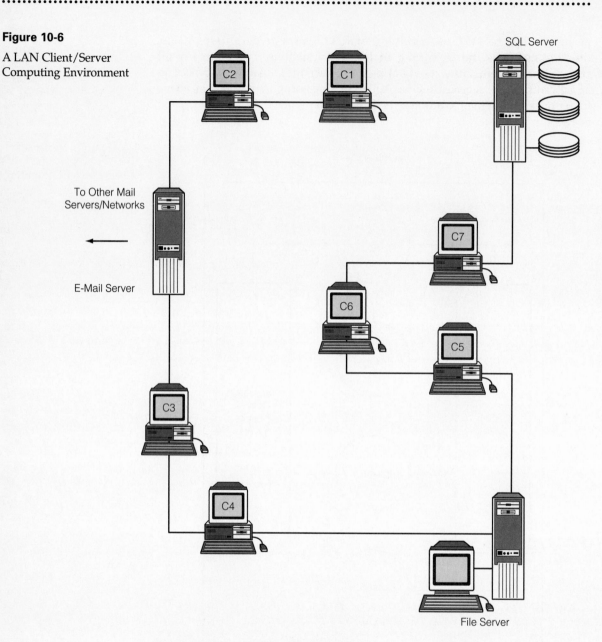

Figure 10-6

A LAN Client/Server
Computing Environment

Advantages of C/S Computing

System Expansion.   Growth is one objective of many companies, and
it is often accompanied by the need for additional computing power. With
C/S computing the computing power is distributed over multiple processors.
Because the computer is the network, in C/S computing we can expand the
computer by adding hardware and software components to the network.
Adding to the network can be done in small, manageable increments. This
means the computer can be scaled up (or down) without incurring large
expenses and major hardware upgrades. Applications also can be easily

expanded. Once the C/S environment is set up, new applications can be quickly installed and can immediately take advantage of the services available. This growth is made easier because the application functions provided by the server processes are already in place, and the work of the applications programmers is reduced.

Figure 10-7

A Peer-to-Peer
Client/Server Environment

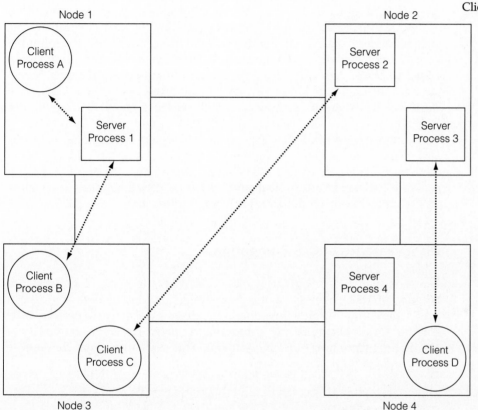

Modular Applications. C/S applications are generally improved because applications are modular. Modularity can reduce the memory required for client applications and provide optimization for server processes. Part of the application logic is contained in the servers and hence does not need to be replicated in the client portion of the code. An analogy may be helpful here. If you are building a house, you would not be likely to do all the jobs yourself because it will be difficult for you to learn all the necessary carpentry, plumbing, electrical, and landscaping skills. However, if you become a client and use the services of those who already know how to do these things, you will likely get the job done faster and better. This analogy applies directly to the concept of C/S computing. Server modules are optimized to perform their function on behalf of their clients, and the clients do not need to be burdened with the logic essential to perform those tasks.

Portability. Some computer systems are better able to perform certain jobs than others. For example, some platforms are noted for their ability to do high-resolution graphics applications, such as computer-aided design and drafting (CAD), whereas other hardware and software combinations are well suited for office automation applications. The combination of the hardware and software of an SQL server also makes the server able to manage data more effectively than a general-purpose computer and operating system. As new technologies emerge, the C/S environment provides a relatively easy way to integrate such technologies into the network. A company can switch among hardware and software vendors to find its ideal computing system. Ordinarily these changes will not affect the remaining components. Using an SQL server as an example, if a new, more powerful server engine becomes available, it should be easy to install the new engine in place of existing SQL servers or to simply add the server to augment existing servers.

Standards. As C/S develops we will likely see new standards for the way clients and servers communicate. Some of these are already being developed by leaders in C/S technology. With interface standards available, software and hardware from many vendors can be integrated to create a modular, flexible, extendible computing environment.

Disadvantages of C/S Computing

One disadvantage of C/S technology on WANs is reduced performance because of the slowness of the communications links. With high-speed LANs, the communication link does not become an obstacle to performance. Another disadvantage of C/S computing on networks is the complexity of creating the optimum C/S environment. This disadvantage is common to WAN and LAN implementations.

C/S Technology

C/S technology on LANs is in its infancy, but its direction has already begun to take shape. In this section we look at some of the technology that underlies C/S computing, the interfaces that exist between clients and servers, and standards that are being developed.

Clients and servers must have a way to communicate with each other. This is done in two basic ways: remote procedure calls and message exchange. You may be familiar with programming languages that support local procedure calls. With local procedure calls, one segment of a program invokes logic in another program segment called a procedure. The procedure does its work, and then the results and processing control are passed back to the point in the program from which the procedure was called. You can think of the procedure as performing a service for the program.

Remote procedure calls extend this concept to allow an application on one computer to call on the services of another process. The process being called could be running in the same computer or, as is typically the case in C/S computing, the process being called could be running in another computer. Moreover, the process being called may not be running at the time of the call. The remote procedure call in this instance initiates the server process on the other computer. **Message exchange** is a more flexible method of communication. The client and the server enter into a session (recall the OSI session layer) and exchange information. The client sends a request and the server responds with the answer to the request.

One issue to be resolved with C/S computing is how to find the server or servers that perform the needed functions. Today, we are looking primarily at clients and servers attached to the same LAN. It is logical to extend this to having servers and clients on different LANs. To maintain the modularity and flexibility of C/S computing, we would like to be able to add servers, delete existing ones, and perhaps move an existing server from one LAN to another. Changes of this nature also should be transparent to the clients, which means the clients should not have to be reprogrammed. This problem can be solved by having servers "advertise" themselves. For example, they might place an entry into a network directory or send messages to all nodes to register their presence.

Clients communicate with servers through an application program interface, as illustrated in Figure 10-8. Standards are being developed that will make forming C/S interfaces easier. Having many different C/S interfaces should be avoided to maintain flexibility. It is better to have one or a few standard interfaces so a company can develop client applications that will be able to access servers created by other companies. These interfaces have come to be called **middleware.** The objective of middleware is to serve as an intermediary between clients and servers, which means the middleware is responsible for making the connection between clients and servers. This is similar to the function performed by the logical link control layer, which, you may recall, is the interface between the network layer and media access control.

Figure 10-8

Client/Server Application
Program Interface

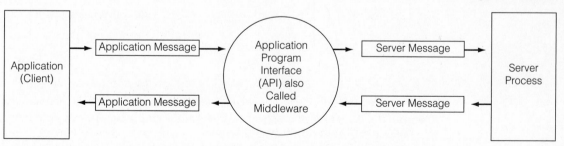

One example of middleware and its standardization efforts is the **Distributed Computing Environment (DCE)** specifications established by the Open Software Foundation. DCE addresses the use of remote procedure calls, security, name services, and messages for C/S computing. Another example is the **Object Request Broker (ORB)** established by the Object Management Group. A client will communicate with a server through the services of the ORB. The ORB will receive a client's request, find a server capable of satisfying that request, send the message to that server, and return the response to the client. The ORB thus provides client and server independence. Any client that can communicate with the ORB is then able to communicate with any server that can communicate with the ORB. This provides both hardware and software independence.

We can use three models to represent the distribution of functions in a C/S environment. First, the majority of the application logic can reside in the client system with only the specialized server logic residing in the server system, as illustrated in Figure 10-9(a). In this model, the server is less burdened and can be more responsive to volumes of client requests. This is usually the model used for database servers. In a database server, the server responds to a client's request for data and data meeting the constraints of the request are returned to the client for processing. This model is sometimes called the **data management model.**

Figure 10-9

Client/Server
Application Models

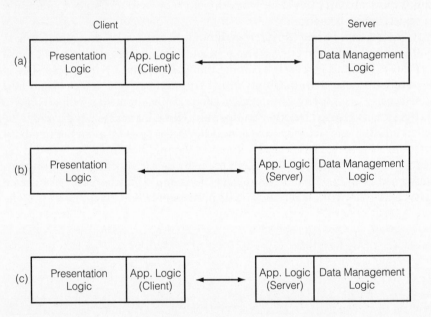

A second model uses the client primarily to display or print data, and the data management and application logic are resident on the server, as illustrated in Figure 10-9(b). This approach could be used for graphics applications wherein a high-speed server processor is used to generate the drawing details and the workstation is responsible for displaying the details on the monitor. This model can be called the **presentation model.**

The third possibility embeds application logic in both the client and the server, as illustrated in Figure 10-9(c). This model might be used in a transaction processing system where the application contains logic about customers and the server contains the application logic for banking accounts.

ADVANTAGES AND DISADVANTAGES OF DISTRIBUTED SYSTEMS

Advantages

Each distributed system just described has numerous advantages. For one, storing data close to the location that uses it most in a network situation minimizes the amount of data that must be transmitted between nodes and provides better response times. Because maintenance of the data is a local responsibility, there is more of a vested interest in keeping the data current. Third, nonlocal transactions are still possible, as are transactions that must span several nodes, the only penalty being slower response times due to slow transmission speeds on the communications links. Distributed systems also give local users more control over their data processing system. This provides users with the flexibility to tailor changes to their own particular needs without disrupting other network nodes. Reliability also is higher than with a centralized system, for the failure of one node does not mean the entire system is down. Each node has most of the data it needs to continue local processing, so applications can continue with only a slight degradation in service.

Disadvantages

Various disadvantages to the distributed approach are discussed below.

Multiple-Node Transactions Are Slower.   Whenever a transaction must span more than one node, response time is longer than if the transaction ran on one node only. Suppose a salesperson for a computer vendor enters an order for a new system consisting of processors, disks, and terminals. The response time for placing the order will be faster if all the equipment is available in the local warehouse than if each component must come from a different location. In the latter case, a message would have to be sent to the other warehouses in sequence until the order was filled.

Maintaining Transaction Integrity.   A transaction is an atomic piece of work. In a centralized database, this atomic property is guaranteed by the database management system's recovery system. However, when a transaction updates files on several nodes, several independent database management systems are involved. Each may be capable of guaranteeing the integrity of the portion of the transaction processed on its system, but there is no coordination among the various database management systems. In fact, it may be difficult to even establish a consistent, unique transaction identifier for node-spanning transactions.

Contention and Deadlock.   Update transactions on multiple nodes increase the risk of contention and deadlock. As discussed in previous chapters, a record being updated is locked until the end of the transaction, to avoid the problems of concurrent updates. Because a transaction that spans several nodes is slower than one on a single node (due to data communications transmission time), affected records remain locked longer. Thus, the probability increases that the records will be needed by another transaction, and hence the amount of contention and the potential for deadlock increase.

Potential for Failure.   The longer response time for transactions that span multiple nodes also increases the probability of a failure that will produce an unsuccessful transaction.

Routing, Transmission, and Processing

In distributed processing, a strategy must be developed for accessing and processing the data. Designers of distributed systems have several options in determining how the remote processing and accesses will be handled. In general, the strategy selected depends on the type of transaction.

Remote Access and Local Processing.   One method for processing with distributed data is **remote access** and **local processing.** This type of transaction is used effectively when most of the data being accessed is needed at the local node. Consider a system for a state's highway patrol force. If a state trooper stops a car and inquires regarding the driver's record, the application on a local node will issue a read request for the driver's files on a remote node. The set of records for the driver is transmitted to the local node and from there to the display device in the trooper's car. In this case, there was a local request for remote access, and all data satisfying that request was sent to the local node for processing. It is possible that the driver is cited for a violation as a consequence of the trooper's work. In this case, the driver's record might be modified locally and then a local request for updating the record in the remote file will be made. The revised record will be transmitted over the network and the database updated as a consequence of the remote update request. The characteristics of the police transaction are that every record accessed was transmitted over the network to the local node, all processing was done locally, and all updates were brought about via local requests. This is similar to the way in which a LAN file server operates.

Partial Remote Processing.   A second method for handling distributed processing requires that the remote node perform some amount of application processing. Consider a transaction to list all employees having more than 10 years of service and a salary less than $20,000: For a company with 100,000 employees, all 100,000 records will need to be accessed to satisfy the query. To pass each of the 100,000 records to the requesting node for selection would place a large load on the communications subsystem and take considerable extra time. A much better alternative is to have a server process on each remote node access the records, perform the selection, and then transmit only the results to the requesting node, where the list will be consolidated.

Total Remote Processing. Consider a transaction that updates records at a remote node. When the record is required locally, the remote record is transmitted to the local node, an update is made, and the record is sent back to the remote node for updating in the database. In some instances the entire update can be performed remotely, as in giving an across-the-board pay raise to employees.

Suppose a company has decided to distribute the personnel and payroll applications and maintains that data in each of five regional processing centers. A manager in the corporate headquarters may have the responsibility for administering a 6-percent pay raise for all 100,000 employees. If the first strategy is used, each of the 100,000 records must be read remotely, transmitted over the network, updated, sent back over the network, and updated in the database. For this transaction, however, there is no need to transmit any data to the local node. A better alternative is to send the request to a server process on the remote node and have all the work done there. You should recognize this type of processing as being equivalent to the capabilities of the local area network's SQL server described in Chapter 4.

Many other examples of the division of activity among nodes could be cited. In essence, there are only the three basic methods just discussed: (1) access remote records, pass them to the local node, process the records locally, and then return them to the remote node(s) for updating as necessary; (2) send messages to remote application servers that accept and process data and then return only the required information to the requesting nodes; or (3) a combination of the two approaches, which is sometimes the best alternative. The design objective is always to make the transaction as efficient as possible, which means minimizing the transmission of many records between nodes.

SUMMARY

Security is a delaying tactic used to deter unauthorized personnel from gaining access to a system and to provide time to catch those who attempt such access. Security of systems and networks is of growing concern to system managers. Security can be implemented at multiple levels within a system. There is an overhead to implementing security precautions, and the cost of the security system should not exceed the potential loss from unauthorized use of the system. Data can be encrypted to prevent unauthorized disclosure.

Groupware applications are changing the way workgroups carry out their duties. Applications such as e-mail, group decision support, electronic meeting, project or work-flow control, time-staged delivery systems, and document coauthoring enable workgroups to be more efficient. These applications provide communication among network users and move data from one node to another in an orderly, timely manner.

With distributed processing, we can turn the network into a large computer, and client/server computing is an architecture for achieving this. In C/S computing, the processing chore is divided among clients and servers.

Clients make requests of servers for processing functions. Consequently, the work required by an application may be processed on several network nodes. C/S computing allows us to configure nodes with hardware and software best suited for the tasks to be run on that node. Furthermore, we are able to distribute data and make it more readily available to all users.

KEY TERMS

ANSI X9.17   300

antiviral software   305

authentication   301

automatic logoff   305

broadcast message   309

call-back unit   303

centralized system   315

cipher text   298

client (requester)   319

client/server (C/S) computing   319

Clipper chip   299

computer virus   305

cooperative computing   320

critical path   310

Data Encryption Standard (DES)   298

data management model   326

decentralized processing system   315

Distributed Computing Environment (DCE)   325

distributed file system (DFS)   318

distributed processing   314

distributed system   313

distribution list   307

document coauthoring system   312

document management software   312

electronic conferencing application   309

encryption algorithm   298

encryption   298

encryption key   298

"grace" login   302

group decision-support software   312

groupware   306

Internet worm   306

intruder detection   304

local processing   328

location restriction   303

mail agent   308

message exchange   325

middleware   325

Object Request Broker (ORB)   326

password   301

password aging   301

personal identification number (PIN)   301

physical security   297

plain text   298

polymorphic virus   306

presentation model   326

Program Evaluation and Review Technique (PERT) chart   310

public key method   299

remote access   328

remote procedure call   324

server   319

server class   320

stealth virus   305

system access   296

time restriction   303

time-staged delivery system   313

transaction log   305

transparent access   318

trapdoor encryption   299

Trojan horse program   306

unauthorized access attempt   304

U.S. Federal Standard 1027   300

user identification   301

user profile   302

work-flow automation   310

workgroup   306

workgroup manager   310

workgroup software   306

worm   306

REVIEW QUESTIONS

1. What is the greatest security risk a company faces? Why is this so?

2. How has data communications complicated the ability to provide security of data?

3. Describe a number of physical security features and how they protect unauthorized access.

4. What is data encryption? What benefits does it provide?

5. What are user identification and authentication? Describe three methods for accomplishing identification and authentication.

6. How can you recognize and overcome unauthorized access attempts?

7. What is a computer virus? How can you protect against computer viruses?

8. What is a workgroup?

9. Describe four classes of groupware.

10. What is work-flow automation? How does it help promote workgroup productivity?

11. How does a document coauthoring and document management system differ from a word processing application?

12. What are the benefits or uses of a time-staged message delivery system?

13. What are the disadvantages of replicating data on multiple nodes?

14. List four current problems in distributed processing.

15. List four applications that are good candidates for distributed processing.

16. Describe the objectives of a distributed file system.

17. What are the advantages and disadvantages of distributed systems?

Acronym Glossary

For a more thorough definition, please refer to the Key Terms Glossary.

ACU   Auto-Call Unit

ADCCP   Advanced Data Communications Control Procedure

ADMD   Administrative Management Domain

AM   Amplitude Modulation

ANSI   American National Standards Institute

API   Application Program Interface

APPN   Advanced peer-to-peer networking

ARP   Address resolution protocol

ASCII   American Standard Code for Information Interchange

ATM   Asynchronous Transfer Mode

BCC   Block Check Character

BCD   Binary Coded Decimal

BISYNC   Binary Synchronous Communications. Also, BSC

BIU   Bus Interface Unit

BPS   Bits Per Second

BSC   Binary Synchronous Communications. Also, BISYNC

CAD   Computer-Aided Design

CAI   Computer-Aided Instruction

CAM   Computer-Aided Manufacturing

CCITT   Consultative Committee on International Telegraph and Telephony

CDDI   Cooper Distributed Data Interface

CICS   Customer Information Control System

CIU   Communications Interface Unit

CLNP   Connectionless Network Protocol

CMIP   Common Management Information Protocol

CMIS   Common Management Information Service

CPU   Central Processing Unit

CRC   Cyclic Redundancy Check

CRT   Cathode Ray Tube

C/S   Client/Server

CSMA/CA   Carrier Sense with Multiple Access and Collision Avoidance

CSMA/CD   Carrier Sense with Multiple Access and Collision Detection

DBMS   Database Management System

DCE   Data Circuit-Terminating Equipment

DCE   Data Communications Equipment

DCE   Distributed Computing Environment

DES   Data Encryption Standard

DFS   Distributed File System

DPSK   Differential Phase Shift Keying

DTE   Data Terminal Equipment

EBCDIC   Extended Binary-Coded Decimal Interchange Code

EDI   Electronic Data Interchange

E-mail   Electronic Mail

FCS   Frame Check Sequence

FDDI   Fiber Distributed Data Interface

FDM   Frequency Division Multiplexing

FEP   Front End Processor

FM   Frequency Modulation

FMS   File Management System

FQDN   Fully Qualified Domain Name

FSK   Frequency Shift Keying

FTP   File Transfer Protocol

GDSS   Group Decision Support System

GUI   Graphical User Interface

HDLC   High-Level Data Link Control

Hz   Hertz

333

IEEE   Institute of Electrical and Electronic Engineers

IP   Internet Protocol

IPC   Interprocess Communication

IPX   Internet Packet Exchange

ISDN   Integrated Services Digital Network

ISO   International Standards Organization

LAN   Local Area Network

LAPB   Link Access Protocol, Balanced

LATA   Local Access and Transport Area

LLC   Logical Link Control

LRC   Longitudinal Redundancy Check

LU   Logical Unit

MAC   Media Access Control protocol

MAU   Multistation Access Unit

Mbps   Million bits per second

MIB   Management Information Base

MIPS   Million Instructions Per Second

MNP   Microcomputer Network Protocols

MTA   Message Transfer Agent

MTBF   Mean Time Between Failures

MTTR   Mean Time To Repair

MUX   Multiplexing

NAU   Network Addressable Unit

NCP   Network Control Program

NFS   Network File System

NIA   Network Interface Adapter (also NIC)

NIC   Network Interface Card (also NIA)

NMS   Network Management System

NOS   Network Operating System

OLE   Object Linking and Embedding

ORB   Object Request Broker

OS   Operating System

OSI   Open Systems Interconnection reference model

PAD   Packet Assembly/Disassembly

PBX   Private Branch Exchange

PC   Personal Computer

PCI   Protocol Control Information

PCM   Pulse Code Modulation

PDN   Packet Distribution Network

PDU   Protocol Data Unit

PERT   Program Evaluation and Review Technique

POP   Point Of Presence

PPP   Point-to-Point Protocol

PRMD   Private Management Domain

PSE   Packet-Switching Equipment

PSK   Phase Shift Keying

PU   Physical Unit

PUCP   Physical Unit Control Point

PVC   Permanent Virtual Circuit

QAM   Quadrature Amplitude Modulation

RAID   Redundant Arrays of Independent Disks

RBOC   Regional Bell Operation Company

RFI   Request For Information

RFP   Request For Proposal

RFQ   Request For Quotation

RFS   Remote File Sharing

RIP   Routing Information Protocol

RJE   Remote Job Entry

RMON MIB   Remote Monitoring Management Information Base

RPC   Remote Procedure Call

SAA   System Application Architecture

SAP   Service Access Point

SBT   Six-Bit Transcode

SDLC   Synchronous Data Link Control

SDU   Service Data Unit

SMDS   Switched Multimegabit Data Service

SMI   Structure of Management Information

SMTP   Simple Mail Transfer Protocol

SNA   Systems Network Architecture

SNADS   SNA Distribution Services

SNMP   Simple Network Management Protocol

SONET   Synchronous Optical Network

SPX/IPX   Sequenced Packet Exchange/Internet Packet Exchange

SQL   Structured Query Language

SSCP   Systems Services Control Point

SSR   Spread Spectrum Radio

STDM   Statistical Time Division Multiplexing

STE   Signaling Terminal Equipment

STP   Shielded Twisted-Pair

SVC   Switched Virtual Circuit

TCP   Transaction Control Process

TCP/IP   Transaction Control Protocol/Internet Protocol

TDM   Time Division Multiplexing

TSAP   Transport Service Access Point

UA   User Agent

UPS   Uninterruptible Power Supply

UTP   Unshielded Twisted-Pair

VDT   Video Display Terminal

VDU   Video Display Unit

VHF   Very-High-Frequency radio waves

VRC   Vertical Redundancy Check

VTAM   Virtual Telecommunications Access Method

WAN   Wide Area Network

WATS   Wide Area Telecommunications or Telephone Service

XTP   Xpress Transfer Protocol

Key Terms Glossary

access time   The total time required in accessing a disk, including seek time, latency, and transfer time.

access method   A software subsystem that provides input and output services as interface between an application and its associated devices. It eliminates device dependencies for an application programmer.

access security   Security that controls a user's access to data. The controls may regulate a user's ability to read and update data, to delete files, and to run programs.

access server   An interconnection utility that allows microcomputers to access LAN resources from remote locations.

active hub   A node connection hub used in an ARCnet LAN that provides signal regeneration and allows nodes to be located up to 2000 feet from the hub.

active node   A node capable of sending or receiving network messages.

active port   The status of a bridge port that will accept packets from the LAN end of the port.

acoustic coupler   An acoustic coupler converts digital signals to analog and analog to digital. It is used mostly in switched communications and uses the telephone handset to pass data between a terminal or computer and the acoustic coupler.

adapter   A device that connects one system to another and allows the two systems to interoperate.

adaptive routing   A routing algorithm that evaluates the existing paths and chooses the one that will provide the best path for a message. Routes may change due to congestion and path failures.

address resolution protocol (ARP)   A protocol used to convert an IP address to the hardware address of a node. For example, if a node on an Ethernet network has an IP address, an internet message will refer to the IP address. The ARP protocol is used to convert the IP address to a hardware address so the message may be delivered over the Ethernet network.

Administrative Management Domain (ADMD)   A domain that represents a private electronic mail system corresponding to a public delivery network in the X.400 standard hierarchy.

Advanced Data Communications Control Procedure (ADCCP)   An ANSI standard bit-oriented data link control. Pronounced "add-cap."

Advanced Peer-to-Peer Networking (APPN)   An IBM network technology that allows two nodes to communicate directly with one another. Under IBM's System Network Architecture (SNA) it is generally the case that communication between two entities requires the involvement of the Systems Services Control Point (SSCP) which runs in an IBM host computer. With APPN, the involvement of the SSCP and host node are not required.

Advanced Program-to-Program Communication   In IBM's System Network Architecture (SNA), the ability for two programs to communicate with each other via an LU 6.2 session.

after-image   The status of a record after it has been processed.

agent   A device component that collects data for the device, which is then stored in the management information base (MIB). In client/server computing, an agent performs information preparation and exchange on behalf of a client or server process. In electronic mail systems, agents can act on behalf of users to operate on mail. For example, a vacation agent could automatically file mail messages and forward them to another user.

aggregate data rate   The amount of information that can be transmitted per unit of time.

alert   A signal given by the network management system that a statistic, such as current line status, line quality, or number of retries on the line, has changed since the last status report. Also known as an alarm.

American National Standards Institute (ANSI)   A U.S. standards-making agency.

American Standard Code for Information Interchange (ASCII)   A code that uses seven or eight bits to represent characters. One of the two common computer codes. *See also* EBCDIC.

amplitude   The height, magnitude, or energy of a waveform.

Amplitude Modulation (AM)   One method of changing the properties of a wave to represent data.

analog line monitor   A diagnostic tool that monitors and displays the analog signals on the communications circuit or on the data communications side of the modem, enabling the user to check for noise and proper modulation.

analog transmission   Refers to measurable physical quantities, which in data communications take the form of voltage and variations in the properties of waves. Data is represented in analog form by varying the amplitude, frequency, and/or phase of a wave or by changing current on a line.

application layer   One of the layers of the International Standards Organization's (OSI) reference model. The functions of this layer are application dependent.

Application Program Interface (API)   In LANs, the interface between application programs and the network software.

ARCnet   Local area network implementation based on Datapoint's attached resource computer network.

Asynchronous Transfer Mode (ATM)   A high-speed transmission protocol in which data blocks are broken into small cells that are transmitted individually and possibly via different routes in a manner similar to packet-switching technology.

asynchronous transmission (Async)   The oldest and one of the most common data link protocols. Each character is transmitted individually with its own error detection scheme, usually a parity bit. The sender and receiver are not synchronized with each other. Also known as start-stop protocol.

AT&T divestiture   In 1984, AT&T was broken up into independent RBOCs and a separate AT&T company. The divestiture ended the regulated monopoly of AT&T as well as freeing AT&T and the RBOCs to enter into business areas previously denied to them.

attenuation   A weakening of a signal as a result of distance and characteristics of the medium.

authentication   A process in which a system user is required to provide and/or verify his or her user identification to gain system access.

authorization   A security procedure that ensures that the entity making a request is allowed to carry out all the activities implied by the request.

Auto-Call Unit (ACU)   A device used to place a telephone call automatically without manual intervention.

availability   All necessary components of a network are operable and accessible when a user requires them.

backbone network   A network used to interconnect other networks or to connect a cluster of network nodes.

backup software   Software that is responsible for reading the files being backed up and writing them to the backup device.

baluns   Adapters that change coaxial cable connectors into twisted-pair wire connectors, allowing transfer from one medium to another or from a connector for one medium to a different medium.

bandwidth   The difference between the minimum and the maximum frequencies allowed. Bandwidth is a measure of the amount of data that can be transmitted per unit of time. The greater the bandwidth, the higher the possible data transmission rate.

baseband transmission   Sends the data along the channel by means of voltage fluctuations. The entire bandwidth of the cable is used to carry data.

batch   A style of computing in which inputs are collected over time and then processed as a group. Processing is carried out without interaction with a user.

Baudot   A code obtained from the telegraph industry that is used in data communications with telegraph lines or equipment originally designed for telegraphy. It is limited in its number of representable characters.

baud rate   A measure of the number of discrete signals that can be observed per unit of time.

before-image   The status of a record before it has been processed.

benchmark   A test in which one or more programs are run on a proposed hardware configuration to verify the ability of the hardware to meet a system's application requirements.

Binary Coded Decimal (BCD)   A coding scheme for the storage of data in digital computers. The code may either be four-bit or six-bit.

Binary Synchronous Communications (BISYNC or BSC) protocol   A transmission protocol introduced by IBM as the data link protocol for remote job entry. It later became a de facto standard for many types of data transmission, particularly between two computers. Data is transmitted a block at a time, and the sender and receiver need to be in time with each other. Specific control characters are used to indicate beginning of text, end of text, start of header, and so on.

bit-oriented synchronous data link protocol   A data link protocol in which one or more bits are used to control the communications link. Bit synchronous protocols are commonly used on both LANs and WANs.

bit parallel transmission   The simultaneous transmission of bits over a wire medium.

bit rate   One method of measuring data transmission speed—bits per second.

Bits Per Second (BPS)   The number of bits that can be transferred over a medium in one second. Bps is a measure of data transmission speed.

bit stuffing   The implementation of transparency in SDLC through bit insertion.

Block Check Character (BCC)   In the error detection methods of longitudinal redundancy check (LRC) or cyclic redundancy check (CRC), an error detection character or characters, called the BCC, is appended to a block of transmitted characters, typically at the end of the block.

block mode   A mode in which data is entered and transmitted in one or more sets or blocks.

breakout box   A passive, multipurpose diagnostic device that is patched or temporarily inserted into a circuit at an interface.

bridge   The interface used to connect networks using similar data link protocols.

broadband transmission   A form of data transmission where data is carried on high-frequency carrier waves; the carrying capacity of the medium is divided into a number of subchannels, such as video, low-speed data, high-speed data, voice, and so on, allowing the medium to satisfy several communication needs.

broadcast message   A message sent to all users on a network.

broadcast radio   Employs AM, FM, and shortwave radio frequencies, with a total frequency range from 500,000 to 108 million cycles per second. Its primary applications include paging terminals, cellular radio telephones, and wireless local area networks.

broadcast routing   Routing in which the message is broadcast to all stations. Only the stations to which the message is addressed accept it.

brouter   A term used to describe bridges that are able to connect two LANs using different data link protocols.

buffer overflow/overrun   A situation that arises when the buffer is either too small or too full to receive the transmitted data. In either case there is no place to store the arriving characters, and the data is lost.

bus   A communications medium for transmitting data or power. A local area network topology.

Bus Interface Unit (BIU)   In a local area network, the bus interface unit provides the physical connection to the computer's I/O bus.

byte count protocol   A type of synchronous protocol that delineates data by including the number of characters being transmitted within the message.

cable tester   A diagnostic tool used to detect faults in cables by generating and monitoring a signal along the cable.

cache memory   High-speed memory that improves a computer's performance.

call-back unit   A security device for switched connections. It operates by receiving a call, verifying the user, severing the call, and calling the user back.

call clearing   The process that dissolves a switched virtual circuit.

Carrier Sense with Multiple Access and Collision Avoidance (CSMA/CA)   A media access control technique that attempts to avoid collisions.

Carrier Sense with Multiple Access and Collision Detection (CSMA/CD)   A media access control technique that attempts to detect collisions and is the most common of the access strategies for bus architectures.

carrier signal   A wave that continues without change. The carrier signal can be modulated by a modem so a receiver can interpret the information.

Carterphone case   A U.S. case regarding attaching devices to a telephone company's network.

CCITT V.10 and V.11   Electrical interfaces for data transmission.

CCITT V.24   A functional interface similar to RS-232-C.

CCITT V.25   A specification for establishing and terminating sessions with an auto-call unit.

CCITT V.28   A specification for electrical interface similar to that of RS-232-C.

CCITT V.32   A modem standard specifying trellis encoding techniques to represent signals.

CCITT V.34   A modem standard for speeds up to 28.8 Kbps using trellis encoding.

CCITT V.35   A standard for data transmission at speeds up to 48,000 bits per second using a 34-pin connection.

CCITT V.42   A modem standard that defines error checking capabilities using cyclic redundancy checking.

CCITT X.20 and X.21   Standards that cover the interface between DCE and DTE for packet distribution networks.

CCITT X.24   A functional interface for packet distribution networks.

Centrex service   A telephone company service that provides PBX capabilities to a company. With the Centrex service, the PBX equipment is located on the telephone company's premises.

character count termination   A transmission termination technique where a transmission is complete when a specified number of characters have been received. Allows the computer to save the data in blocks and avoid buffer overflow.

character synchronous protocol   A type of synchronous protocol oriented toward specific data codes and specific characters within those codes.

checksum   A technique used to check for errors in data. The sending application generates the checksum from the data being transmitted. The receiving application computes the checksum and compares it to the value computed and sent by the sending station.

ciphertext   The encrypted version of a message or data.

circuit   Either the medium connecting two communicating devices or a path between a sender and a receiver where there may be one or more intermediary nodes. The exact meaning depends on the context.

client   A software application that requests services from the server in a client/server computing environment. Some systems may refer to the client as a requester.

client/server protocol   An application framework in which the processing load is divided among several processes called clients and servers. Clients issue requests to servers, which provide specialized services such as database processing and mail distribution. Within this framework, clients are able to concentrate on business logic while servers can use specialized hardware and software that allows them to provide their services more efficiently. When clients and servers are located in different computers, application processing is distributed over multiple computers and, in effect, the network becomes the computer.

closed system   A proprietary system wherein the interface specifications are not made readily available to other manufacturers. Thus, a closed system does not provide support for OSI or ANSI standard protocols and interfaces.

cluster controller   A device that manages multiple terminals by buffering data transmitted to and from the terminals and performing error detection and correction.

coaxial cable   A transmission medium consisting of one or two central data transmission wires surrounded by an insulating layer, a shielding layer, and an outer jacket. Coaxial cable has a high data-carrying capacity and low error rates.

code independence   The ability to successfully transmit data regardless of the data code, such as ASCII or EBCDIC.

collision   In a CSMA/CD media access control protocol, a collision occurs when two stations attempt to send a message at the same time. The messages interfere with each other, so correct communication is not possible.

common carrier   A public utility that provides public transmission media, such as the telephone companies and satellite companies.

Common Management Information Protocol (CMIP) Guidelines issued by the International Standards Organization for creating network management software products. Also known as the Communications Management Information Protocol.

Common Management Information Service (CMIS)   An International Standards Organization (ISO) standard for services to be provided by a network management system. CMIS, together with the common management information protocol form the ISO network management protocol.

communications controller   A computer that serves as a front end processor for a host machine. The communications controller provides the data link protocols and the physical devices attached to communications lines.

Communications Interface Unit (CIU)   In a local area network, the communications interface unit provides the physical connection to the transmission medium.

communications server   A server that monitors connections to the host by determining whether there is a free port to make the connection and granting or denying the request accordingly.

Computer-Aided Design (CAD)   An application of computers in the design process. One component is computer drafting.

Computer-Aided Instruction (CAI)   The use of computers to facilitate the education process.

Computer-Aided Manufacturing (CAM)   The use of computers to solve manufacturing problems. CAM includes robotic control, machine control, and process control components.

concentrator   A computer that provides line-sharing capabilities, data editing, polling, error handling, code conversion, compression, and encryption.

conditioning   A service provided by telephone companies for leased lines. It reduces the amount of noise on a line, providing lower error rates and increased speed.

conducted media   Media that use a conductor such as a wire or fiber optic cable to move a signal from sender to receiver.

congestion control   The reduction of transmission delays.

Connectionless Network Protocol (CLNP)   The counterpart to the Internet Protocol (IP), this protocol provides message services such as message priorities, route selection parameters, and security parameters.

connector   Establishes the physical connection between the computer and the medium.

consistency   A consistent system is one that works predictably with respect both to the people who use the system and to response times.

Consultative Committee on International Telegraph and Telephony (CCITT) An international standards organization.

contention   A convention whereby devices obtain control of a communications link. In contention mode, devices compete for control of the line either by transmitting directly on an idle line or by issuing a request for line control.

contention mode   A mode in which the host and the terminal contend for control of the medium by issuing a bid for the channel.

context data   A requirement of multithreaded processes that entails unifying the work by keeping track of the completed parts as well as the parts yet to be worked on, and ensuring that an interrupted transaction is restarted at the correct point.

control center   A network component responsible for monitoring the network and taking corrective action when necessary.

conversational mode   A mode in which the terminal and the host exchange messages.

cooperative computing   A data-processing model in which two or more processes collaborate on the processing necessary for a single transaction or application. The cooperating processes may reside in different computers.

Copper Distributed Data Interface (CDDI)   An ANSI LAN standard for twisted-pair-wire LANs spanning a distance of approximately 200 kilometers and providing speeds of 100 Mbps. An extension of the fiber distributed interface LAN.

corporate license   A license that gives a corporation unlimited use of software at all locations.

CPU time   The amount of time required for the CPU to execute the processing instructions, including those executed by the database management system, operating system, data communications software, and applications programs.

critical path   The sequence of events in a project that takes the longest to complete.

crosstalk When the signals from one channel distort or interfere with the signals of a different channel.

current loop A transmission technique that uses changes in current flow to represent data. Does not require a modem and operates at speeds up to 19.2K bits per second.

Customer Information Control System (CICS) A TCP provided by IBM. Its primary function is as an interface between terminal users on one side and application programs or the database on the other.

Cyclic Redundancy Check (CRC) An error detection algorithm that uses a polynomial function to generate the block check characters. CRC is a very efficient error detection method.

daisy chain A connection arrangement in which each device is connected directly to the next device. For example, a daisy chain of devices A, B, C, and D might have A connected to B, B connected to C, and C connected to D. Also known as cascading.

Database Management System (DBMS) A system that organizes data into records, organizes records into files, provides access to the data based on one or more access keys, and provides the mechanism for relating one file to another.

database server A computer that allows microcomputers on a network to request database processing of records, returning a single figure answer rather than the set of records essential to determining the answer.

data communications The transmission of data to and from computers and components of computer systems.

Data Communications Equipment (DCE) One class of equipment in data communications, including modems, media, and media support facilities.

Data Encryption Standard (DES) An algorithm that uses an encryption key to transform data, called plaintext, into an encoded form, called encrypted or cipher-text.

data flow control layer Layer 5 in IBM's SNA networks. The data flow control layer provides a set of protocols between two end users. These protocols provides for the orderly flow of information between the two users.

datagram One type of connection option for a PDN. The message fits into the data field on one packet. There is less accountability for packet delivery than for other connection types.

data link control layer Layer 2 in IBM's SNA networks. The data link control layer is responsible for protocols in node-to-node transfers, for example, synchronous and asynchronous transmissions. The data link control layer is also responsible for error detection and recovery across a link. Similar in function to the OSI Reference Model data link layer.

data link layer One of the layers of the International Standards Organization's OSI reference model. The data link layer is responsible for node-to-node-message transfers.

data link protocol Convention that governs the flow of data between a sending and a receiving station.

data switch A device implemented on sub-LANs to provide connections between microcomputers.

dataset/modem Short for modulator-demodulator. A device that changes digital signals to analog signals for transmitting data over telephone circuits. Also used for some fiber optic transmission (digital fiber optics do not require a modem) and any transmission mode requiring a change from one form of signal to another.

Data Terminal Equipment (DTE) The second class of equipment in data communications, including terminals, computers, concentrators, and multiplexers.

deadlock A state that exists when two or more processes are unable to proceed. It occurs when two or more transactions have locked a resource and request resources that other involved processes already have locked.

dedicated printer A printer that can be used only by a person at the workstation to which the printer is attached.

dedicated server One or more computers that operate only as designated file, database, or other types of servers.

dibits A transmission mode in which each signal conveys two bits of data.

Differential Phase Shift Keying (DPSK) A modulation technique that uses phase modulation. DPSK changes phase each time a 1 bit is transmitted and does not change phase for 0 bits.

digital transmission A transmission mode in which data is represented by binary digits rather than by an analog signal.

direct sequencing Sends data out over several different frequencies simultaneously to increase the probability of success.

discovery packet A packet sent by the sending station on all available routes to evaluate and determine the best route from the information collected by the packet.

disk caching Similar in function to cache memory except that main memory serves as a high-speed buffer for slower disk drives.

disk drive interface/controller Sets the standards for connecting the disk drive to the microprocessor and the software commands used to access the drive.

diskless workstation A workstation that has no local disk drives, reducing the ways in which a virus can be introduced.

disk seek enhancement An I/O optimization technique that reduces the head movement during seeks and improves performance.

Distributed Computing Environment (DCE) A standardization for middleware established by the Open Software Foundation that specifies the use of remote procedure calls, security, name services, and messages for client/server computing.

distributed database A database wherein data is located on two or more computing systems connected via a data communications network. The fact that data is distributed should be transparent to database users.

Distributed File System (DFS) Network software responsible for making network resources available to multiple users regardless of their location in the network.

distributed processing The geographic distribution of hardware, software, processing, data, and control.

distributed query processing   A condition in which a user at one node can start a query involving data on other nodes.

distributed routing determination   A routing algorithm in which each node calculates its own routing table based on status information periodically received from other nodes.

distributed transaction management   In a distributed database, a transaction may be operated on by several processes in different computer nodes. Transactions of this type must be managed by the distributed database system to ensure database integrity either by completing the transaction or by reversing any updates done by a transaction that cannot be completed.

distribution list   A predefined list of individual users, represented by a single E-mail address, that replaces the need to enter each user's individual address when sending a message to them collectively as a workgroup.

document co-authoring system   A system that allows two or more workers to work on one document concurrently.

document management system   A system that helps an organization manage and control its documents.

domain   In IBM's SNA, the network components managed by a systems services control point.

dotted quad   The four-octet address representation on the Internet.

double buffering   Used when buffer overflow/overrun occurs to avoid losing characters.

downloaded   The process of transferring data or an application from the server to the workstation.

DS1/T1 through T4/DS4   High-speed data transmission circuits from a common carrier.

dumb terminal   A terminal that passively serves for input and/or output but performs no local processing.

duplexed servers   The fault-tolerance technique in which one server can fail and another is available to continue working.

echo   The reflection or reversal of the signal being transmitted. Also used to define a transmission convention in which the receiver of data sends the data back to the sender to assist in error detection.

echo suppresser   A device that allows a transmitted signal to pass in one direction only, thus minimizing the echo effect.

effectiveness   A measure of how well a system serves users' needs.

electronic appointment calendar   A work-group productivity tool that is stored on the network, so that users can consult each other's appointment calendars.

electronic conferencing   An application that assists users in arranging and conducting meetings electronically.

electronic mail (E-mail)   An online service equivalent to the postal system which allows users to send and receive messages from other users electronically.

electronic meeting systems   Network software that allows participants to exchange machine readable information in the form of graphics, text, audio, and full-motion video.

emulator   A diagnostic tool that enables the user to check for adherence to a specific protocol.

encryption   A process in which transmitted data is scrambled at the sending location and reconstructed into readable data at the receiving end.

end office   A telephone company office to which a subscriber is connected. Also called a class 5 office.

enterprise network   A network of two or more LANs connected to each other, or one or more LANs connected to a WAN.

ergonomics   The science of designing equipment to maximize worker productivity by reducing operator fatigue and discomfort while improving safety.

Ethernet   A local area network implementation using the CSMA/CD protocol on a bus. The IEEE 802.3 standard is based on Ethernet. One of the popular local area network implementations.

exclusive open mode   A file open mode in which an open request is granted only if no other user has the file opened already.

Extended Binary-Coded Decimal Interchange Code (EBCDIC)   A code that uses eight bits to represent a character of information. One of the most common computer codes. See also ASCII.

external specification   Specifications detailing end-user interfaces to a system and information available to the user.

fault tolerance   A combination of hardware and software techniques that improve the reliability of a system.

Fiber Distributed Data Interface (FDDI)   An ANSI LAN standard for fiber optic LANs spanning a distance of approximately 200 kilometers and providing speeds of 100 Mbps.

fiber optic cable   A transmission medium that provides high data rates and low errors. One or more glass or plastic fibers are woven together to form the core of the cable. This core is surrounded by a glass or plastic layer called the cladding. The cladding in turn is covered with plastic or other material for protection. The cable requires a light source, most commonly laser and light-emitting diodes.

file exchange utilities   A work-group productivity tool that allows files to be easily copied from one network node to another.

File Management System (FMS)   A system that provides a subset of a database management system's capabilities. An FMS provides functions such as storage allocation and file access methods for a single file.

file server   A computer that allows microcomputers on a network to share resources such as data, programs, and printers. The file server's software controls access to shared files, as opposed to the operating system of the microcomputer.

file transfer protocol (FTP)   A capability of the TCP/IP protocol suite that allows files to be transferred from one node to another over the network.

file transfer utility   An intrinsic part of many routers, this utility allows files to be moved between network nodes.

filter　A software component used to screen and format data sent to the management center.

flooding　A technique used by a bridge to locate a destination address not present in the bridge's routing table by sending a packet out on all possible paths. An acknowledgment from the receiving station will contain the destination address of the packet, which can then be added to the bridge's routing table.

flow control　A mechanism used by network protocols to provide message pacing so the sender does not send data faster than the receiver is able to accept it.

Fractional T-1　A T-1 service that fills the void of high speed transmission options between 64 Kbps and 1.5 Mbps by providing a portion of T-1 line to customers.

frame　A term used to describe a transmission packet in bit-oriented protocols.

frame relay　A fast packet switching protocol that is similar to X.25 packet switching. Frame relay does not perform as exhaustive error checking as X.25 and is thus able to switch packets at a higher rate than X.25.

framing protocol　A type of synchronous protocol that uses reserved characters or bit patterns to delineate data and control fields within the message.

frequency division multiplexing (FDM)　A technique that divides the available bandwidth of the circuit into subchannels of different frequency ranges, each of which is assigned to one device.

frequency hopping　Data is transmitted at one frequency, the frequency changes, and the data is transmitted at the new frequency. Each piece of data is transmitted over several frequencies to increase the probability that the data will be successfully received.

Frequency Modulation (FM)/Frequency Shift Keying (FSK)　One method of changing the characteristics of a signal to represent data. The frequency of the carrier signal is changed. Often used by lower speed modems.

Front-End Processor (FEP)　A communications component placed at the host end of a circuit to take over a portion of the line management work from the host. Also referred to as a communications controller or a message switch.

full duplex　A data transmission mode in which data is transmitted over a link in both directions simultaneously.

Fully Qualified Domain Name (FQDN)
The computer.domain notation used to specify addresses in the Internet.

functional specification　An agreement between management and designers outlining design objectives, such as the product to be produced, and design constraints, such as time and cost.

functional testing　Testing individual modules to ensure that they produce the desired results.

gateway　The interface used to connect two dissimilar networks or systems by providing conversion from one network to another.

geosynchronous orbit　A satellite orbit in which the satellite is stationary with respect to the earth. The satellite is always positioned over the same location.

Group Decision Support System (GDSS)　System that assists individuals and groups in the decision-making process and helps them set objectives.

groupware　A collective of work-group productivity tools that allows a group of users to communicate and to coordinate activities.

guardbands　Subchannel separators that are implemented in frequency division multiplexing to avoid crosstalk.

half duplex　A data transmission mode in which data can travel in both directions over a link but in only one direction at a time.

half-session layer　Represents a single layer (transmission control, flow control, and presentation service) in the four-layer definition of SNA functional layers.

Hertz (Hz)　The term used to denote frequency; one hertz is one cycle per second.

heterogeneous　In networks, a network made up of a variety of equipment, particularly, equipment and software from a variety of vendors.

hierarchical topology　A network topology in which the nodes are arranged hierarchically. Also known as a tree structure.

High-Level Data Link Control (HDLC)　A positional synchronous protocol that operates in full duplex mode in both point-to-point and multipoint configurations. Data is transmitted in fixed-format frames consisting of start flag, address, control information, block check character (CRC), an end-of-frame flag. HDLC is an International Standards Organization standard similar to IBM's SDLC.

hub　A wiring concentrator for connecting workstations on a token ring or 10Base-T local area network.

Hush-a-Phone Case　A U.S. case that set a precedent regarding attaching equipment to telephone networks.

I/O driver　The part of the operating system that manages the input/output subsystem by providing low-level access to devices.

I/O optimization　A variety of ways to optimize the task of file access which increases the performance of the server.

identification　Information assigned to a specific user of a system for security and control purposes. User identification ranges from simple user names to high-security measures such as voice print and fingerprint identification.

IEEE 802.1 High-Level Interface Subcommittee　The high-level subcommittee that addresses matters relating to network architecture, management, and interconnections.

IEEE 802.2 Logical Link Control Subcommittee　This subcommittee defines the functions of the logical link control sublayer of the OSI Reference Model data link layer. The objective of the LLC is to provide a consistent, transparent interface to the media access control (MAC) layer, so the network layers above the data link layer are able to function correctly regardless of the MAC protocol.

IEEE 802.3 standard   A standard that covers a variety of CSMA/CD architectures that are generally based on the Ethernet.

IEEE 802.4 standard   A subcommittee that sets standards for token bus networks.

IEEE 802.5 standard   A subcommittee that sets standards for token-ring networks.

IEEE 802.6 standard   A metropolitan area network (MAN) standard similar to the FDDI family of technologies. The IEEE 802.6 standard has also been adopted by ANSI. The standard is also referred to as the distributed queue dual bus (DQDB) standard. As the name DQDB indicates, the architecture uses two buses. Each bus is unidirectional, meaning that data is transmitted in one direction on one bus and in the other direction on the second bus.

IEEE 802.7 Broadband Technical Advisory Group
This group provides guidance and technical expertise to other groups that are establishing broadband LAN standards, such as the 802.3 subcommittee for 10Broad36.

IEEE 802.8 Fiber Optic Technical Advisory Group
This group provides guidance and technical expertise to other groups that are establishing standards for LANs using fiber optic cable.

IEEE 802.9 Integrated Data and Voice Networks Subcommittee   This committee sets standards for networks that carry both voice and data. Specifically, it is setting standards for interfaces to the Integrated Services Digital Networks (ISDNs).

IEEE 802.10 LAN Security Subcommittee   This committee addresses the implementation of security capabilities like encryption, network management, and the transfer of data.

IEEE 802.11 Wireless LAN Subcommittee   This committee sets standards for multiple wireless transmission methods for LANs.

IEEE 802.12 Demand Priority Access Method Subcommittee
This subgroup is developed the specifications for the 100VG-AnyLAN protocol. The protocol specifies 100 Mbps speeds over twisted-pair wires.

impulse noise   A noise characterized by signal "spikes." In telephone circuits it can be caused by switching equipment or by lightning strikes and in other situations by transient electrical impulses such as those occurring on a shop floor. Impulse noise is a common cause of transmission errors.

inactive node   A node that may be powered down and is incapable of sending or receiving messages.

inactive port   The status of a bridge port that will not accept packets from the LAN end of the port.

information superhighway   A national information system geared toward moving the raw materials (data) and finished goods (information and ideas) of information to their needed locations.

infrared transmission   Uses electromagnetic radiation of wavelengths between visible light and radio waves. It is a line-of-sight technology used to provide local area connections between buildings and is also the medium used in some wireless local area networks.

Institute of Electrical and Electronic Engineers (IEEE)
A professional society that establishes and publishes documents and standards for data communications. IEEE has established several standards for local area networks, including the IEEE 802.3 and IEEE 802.5 standards for LAN technology.

Integrated Services Digital Network (ISDN)   The integration of voice and data transmission (and other formats such as video and graphics images) over a digital transmission network. This network configuration is proposed by numerous common carriers.

integrated testing   A procedure which ensures that all parts of a system are functionally compatible.

intelligent terminal   A terminal that has both memory and data processing capabilities.

interactive   A computing paradigm in which users interact with the programs.

interconnected (plex or mesh) network   A network topology in which any node can be directly connected to any other node.

intermodulation noise   A special form of crosstalk, which is the result of two or more signals combining to produce a distorted signal.

internal specification   Specifications or "blueprints" for developing a software system.

International Standards Organization (ISO)   An organization that is active in setting communications standards.

Internet   A specific collection of interconnected networks spanning more than 40 countries throughout the world. When used with a small letter I, an internet is any interconnection of two or more computer networks.

Internet Packet Exchange (IPX)   The network layer protocol used by Novel NetWare LANs.

interoperability   The ability of all network components to connect to the network and to communicate with shared network resources.

interrupt   A signal issued by hardware or an application requesting a service from the operating system.

interrupt characters   A set of characters that terminate a message or cause an interruption in transmission to perform a special action, such as a backspace.

inventory software   A management tool used to collect LAN component data, such as network addresses and CPU types, that will assist a network administrator in managing and fixing a network.

inverse multiplexer   A mux that provides a high-speed data path between two devices by separating data onto multiple lower-speed communications circuits.

key disk   A security system in which a flexible disk must be in the disk drive when the application is run.

LAN analyzer   A diagnostic tool that monitors network traffic, captures and displays data sent over the network, generates network traffic to simulate load or error conditions, tests cables for faults, and provides data helpful for system configuration and management.

LAN Server (IBM)   An example of LAN software that runs under an existing OS, OS/2.

latency   The average time required for the requested data to revolve under the read/write heads.

learning bridge   Bridge that builds its own routing table from the messages it receives, rather than having a predefined routing table. Also known as a transparent bridge.

leased lines   Lines leased from common carriers. Lines are leased when the connection time between locations is long enough to cover the cost of leasing or if speeds higher than those available with switched lines must be attained.

license agreement   An agreement that covers the rules under which you are allowed to use a product.

line monitor   A device used to diagnose problems on a communications link. Also known as a protocol analyzer.

link   The circuit established between two adjacent nodes, with no intervening nodes.

Link Access Procedure, Balanced (LAPB)   A bit synchronous protocol similar to high-level data link control. LAPB is the protocol specified for X.25 networks.

Local Access and Transport Areas (LATA)   The region served by a regional Bell operating company(RBOC). Following the divestiture of AT&T the U.S. was divided into local access and transport areas. LATAs are not rigidly defined, but calls within a LATA are handled exclusively by the RBOC (the call is not handled by a long-distance carrier but still may be a toll call).

Local Area Network (LAN)   A communications network in which all of the components are located within several kilometers of each other and that uses high transmission speeds—generally one million bits per second or higher.

local procedure calls   In programming, one procedure in a program can call another procedure in the same program. The called procedure carries out a processing task for the calling procedure. Generally, the two procedures exchange information through a list of parameters that are passed between the calling and the called procedure.

locks   Record or file-level control that overcomes the problem with file open contention.

log file   A monitoring tool used for both diagnostic functions and predictive or management functions.

Logical Link Control (LLC)   A sublayer of the OSI reference model data link layer. The logical link control forms the interface between the network layer and the media access control protocols.

Logical Unit (LU)   In IBM's SNA, a unit that represents a system user. Sessions exist between LUs or between an LU and the SSCP. Several types of LUs have been defined.

Longitudinal Redundancy Check (LRC)   An error-checking technique in which a block check character is appended to a block of transmitted characters, typically at the end of the block. The block check character checks parity on a row of bits.

LU 6.2   An SNA logical unit type representing a program-to-program session.

mail agent   A software module that can automatically act on behalf of a user to forward mail or alert other users that the recipient is unavailable.

Management Information Base (MIB)   A database that defines the hardware and software elements to be monitored in the SNMP.

matrix switch   A device that allows terminal connections to be switched among the available processors.

Mean Time Between Failures (MTBF)   A measure of the average amount of time a given component may be expected to operate before failing.

Mean Time To Repair (MTTR)   The average amount of time required to repair a broken piece of equipment and restore it to service.

Media Access Control (MAC) protocol   A sub layer of the OSI reference model's data link layer. The media access control protocol defines how a station gains access to the media for data transmission. Common MAC protocols are carrier sense with multiple access and collision detection (CSMA/CD) and token-passing.

medium   In data communications, the carrier of data signals. Twisted-pair wires, coaxial cables, and fiber optic cables are the most common LAN media.

menuing software   A management tool used to provide users options via a menu of choices.

message logging   Also referred to as safe storing, this recovery system writes the message to a file prior to acknowledgment so the message may be reviewed or recovered later if necessary.

message sequence numbers   A system in which each transmitted message is given a sequential number, allowing multiple messages to be transmitted without acknowledgment.

Message Transfer Agent (MTA)   An interface between E-mail user agents.

metering software   A monitoring tool used on LANs to enforce adherence to software license agreements by keeping track of the number of times an application is executed.

Microcomputer Network Protocols (MNP)   A set of modem protocols providing for data compression and error checking, such as MNP Level 4 and MNP Level 5.

microwave radio   A method of transmitting data using high-frequency radio waves. It requires a line of sight between sending and receiving stations. Capable of high data rates, microwave is used for wide area networks and wireless LANs.

middleware   A software interface that functions as an intermediary between clients and servers.

mirrored disks   A fault tolerance technique in which two disks containing the same data are provided so that if one fails, the other is available, allowing processing to continue.

mobile computing   Has expanded the role of broadcast radio in data communications. It requires a wireless medium such as cellular radio, radio nets, and low orbit satellites.

modem eliminator   A device that allows data transmission over short distances without a modem. Provides for signal timing as well as data transmission.

modem turnaround time   The time required for a modem to make the transition from sender to receiver on half duplex links. It includes the time for the old sender to drop the carrier signal, for the new sender to recognize that the carrier signal has been dropped, and for the new sender to raise the carrier signal that must be detected by the new receiver.

modular expansion   A system that allows the user to upgrade from a small system to a more powerful system by adding more of the same type of processor to the existing system.

multidrop   See multipoint connection.

multimedia technology   Technology that extends a computer's capabilities by adding audio and video to data.

multimode graded-index fiber   Acts to refract the light toward the center of the fiber by variations in the density of the core.

multimode step-index fiber   The oldest of the fiber optic technologies, in which the reflective walls of the fiber move the light pulses to the receiver.

multiple access   The ability for nodes to access a medium that is not carrying a message.

multiplexer   A hardware device that allows several devices to share one communications channel.

multiplexing   A line-sharing technology that allows multiple signals to be transmitted over a single link.

multipoint connection   A connection in which several terminals share one communications link.

Multistation Access Unit (MAU)   In an IBM token ring LAN, a MAU is used to interconnect workstations.

multithreading   The capacity a process has to work on multiple requests at once.

NetView   IBM's network management system. NetView has three major subsystems, NetView, NetView/PC, and NetView/6000.

NetWare   A leading example of the integrated LAN operating system software approach by Novell.

network   Two or more computers connected by a communications medium, together with all communications, hardware and software components. Alternatively, a host processor together with its attached terminal, workstations, and communications equipment, such as transmission media, modems, and so on.

Network Addressable Unit (NAU)   In IBM's SNA, any device that has a network address, such as logical units and physical units.

network architecture   The way in which media, hardware, and software are integrated to form a network

network configuration tool   A monitoring tool used to plan the optimum network configuration with respect to sources and types of circuits.

network control   Involves the sending and receiving of node status information to other nodes to determine the best routing for messages.

Network Control Program (NCP)   A data communications program that helps manage a communications network.

Specifically, a program that runs in IBM's 37xx line of communications controllers.

network directory services   A database that contains the names, types, and network addresses of network resources. Examples of resource types include users, printers, and servers. The directory database may be replicated on several network nodes, thus allowing users and processes to locate resources they need to complete their work.

Network File System (NFS)   A distributed file system developed by Sun Microsystems that is also compatible with DOS and UNIX-based systems.

network layer   One of the layers of the International Standards Organization's OSI reference model. The network layer is responsible for end-to-end message routing.

Network Management System (NMS)   A combination of hardware and software used by network supervisors to monitor and administer a network.

network manager   An individual or management team responsible for configuring, planning, tuning, and establishing standards and procedures for a network.

network routing manager   A designated node that has an overview of network functioning, location of any bottlenecks, and location of utilized facilities.

network routing table   In the process of message transmission, a table in which the network layer looks up the destination address to find the next address along the path.

network statistics   Information, such as error rates, data rates, and the number of retransmission attempts resulting from errors, that is collected to analyze network performance trends.

network topology   A model for the way in which network nodes are connected. Network topologies include bus, ring, and star.

neutral working   A method of transmitting data in a current loop where current represents a 1 bit and the absence of current indicates a 0 bit.

next received   See number received.

next sent   See number sent.

node   A processor in a network, either a LAN or a WAN.

non-dedicated server   A computer that can operate as both a server and a workstation.

null modem   A cable in which the transmit and send leads are crossed. A null modem allows two devices to communicate over short distances (typically 50 feet or less) without using a modem.

number received (Nr) subfield   In bit synchronous transmission such as HDLC, a field on the transmission frame and on the receiver's system used to represent the frame sequence number the receiving station expects to receive next.

number sent (Ns) subfield   In bit synchronous transmission such as HDLC, a field on the transmission frame and on the sender's system used to represent the frame sequence number being transmitted.

Object Request Broker (ORB) A standardization for middle-ware established by the Object Management Group that assures hardware and software independence by locating a server that is capable of satisfying a client's request.

octet A group of eight bits used in bit synchronous protocols. Data, regardless of its code, is treated as octets.

office automation systems A special case of a distributed system, with both data and processing distributed among several different components.

open architecture Architecture whose network specifications are available to any company. This allows a variety of companies to design hardware and software components that can be easily integrated into new and existing networks.

open system See open architecture.

Open System Interconnection (OSI) Management Framework The part of the OSI Reference Model standard that provides the model for network management standards.

Open Systems Interconnection (OSI) Reference Model A seven-layered set of functions for transmitting data from one user to another. Specified by the International Standards Organization.

Operating System (OS) The overall manager of the computing system that performs all of its functions transparent to the applications program and the programmer.

pacing See flow control.

packet A unit of data transmission. The packet consists of the data to be transmitted together with the headers and trailers affixed by the various layers in the OSI Reference Model.

Packet Assembly/Disassembly (PAD) A function in a packet-switching network that breaks messages into packets for transmission and reassembles packets into messages at the message's destination.

packet switching The transmission of a message by dividing the message into fixed length packets and then routing the packets to the recipient. Packets may be sent over different paths and arrive out of order. At the receiving end, the packets are reordered. Routing is determined during transmission of the packet. Also known as packet distribution network (PDN), public data network, X.25 network, or value-added network.

Packet-Switching Equipment (PSE) Equipment that accepts and forwards messages in a packet distribution network.

parity check/Vertical Redundancy Check (VRC) The same as parity error checking. For each character transmitted, an additional bit, the parity bit, is attached to help detect errors. The bit is chosen so that the number of 1 bits is even (even parity) or odd (odd parity).

parity data In RAID technology, additional data that provides the ability to reconstruct data that has been corrupted.

passive hub A node connection hub used in an ARCnet LAN that does not provide signal regeneration, so nodes can be located no farther than 100 feet from the hub.

password A secret expression used by authorized persons to prove their right to access a system.

path A group of links that allows a message to move from its point of origin to its destination.

path control layer The third layer in IBM's SNA. Path control provides end-to-end routing.

peer layers Corresponding layers in the OSI Reference Model. For example, the network layers in two nodes are peer layers.

peer-to-peer A type of communication in which any two devices can communicate on essentially equivalent basis. A peer-to-peer architecture is a LAN option that allows nodes to communicate on an equal basis and share resources (as opposed to a server-based LAN).

performance monitor A monitoring tool that provides snapshots of how a system is actually functioning, which helps the network management team identify trends in the use or misuse of the network.

Permanent Virtual Circuit (PVC) One of three types of connection for a packet distribution network. A PVC provides a permanent link (like a leased line) between two nodes. It is usually selected when two nodes require continual transmission.

phase jitter A variation in the phase of a continued signal from cycle to cycle.

phase modulation A change in the phase of a carrier signal. Commonly used alone or in conjunction with amplitude modulation to provide high-speed transmission (4800 bits per second and higher).

Phase Shift Keying (PSK) A form of phase modulation.

physical control layer Layer 1 in IBM's SNA networks. The physical control layer covers physical interfaces similar to the physical layer of the OSI Reference Model.

physical layer One of the layers of the International Standards Organization's OSI reference model. The physical layer specifies the electrical connections between the transmission medium and the computing system.

physical security Measures, such as door locks, safes, and security guards, taken to deny physical access to restricted areas.

Physical Unit (PU) In SNA, a hardware unit. Four physical units have been defined: Type 5, host processor; Type 4, communications controller; Type 2, cluster or programmable controller; and Type 1, a terminal or controller that is not programmable.

Physical Unit Control Point (PUCP) In IBM's systems network architecture (SNA), a physical unit control point resides in nodes that do not contain a systems services control point (SSCP). The PUCP is responsible for connecting the node to and disconnecting the node from the network.

plain text The unencrypted or properly decrypted version of a message or data. Plain text is intelligible. Also known as clear text.

Point Of Presence (POP) A point of presence in the U.S. public telephone network. A point of presence is a point at which a transfer is made from a local telephone company to the long-distance carrier.

point-to-point connection A connection using a communication line to connect one terminal or computer to a host computer.

point-to-point protocol   A protocol that allows routers to establish data link connections and to exchange configuration information.

polar working   One method used to implement current loop transmission.

polling   The process of asking terminals whether they have data to transmit.

port concentrator   A device that allows multiple input streams from a multiplexer to be passed to the host through a single communications port.

port selector   A device that helps determine which users are granted access to applications where the number of potential terminal users far exceeds the number of available lines. Also known as a data switch.

positional protocol   A type of synchronous protocol that delineates fields by the use of fixed-length fields on the message, by indicating the size of the message with a character count embedded in the message, or both.

presentation layer   One of the layers of the International Standards Organization's OSI reference model. The presentation layer addresses message formats.

presentation services layer   Layer 6 in IBM's SNA networks. The presentation services layer is involved in formatting data received from and sent to a user.

primary center   A telephone company class 3 station. A primary center is one station higher than a toll center.

printer driver   A software module that determines how to format data for proper printing on a specific type of printer.

print server   A computer that allows several users to direct their printed output to the same printer.

Private Branch Exchange (PBX)   Telephone switching equipment located on corporate premises and owned by the corporation. A PBX allows telephone calls within an office to be connected locally without using the telephone company's end office or transmission circuits.

private lines   Communication lines owned by a user; alternatively communications lines leased from a common carrier.

Private Management Domain (PRMD)   A domain that represents a delivery and interconnection network corresponding to a company in the X.400 standard hierarchy.

Program Evaluation and Review Technique (PERT)   A technique that tracks a project's progress to determine its critical path and to monitor personnel, schedules and project resources.

project management system   A management tool that assists in planning projects and allocating resources.

propagation delay   The amount of time it takes for a signal to travel from its source to its destination.

protected open mode   A file open mode that is granted only if no other user has already been granted exclusive or protected mode.

protocol   Convention used for establishing transmission rules. Protocols are used to establish rules for delineation of data, error detection, control sequences, message lengths, media access, and so on.

protocol control information (PCI)   A header attached to a service data unit. The protocol control information together with the service data unit (SDU) form a protocol data unit(PDU).

protocol converter   A special-purpose device that allows a terminal to look like a different type of terminal in order to facilitate interconnection between different computer systems.

protocol data unit (PDU)   A unit of information exchanged between peer protocols in the OSI Reference Model.

protocol stacks   A protocol stack allows a collection of protocols to interoperate. The stack defines the order of operation of the protocols. The top of the stack is oriented toward the application layer while the protocols at the bottom of the stack deal with communication protocols, for example those at the data link and network layers.

proxy agent   Software that provides an interface between different network management protocols.

public key encryption   An encryption algorithm. Two keys are created, the public and private keys. Encryption is accomplished with the public key. Decryption is done with the private key.

Pulse Code Modulation (PCM)   A method for transmitting data in digital format.

quadbits   A technique in which each signal carries four bits of data. Requires 16 different signals.

Quadrature Amplitude Modulation (QAM)   A modulation technique using both phase and amplitude modulation.

queuing time   The amount of time the transaction must wait in queues for service.

radiated media   Media that use radio waves of different frequencies or infrared light to broadcast through air or space and accordingly do not need a wire or cable conductor to transmit signals.

recovery   The act of restoring a system to operational status following a failure.

redirector   A software module that intercepts and reroutes network application I/O requests before they get to the workstation's OS.

Redundant Arrays of Independent Disks (RAID)   A fault-tolerance disk storage technique that spreads one file plus the file's checksum information over several disk drives. If any single disk drive fails, the data stored thereon can be reconstructed from data stored on the remaining drives.

Regional Bell Operating Company (RBOC)   The AT&T divestiture resulted in the formation of RBOCs and a separate AT&T company. An RBOC is responsible for local telephone services within a region of the United States.

regional center   A class 1 telephone station.

reliability   The probability that the system will continue to function over a given time period.

remote control software   A diagnostic tool that allows a LAN administrator to remotely view a user's monitor and take control of the user's keyboard.

remote data access (RDA)   An OSI standard that defines a service that allows application programs to access data located on another node. RDA is intended to allow such access independent of the database management systems or operating systems being used.

Remote File Sharing (RFS) A distributed file system that is only supported by UNIX-based systems.

Remote Job Entry (RJE) An application of data communications. Batches of data are collected at a remote site and transmitted to a host for processing. In early implementations the input was card format and the output was printer format (between the remote terminals and the host processor).

remote login facility A network utility that allows users to log onto a remote system thereby establishing the user as a local user on the remote node.

Remote Monitoring MIB (RMON MIB) An SNMP standard that describes nine different device groups. A vendor must choose an appropriate group for a device adhering to this standard and is required to support all the data objects defined for that group.

remote procedure call (RPC) A remote procedure call is similar to a local procedure call except that the calling and called procedures are not a part of the same program. The called and calling procedures may be located in the same computer or in different networked computers.

repeater A device used to amplify signals on a network. Repeaters allow the medium distance to be extended.

Request For Information (RFI) An informal method of investigating hardware and software solutions by presenting a brief statement of a problem to be solved and a list of questions soliciting solutions to the problem.

Request For Proposal (RFP) Sometimes referred to as a Request For Quotation (RFQ), a formal document describing the problem to be solved and requesting qualified vendors to submit plans and costs for solving the problem.

response time The amount of time required for a user to receive a reply to a request. Usually the time elapsed between the user pressing the Enter key to send the request (or the equivalent) and the return of the first character of the response.

reverse channel Allows transmission in both directions on a line that is essentially half duplex. The reverse channel generally has a lower transmission rate than the forward channel and is used to acknowledge receipt of data. Reverse channels help reduce the need for modem turnaround.

ring topology A network configuration commonly used to implement local area networks. The medium forms a loop to which workstations are attached. Data is transmitted from one station to the next around the ring. Generally the access protocol is token-passing.

root bridge The bridge assigned the highest priority.

router A network interconnection device and associated software that links two networks. The networks being linked can be different, but they must use a common routing protocol.

routing An algorithm used to determine how to move a message from its source to its destination. Several algorithms are used.

routing information protocol (RIP) One of the protocols used by routers to exchange routing information and thus update their network routing tables.

routing table An information source containing node addresses and the identification of the path to be used in transmitting data to those nodes.

RS-232-C standard An Electronic Industries Association (EIA) standard for asynchronous transmission.

RS-366 standard An Electronic Industries Association (EIA) standard for automatic-call unit interface.

RS-449 standard An Electronic Industries Association (EIA) standard that improves on the capabilities of RS-232-C.

satellite radio transmission Transmits data via very-high-frequency (VHF) radio waves and requires line-of-sight transmission between stations.

sectional center In the telephone network, a class 2 station.

security Controls implemented by network management to delay unauthorized access to a system.

seek time In disk accessing, the time it takes to move the read/write heads to the proper cylinder.

serial binary transmission The successive transmission of bits over a wire medium.

server In client/server computing, the software application that provides clients with the services they request. A computer that provides LAN services.

server license A license that allows an application to be installed on one server.

service data unit (SDU) The basic data unit consisting of data assembled at the application layer. Protocol control information is attached to the SDU forming a protocol data unit.

session The dialog between two system users.

session layer One of the layers of the International Standards Organization's OSI reference model. The session layer is responsible for establishing a dialogue between applications.

shared open mode A file open mode that allows several users to have a file open concurrently.

shared printer A printer controlled by a server and available to designated users.

shielded twisted-pair (STP) wires Twisted-pair wires that have a metalized or foil outer covering shield around them to reduce the probability of noise affecting the signal transmitted over the wires.

Signaling Terminal Equipment (STE) Node used to provide an interface between two different packet-switching networks.

simple mail transfer protocol (SMTP) A protocol within the TCP/IP protocol suite. SMTP is an application layer protocol used to implement mail services and message transfer.

Simple Network Management Protocol (SNMP) SNMP provides a guideline for creating network management software products. SNMP has four key components: the SNMP protocol, structure of management information (SMI), management information base (MIB), and the network management system (NMS).

simplex transmission   A mode of data transmission in which data may flow in only one direction. One station is always a sender and another is always a receiver over a simplex link.

simulation model   A monitoring tool that allows the user to describe network and system activities and to receive an analysis of how the system can be expected to perform under the described conditions.

single mode transmission   The fastest fiber optic technique, in which the light is guided down the center of an extremely narrow core.

single threading   A technique in which only one operation is processed at a time.

site license   A license that gives the user unlimited rights to use the software at a given site.

Six-Bit Transcode (SBT)   A six-bit computer code developed by IBM primarily for RJE.

sizing   The analysis conducted to determine the amount of hardware required to support a system. Sizing must consider the system throughout and the required transaction response times during peak processing periods.

smart terminal   A terminal that can save data entered by the operator into memory.

SNA Distribution Services (SNADS)   An SNA facility that provides asynchronous distribution of documents throughout a network.

socket   A combination of a transmission control protocol (TCP) port number and an internet address. Sockets are used in TCP/IP and other systems to provide connections between two entities.

software license agreement   A document provided by the software vendor that specifies the rights and restrictions of using the software.

source routing   A learning bridge algorithm in which the sending node is responsible for determining the route to the destination node. The routing information is appended to the message and the bridges along the route use the routing information to move the message from the source to destination.

spanning tree   A method by which learning bridges build their own routing table.

spanning tree algorithm   A learning bridge algorithm in which bridges exchange routing information with one another. Based on the routing information thus received, each bridge maintains a routing table that shows how to route messages to other LANs.

spooler   A software system that collects printer output (typically on disk) and schedules the data for printing. SPOOL is an acronym for Simultaneous Peripheral Operation On Line.

Spread Spectrum Radio (SSR)   The primary application for data communications is for use with wireless LANs. It has a characteristic reliability in environments where signal interference is likely.

STARLAN   A configuration similar to the basic star topology in that each workstation is connected to a wiring hub. The primary medium used for implementations is twisted-pair wires.

star topology   A network topology using a central system to which all other nodes are connected. All data are transmitted to or through the central system. Also known as star network.

star-wired LAN   A variation of star topology in which a wiring hub is used to form the connection between network nodes.

static routing   A form of routing in which one particular path between two nodes is always used.

Statistical Time Division Multiplexing (STDM)   A technique that provides improved time-sharing efficiency by transmitting data only for those lines with data to send, rather than allowing idle lines to occupy carrying capacity of the communications circuit. Also known as a stat mux.

stealth virus   A computer virus that has the ability to change its signature or identity, thus making the virus more difficult to detect and eradicate. Also known as a polymorphic virus.

store-and-forward system   When transmitting data between two nodes, the messages are logged at intermediate nodes, which then forward them to the next node.

StreetTalk (Banyan)   A database that provides network directory services.

stress testing   A procedure that ensures that the system can sustain the designated workload.

Structure of Management Information (SMI)   A component of the SNMP that details how information is represented in the management information base (MIB).

Structured Query Language (SQL)   A relational database language developed by IBM and later standardized by the American National Standards Institute (ANSI).

subarea   A portion of an SNA network consisting of a subarea node (a host node or communications controller — PU Types 5 and 4 respectively) together with all of the network resources supported by the subarea node.

sub-LAN   A network that provides a subset of LAN capabilities, primarily peripheral sharing and file transfer, but has lower data transfer rates and diminished transparency than a LAN.

subnet   The first set of numbers in an Internet address representing the network identification of a node's network.

switched connection   A communications link established when one station dials a telephone number to connect to another station. A switched connection uses voice circuits. The circuit exists for the duration of the session.

Switched Multimegabit Data Services (SMDS)   A high-speed connectionless digital transmission service.

Switched Virtual Circuit (SVC)   One of three types of circuits in a packet distribution network. When a session is required between two users, an end-to-end circuit is determined and allocated for the duration of the session. Similar to a switched connection.

synchronous   A transmission protocol where the sender and receiver are synchronized. Data is generally transmitted in blocks, rather than a character at a time as in asynchronous transmission.

Synchronous Data Link Control (SDLC) An IBM positional synchronous protocol that operates in full duplex or half duplex mode in both point-to-point and multipoint configurations. Data is transmitted in fixed-format frames consisting of start flag, address, control information, block check character (BCC) and end-of-frame flag.

synchronous protocol See synchronous.

Systems Network Architecture (SNA) IBM's architecture for building a computer network. Encompasses hardware and software components, establishing sessions between users, and capabilities such as office and message/file distribution services.

Systems Services Control Point (SSCP) In IBM's SNA, the process that controls a domain. It is responsible for initiating network components, establishing sessions, and maintaining unit status.

T-1 Communications A high speed common carrier service that provides 1.54 Mbps. T-1 service is also know as DS-1 signaling.

T-2 Communications A high speed common carrier service that provides 6.3 Mbps. T-2 service is also know as DS-2 signaling.

T-3 Communications A high speed common carrier service that provides 45 Mbps. T-3 service is also know as DS-3 signaling.

T-4 Communications A high speed common carrier service that provides 274 Mbps. T-4 service is also know as DS-4 signaling.

TELNET A TCP/IP protocol that allows entry form a keyboard to be passed from a local system to a remote system. Through this protocol, an application on the remote node believes it is communicating with a locally attached device.

terminal An input/output device that can be connected to a local or remote computer called a host computer.

terminal emulation A software program and a hardware interface that allow one microcomputer to function as a variety of terminals in support of changing requirements.

terminator A resistor at a cable end that absorbs the signal and prevents echo or other signal noise.

think/wait time The amount of time an operator will wait or think while entering data for each transaction.

throughput The amount of work performed by a system per unit of time.

Time Division Multiplexing (TDM) A technique that divides transmission time by allotting to each device a time slot during which it can send or receive data.

time-out interval A period of time allowed for an event to occur. If the event does not happen, the time-out expires and the process initiating the event is notified.

time-staged delivery system Software that allows users to identify a transmission package, designate one or more recipients of the package, and specify a delivery priority.

token A special frame that is passed between nodes on a LAN. The node that receives the token has the right to transmit data. In some LANs there is one and only one token allowed to circulate. In metropolitan area networks like FDDI, several tokens may be circulating at one time.

token-passing A media access control protocol in which a string of bits called the token is distributed among the network nodes. A computer that receives the token is allowed to transmit data onto the network. Only the stations receiving a token can transmit. Token-passing is implemented on ring and bus LANs.

token-passing bus A LAN architecture using a bus topology and token passing media access control protocol.

token-passing ring A LAN architecture using a ring topology and token passing media access control protocol.

toll center In the telephone network, a toll center is a class 4 switching office. Also called a class 4 station.

topology The physical layout of a network. Common LAN topologies are bus, ring, and star. Common WAN topologies include star, hierarchical, and plex or interconnected.

transaction A user-specified group of processing activities that either are entirely completed or leave the database and processing system in the same state as before the transaction was initiated.

Transaction Control Process (TCP) A process that receives inputs from terminals and routes them to the proper application processes. TCPs also may edit input data, format data to and from a terminal, log messages, and provide terminal job sequencing. Examples include IBM's CICS and Tandem's Pathway. Also called a teleprocessing monitor or message control system.

transaction log Records all of the data received and is used in recovering from failures and in system auditing.

transaction routing The routing of a transaction received from a terminal to one or more application programs.

transaction services layer Layer 7 if IBM's SNA networks. Transaction services addresses application level processing.

transceiver A device that receives and sends signals. A transceiver helps form the interface between a network node and the medium.

transfer time The amount of time required for the data to be sent over the channel to the CPU's memory.

transmission control layer Layer 4 if IBM's SNA networks. Transmission control addresses initiating and terminating sessions, flow control, and message sequencing for end-to-end reliability. Transmission control contains functions found in both the session and transport layers of the OSI Reference Model.

Transmission Control Protocol/Internet Protocol (TCP/IP) A suite of internetwork protocols developed by the U.S. Department of Defense for internetwork file transfers, electronic mail transfer, remote logons, and terminal services.

transparency The ability to send any bit string as data in a message. The data bits are not interpreted as control characters.

transparent access The ability of a user to access distributed files as though they were located on the user's local node.

transparent bridge   A learning bridge. Transparent bridges are able to use information contained in the data link packets to determine the path along which to send packets.

transponder   In satellite communications, a transponder receives the transmission from earth (uplink), amplifies the signal, changes frequency, and retransmits the data to a receiving earth station (downlink).

transport layer   One layer of the International Standards Organization's OSI reference model. The transport layer is responsible for generating the end user's address and for the integrity of the receipt of message blocks.

Transport Service Access Point (TSAP)   An address used by the transport layer to uniquely identify session entities.

trapdoor encryption   An encryption algorithm that utilizes large prime numbers and two keys, one key made public and the other kept secret by the message recipient. The public key encrypts the data, and the private key decrypts the ciphertext. Also known as the public key method.

tribits   A method of modulation that allows three bits to be represented by each signal.

twisted-pair wires   A type of wire that consists of pairs of wires (typically two or four pairs) in a LAN). Each pair of wires are twisted around one another to reduce noise from adjacent pairs and to enhance their ability to transmit data. Twisted-pair wires can be shielded or unshielded.

Uninterruptible Power Supply (UPS)   A backup power unit that continues to provide power to a computer system during the failure of the normal power supply. A UPS is frequently used to protect LAN servers from power failures.

unipolar signaling   A digital transmission signaling technique that uses a single voltage to represent a 1-bit and zero voltage to represent a 0-bit.

UNIX   A popular multi-user operating system. UNIX is available on a wide variety of hardware platforms and has numerous capabilities that make it effective as a network operating system.

unshielded twisted-pair (UTP) wires   A type of twisted-pair wire that has no metalized outer covering to shield the wires from external interference.

uploading   The transfer of files or programs from the terminal to the host.

User Agent (UA)   A mail agent that allows a user to compose a message, provides recipient addresses, and receives messages.

user login script   A set of actions to be taken when the user logs in, such as setting search paths and initial menus.

user profile   Information needed to define the applications and transactions a user is authorized to execute.

V.nn   One of a variety of CCITT protocols. See CCITT V.nn.

Video Display Unit (VDU)   A terminal that uses a technique such as a cathode ray tube or a liquid crystal display to represent data. Also referred to as a Video Display Terminal (VDT) or Cathode Ray Tube (CRT).

Vines (Banyan)   An example of LAN software that runs under an existing OS, UNIX.

virtual circuit   A connection, established when setting up a communications session, between a sender and a receiver in which all messages are sent over the same path.

virtual routing   No permanently established path exists; instead each node consults its routing table to determine which node should next receive the message.

Virtual Telecommunications Access Method (VTAM)   One of IBM's telecommunications access methods.

virus detection software   Software that analyzes a system and attempts to discover and remove any viruses that have infected the system.

weighted routing   When multiple paths exist, each is given a weight according to perceived utilization. A random number is generated to determine which of the available paths to use based upon their weights.

white noise   One source of data communication errors. It results from the normal movements of electrons and is present in all transmission media at temperatures above absolute zero. Also known as thermal noise and Gaussian noise.

Wide Area Network (WAN)   A network that typically covers a wide geographical area and operates at speeds lower than LAN speeds.

Wide Area Telecommunications or Telephone Service (WATS)   An inbound or outbound telephone service that allows long-distance telephone service. In the United States the inbound service is associated with the 800 area code toll-free numbers.

Windows NT   A leading example of the integrated LAN operating software approach by Microsoft.

wireless LAN   A LAN implemented without using conducted media. A wireless LAN may use spread spectrum radio, broadcast radio, microwave radio, or infrared light transmission to connect the workstations together. Some LANs may use both conducted and wireless media.

wiring hub   Used by some LAN implementations to provide node-to-node connection.

workgroup software   Often referred to as groupware, this software facilitates the activities of a group of two or more workers by reducing the time and effort needed to perform group tasks such as meetings, office correspondence, and group decision making.

workload generator   A monitoring tool that generates transaction loads and pseudo-application processes for execution on a proposed configuration to illustrate how a system will actually function.

X.25 network   A network defined by CCITT X.25 standard. An X.25 network uses packet switching, and is also known as a packet switching network or value added network. See packet switching network.

X.400 standard   A standard developed by the CCITT that provides a platform for the implementation of a worldwide electronic message-handling service.

X.500 standard   A standard that specifies the procedure for creating a directory system to maintain electronic mail user names and their network addresses as well as the names and addresses of other network resources such as printers and servers.

Xpress Transfer Protocol (XTP)   An extension of TCP/IP that enhances performance by reducing the amount of processing and allowing some functions to be worked on simultaneously.

zero-slot LAN   A low-speed LAN using "standard" microcomputer components that do not require an additional slot on the motherboard for a LAN adapter.

Index

....

Instructions for using the index with the computer based training (CBT) modules

Entries in this index relating to the CBT modules are displayed in bold. To relate a CBT entry to the modules themselves, use the table below. The table references each of the 12 CBT modules by a number, for example, CB3, a book location, for example Section 1, Chapter 2, and a name, for example, LAN Transmission Media. Index references refer to CBT module numbers and a page number within that module. For example, CB3-7 refers to module number 3 (LAN Transmission Media) and page 7 within that module.

Number	Book Location	Name
CB1	Section 1, Chapter 1	OSI Reference Model
CB2	Section 1, Chapter 2	Modems and Media
CB3	Section 1, Chapter 2	LAN Transmission Media
CB4	Section 2, Chapter 6	Enterprise Network Evolution
CB5	Section 2, Chapter 4	Media Access
CB6	Section 2, Chapter 5	Network Operating System Overview
CB7	Section 2, Chapter 7	SNA Session Flows
CB8	Section 2, Chapter 6	HDLC/SDLC
CB9	Section 3, Chapter 8	X.25 Frame Relay
CB10	Section 3, Chapter 8	Bridge/Router Flows Through Layers
CB11	Section 3, Chapter 9	System Management Issues
CB12	Section 3, Chapter 9	Network Management Overview

By default, CBT page numbers are not displayed when viewing the modules. To display the page numbers, choose Page from the main menu and select the Show Page Numbers F12 option. (Alternatively, you could press the F12 function key.) The Show Page Numbers F12 option acts as a toggle; that is, if page number display is off, selecting the option will turn page number display on, and if page number display is on, selecting the option will discontinue displaying of page numbers.

Finding a CBT index reference

The following example shows the steps necessary to locating a CBT index reference. We will use the following index entry for our example:

propagation delay CB2-25, CB2-26, CB8-7

The term **propagation delay** may be found in CB2 on pages 25 and 26 and in CB8 on page 7. Let us locate the CB8 reference. Looking in the table above we see that CB8 is the HDLC/SDLC module and correlates to Chapter 6. This module can be found in the CBT Main Menu option Section 2, Chapters 4 - 7. The following steps can be used to find the reference.

1. Start the CBT software.
2. Go to the main menu.
3. Select "Section 2 Chapters 4 - 7."
4. Select "HDLC/SDLC."
5. Turn page numbering on.
6. Move forward in the module to page 7.

Note that in some modules, you cannot reach a page by simply selecting the forward (right arrow) button. In some instances, it is necessary to first select a topic to explore in more detail and then use the forward button. In these instances the method of proceeding should be clear from the information displayed on the screen and the reference you are attempting to locate. For example, under the topic of security in the module CB11, System Management Issues, there is a reference to User Ids. When security is presented in the module, an array of security features are presented, for example, User IDs, Accounting, Auditing, and so on. To get to a page referenced under Security with the subtopic of User IDs, you will need to first select the User ID option from the array of options and then use the forward button to reach the desired page.

END-USER WARRANTY AND LICENSE AGREEMENT

IMPORTANT: BY OPENING THE SEALED SOFTWARE ENVELOPE, YOU AGREE TO BE BOUND BY THE TERMS AND CONDITIONS OF THIS LICENSE AGREEMENT. THESE ARE THE ONLY TERMS UPON WHICH ADDISON WESLEY LONGMAN PRODUCTS ARE LICENSED. IF YOU DO NOT AGREE TO THESE TERMS, YOU MAY, WITHIN FIFTEEN (15) DAYS, RETURN THIS ENTIRE PACKAGE, INCLUDING THE UNOPENED SOFTWARE ENVELOPE, TO THE LOCATION WHERE YOU ACQUIRED IT FOR A FULL REFUND.

1. Grant of License
Addison Wesley Longman Publishing Company ("Addison Wesley Longman") has authorized distribution of this copy of the enclosed program (the "Software") to you pursuant to a license from The Saratoga Group, Inc. for the Software to accompany *Essentials of Data Communications,* and retains ownership of this copy of the Software. The Saratoga Group, Inc. retains ownership of the Software itself. Addison Wesley Longman grants you a nonexclusive, nontransferable license to use the Software according to the terms and conditions herein. This License Agreement permits you to install software for your use only. This License permits you to make only one backup copy of the Software.

2. Restrictions
You shall not: (1) modify, translate, reverse engineer, decompile, or disassemble the Software; (2) rent, or transfer all or part of the Software, Documentation, or any rights granted hereunder to any other person; (3) remove any proprietary notices, labels, or marks from the Software; (4) use the Software outside the country in which it was purchased; and (5) utilize any computer hardware or software designed to defeat any hardware copy protection device, should the software you have licensed be equipped with such protection. You agree that this product is FOR EDUCATIONAL USE ONLY and will comply to this restriction.

3. Copyright
Title and copyrights to the Software and accompanying materials and any copies made by you remain with Addison Wesley Longman and The Saratoga Group, Inc. Unauthorized copying of the Software or Documentation, or failure to comply with the above restrictions, will result in automatic termination of this license. Unauthorized duplication of the Software constitutes copyright infringement and in the United States is punishable in a federal criminal action by a fine of up to US$250,000 and imprisonment for up to five (5) years. In addition, federal civil penalties allow the recovery of actual damages based on the number of copies produced or liquidated damages of up to US$100,000 for willful copyright infringement.

4. Limited Warranty
Addison Wesley Longman warrants that, for a period of ninety (90) days from the date of delivery to you as evidenced by a copy of your receipt, the media on which the Software is furnished under normal use will be free from defects in materials and workmanship. EXCEPT FOR THE ABOVE EXPRESS LIMITED WARRANTIES, ADDISON WESLEY LONGMAN MAKES AND YOU RECEIVE NO WARRANTIES, EXPRESS, IMPLIED, STATUTORY OR IN ANY COMMUNICATION WITH YOU, AND ADDISON WESLEY LONGMAN SPECIFICALLY DISCLAIMS ANY OTHER WARRANTY INCLUDING THE IMPLIED WARRANTY OF MERCHANTABILITY OR FITNESS FOR A PARTICULAR PURPOSE. ADDISON WESLEY LONGMAN DOES NOT WARRANT THAT THE OPERATION OF THE SOFTWARE WILL BE UNINTERRUPTED OR ERROR FREE. If the Software was purchased in the United States, the above exclusions may not apply to you as some states do not allow the exclusion if implied warranties. In addition to the above warranty rights, you may also have other rights that vary from state to state.

5. Remedies
The entire liability of Addison Wesley Longman and your exclusive remedy under the warranty provided herein will be, at the option of Addison Wesley Longman, to attempt to correct or work around errors, to replace the media or to refund the purchase price and terminate this Agreement. This remedy is subject to the return of the Software to the location from which it was obtained with a copy of your receipt.

6. Limitation of Liability
IN NO EVENT WILL ADDISON WESLEY LONGMAN BE LIABLE FOR ANY DAMAGES, WHETHER ARISING FOR TORT OR CONTRACT, INCLUDING LOSS OF DATA, LOST PROFITS, COST OF COVER OR OTHER SPECIAL, INCIDENTAL, CONSEQUENTIAL, OR INDIRECT DAMAGES ARISING OUT OF THE USE OR INABILITY TO USE THE PROGRAM OR ACCOMPANYING DOCUMENTATION, HOWEVER CAUSED AND ON ANY THEORY OF LIABILITY. THIS LIMITATION WILL APPLY EVEN IF ADDISON WESLEY LONGMAN OR ANY AUTHORIZED ADDISON WESLEY LONGMAN DEALER DEALER HAS BEEN ADVISED OF THE POSSIBILITY OF SUCH DAMAGE. YOU ACKNOWLEDGE THAT THE LICENSE FEE REFLECTS THIS ALLOCATION OF RISK.

8. Canadian Sales
If you purchased this product in Canada, you agree the following:

The parties hereto confirm that it is their wish that this Agreement, as well as other documents relating hereto, including Notices, have been and shall be written in the English language only.

Les parties aux présentes confirment leur volonté que cette convention de meme que tous les documents y compris tout avis qui s'y rattache, soient rédigés en langue anglaise.

9. General
This agreement shall not be governed by the 1980 U.N. Convention on contracts for the Sale of Goods; rather this Agreement shall be governed by the laws of the State of California, including its Uniform Commercial Code without reference to conflict of laws principles. This Agreement is the entire agreement between us and supersedes any other communications or advertising with respect to the Software and Documentation. If you have any questions regarding the Software to accompany *Essentials of Data Communications,* please contact in writing: The Saratoga Group, Inc., 12980 Saratoga Avenue, Suite E, Saratoga, CA 95070.